**HMH**

# ALGEBRA 1

## Analyze • Connect • Explore

# Assessment Resources

COMMON CORE EDITION

# Contents

## Introduction

Algebra 1 Assessment Options ..................................................................................... vii

Using the Assessment Resources ............................................................................... viii

## Individual Student Profiles

Placement Test: Individual Student Profile ................................................................... ix

Beginning-of-Year Diagnostic Test: Individual Student Profile ...................................... x

## Performance Tasks

Performance Tasks: Teacher's Guide ........................................................................... xii

Performance Tasks: Scoring Rubric for Students ........................................................ xiii

Performance Tasks: Teacher's Guide Scoring Rubric ................................................. xiv

# Contents

**Placement Test** ............................................................................................... 1

**Beginning-of-Year Diagnostic Test** ................................................. 5

## Quizzes

Module Quiz 1: B ....................................................................................... 15

Module Quiz 1: D ....................................................................................... 17

Module Quiz 2: B ....................................................................................... 19

Module Quiz 2: D ....................................................................................... 21

Module Quiz 3: B ....................................................................................... 23

Module Quiz 3: D ....................................................................................... 25

Module Quiz 4: B ....................................................................................... 27

Module Quiz 4: D ....................................................................................... 29

Module Quiz 5: B ....................................................................................... 31

Module Quiz 5: D ....................................................................................... 33

Module Quiz 6: B ....................................................................................... 35

Module Quiz 6: D ....................................................................................... 37

Module Quiz 7: B ....................................................................................... 39

Module Quiz 7: D ....................................................................................... 41

Module Quiz 8: B ....................................................................................... 43

Module Quiz 8: D ....................................................................................... 45

Module Quiz 9: B ....................................................................................... 47

Module Quiz 9: D ....................................................................................... 49

Module Quiz 10: B ..................................................................................... 51

Module Quiz 10: D ..................................................................................... 53

Module Quiz 11: B ..................................................................................... 55

Module Quiz 11: D ..................................................................................... 57

Module Quiz 12: B ..................................................................................... 59

Module Quiz 12: D ..................................................................................... 61

Module Quiz 13: B ..................................................................................... 63

Module Quiz 13: D ..................................................................................... 65

Module Quiz 14: B ..................................................................................... 67

Module Quiz 14: D ..................................................................................... 69

Module Quiz 15: B ..................................................................................... 71

Module Quiz 15: D ..................................................................................... 73

Module Quiz 16: B ........................................................... 75

Module Quiz 16: D ........................................................... 77

Module Quiz 17: B ........................................................... 79

Module Quiz 17: D ........................................................... 81

Module Quiz 18: B ........................................................... 83

Module Quiz 18: D ........................................................... 85

Module Quiz 19: B ........................................................... 87

Module Quiz 19: D ........................................................... 89

# Unit Tests and Performance Tasks

Unit Test 1A: A ............................................................. 91

Unit Test 1A: B ............................................................. 93

Unit Test 1A: C ............................................................. 95

Unit Test 1A: D ............................................................. 97

Unit 1A Performance Task ................................................. 99

Unit Test 1B: A ............................................................. 100

Unit Test 1B: B ............................................................. 102

Unit Test 1B: C ............................................................. 104

Unit Test 1B: D ............................................................. 106

Unit 1B Performance Task ................................................. 108

Unit Test 2A: A ............................................................. 109

Unit Test 2A: B ............................................................. 111

Unit Test 2A: C ............................................................. 113

Unit Test 2A: D ............................................................. 115

Unit 2A Performance Task ................................................. 117

Unit Test 2B: A ............................................................. 118

Unit Test 2B: B ............................................................. 120

Unit Test 2B: C ............................................................. 122

Unit Test 2B: D ............................................................. 124

Unit 2B Performance Task ................................................. 126

Unit Test 3: A ............................................................... 127

Unit Test 3: B ............................................................... 129

Unit Test 3: C ............................................................... 131

Unit Test 3: D ............................................................... 133

Unit 3 Performance Task ................................................... 135

Unit Test 4: A .............................................................................. 136
Unit Test 4: B .............................................................................. 138
Unit Test 4: C .............................................................................. 140
Unit Test 4: D .............................................................................. 142
Unit 4 Performance Task ............................................................. 144
Unit Test 5: A .............................................................................. 145
Unit Test 5: B .............................................................................. 147
Unit Test 5: C .............................................................................. 149
Unit Test 5: D .............................................................................. 151
Unit 5 Performance Task ............................................................. 153

# Benchmark Tests

Benchmark Test Modules 1–5 ...................................................... 154
Mid-Year Test Modules 6–11 ...................................................... 158
Benchmark Test Modules 12–16 .................................................. 162

# End-of-Year Test .............................................. 166

# Answer Key .................................................... 176

# Algebra 1 Assessment Options

| | Assessment Resources | Student Edition and Teacher's Edition | Online |
|---|---|---|---|
| | | | **Personal Math Trainer** Online Assessment and Intervention — my.hrw.com |
| **Diagnostic/ Entry Level** | • Placement Test<br>• Beginning-of-Year Diagnostic Test | • Are You Ready? | • Diagnostic Test<br>• Are You Ready? Intervention and Enrichment |
| **Formative/ Progress Monitoring** | • Module Quizzes (Levels B, D) | • Your Turn<br>• Math Talk<br>• Reflect<br>• Questioning Strategies<br>• Essential Questions<br>• Lesson Quizzes<br>• Ready to Go On? Quizzes<br>• Module Mixed Review: Assessment Readiness | • Ready to Go On? Intervention and Enrichment<br>• Online Homework<br>• Module Mixed Review: Assessment Readiness<br>• Online Quizzes and Tests |
| **Summative** | • Unit Tests (Levels A, B, C, D)<br>• Unit Performance Tasks<br>• Quarterly Benchmark Tests<br>• Mid-Year Test<br>• End-of-Year Test | • Unit Assessment Readiness<br>• Unit Performance Tasks | • Assessment Readiness Practice Tests<br>• Online Quizzes and Tests |

# Using the Assessment Resources

The *Assessment Resources* provides the following tests to assess mastery.

| | | |
|---|---|---|
| **Diagnostic/ Entry Level** | **Placement Test**<br>• Use to assess prerequisite skills mastery before beginning the school year.<br>• For students who require intervention, use the online *Are You Ready?* Intervention. | **Beginning-of-Year Diagnostic Test**<br>• Use to assess knowledge of the key objectives that will be taught in the current school year.<br>• Use as a baseline for a student's mastery of math concepts and skills, and to evaluate growth during the school year. |
| **Formative/ Progress Monitoring** | **Module Quizzes**<br>• Use to assess mastery of the concepts and skills taught in the Modules.<br>• Use Level D for students who are considerably below level and require modified materials. For all other students use Level B. | |
| **Summative** | **Unit Tests**<br>• Use to assess mastery of the concepts and skills taught in the Units.<br>• Level A: for students who are slightly below level<br>• Level B: for students who are on level<br>• Level C: for advanced students<br>• Level D: for students who are considerably below level and require modified materials | **Benchmark Tests**<br>• Use for Assessment Readiness.<br>• There are four Benchmark Tests: two quarterly tests, the Mid-Year Test, and the End-of-Year Test. |
| | **Performance Tasks**<br>• Use to provide alternate assessment at the end of each Unit.<br>• These tasks are accessible to all students and suitable to be completed in a classroom.<br>• Before starting the Performance Task, provide students with the *Scoring Rubric for Students* to establish the expectations and scoring rubrics for the task. Use the *Teacher's Guide Scoring Rubric* to assess students' work and their competency with applying the Mathematical Practices. | |

# Placement Test

## *Individual Student Profile*

The Proficient? column provides a snapshot of a student's mastery of previous grade-level standards.

Each Student Edition Module begins with *Are You Ready?*, a tool to assess whether students have the prerequisite skills needed to be successful in Algebra 1. *Are You Ready?* Intervention is also available online.

Name _____ Date _____ Class _____

| COMMON CORE | Placement Test Items | Proficient? Yes/No |
|---|---|---|
| 8.NS.2 | 1, 2 | |
| 8.EE.3 | 3, 4 | |
| 8.EE.5 | 5, 6 | |
| 8.EE.6 | 7 | |
| 8.EE.7 | 13 | |
| 8.EE.8a | 14 | |
| 8.EE.8b | 15 | |
| 8.EE.8c | 16 | |
| 8.F.1 | 11, 12 | |
| 8.F.3 | 9 | |
| 8.F.4 | 8, 10 | |
| 8.G.2 | 19 | |
| 8.G.3 | 18, 20 | |
| 8.G.4 | 17 | |
| 8.G.5 | 21, 22 | |
| 8.G.6 | 25 | |
| 8.G.7 | 24 | |
| 8.G.8 | 23 | |
| 8.G.9 | 26, 27 | |
| 8.SP.1 | 28 | |
| 8.SP.2 | 29 | |

# Beginning-of-Year Diagnostic Test

## *Individual Student Profile*

The Proficient? column provides a snapshot of a student's knowledge of key objectives that will be taught in Algebra 1. The Diagnostic Test can be used as a baseline for a student's mastery of objectives and to evaluate growth.

Name _____ Date _____ Class _____

| COMMON CORE | Student Edition Modules | Diagnostic Test Items | Proficient? Yes/No |
|---|---|---|---|
| N.RN.1 | 2 | 6 | |
| N.RN.2 | 2, 10 | 7, 44 | |
| N.RN.3 | 2 | 8, 9 | |
| N.Q.1 | 1 | 4, 5 | |
| N.Q.3 | 1 | 1, 2, 3 | |
| A.SSE.1.b | 3 | 10, 11 | |
| A.SSE.2 | 3, 3, 13, 13, 13 | 12, 13, 51, 52, 53, 54 | |
| A.APR.1 | 12, 12, 12, 12 | 47, 48, 49, 50 | |
| A.CED.2 | 6 | 23 | |
| A.CED.4 | 19 | 75 | |
| A.REI.3 | 4, 4 | 14, 15, 16 | |
| A.REI.4.a | 15, 15 | 59, 60 | |
| A.REI.4.b | 15 | 61 | |
| A.REI.5 | 9 | 37 | |
| A.REI.6 | 9, 9, 9 | 35, 36, 38 | |
| A.REI.10 | 5 | 17, 18 | |
| A.REI.11 | 6 | 25 | |
| A.REI.12 | 7 | 30 | |
| F.IF.1 | 5, 19 | 19, 73 | |
| F.IF.2 | 5 | 20 | |
| F.IF.3 | 5, 7, 10 | 21, 28, 43 | |

# Beginning-of-Year Diagnostic Test

## Individual Student Profile (continued)

Name _____ Date _____ Class _____

| COMMON CORE | Student Edition Modules | Diagnostic Test Items | Proficient? Yes/No |
|---|---|---|---|
| F.IF.5 | 19 | 74 | |
| F.IF.6 | 6 | 24 | |
| F.IF.7 | 19 | 76 | |
| F.IF.7.a | 6, 14, 14, 14, 15 | 22, 55, 56, 58, 63 | |
| F.IF.7.b | 18 | 70, 71 | |
| F.IF.7.c | 15.8 | 62 | |
| F.IF.9 | 6 | 26 | |
| F.BF.1 | 7, 7 | 27, 29 | |
| F.BF.3 | 14, 18 | 57, 72 | |
| F.LE.1.a | 10 | 39 | |
| F.LE.1.c | 10 | 42 | |
| F.LE.2 | 10 | 40, 41 | |
| S.ID.1 | 17, 17 | 67, 68 | |
| S.ID.2 | 17 | 66 | |
| S.ID.3 | 17 | 69 | |
| S.ID.5 | 16, 16 | 64, 65 | |
| S.ID.6.a | 11 | 45 | |
| S.ID.6.b | 8, 11 | 34, 46 | |
| S.ID.6.c | 8 | 33 | |
| S.ID.7 | 8 | 32 | |
| S.ID.8 | 8 | 31 | |

**Mathematical Practices**

# Performance Tasks

## *Teacher's Guide*

Performance Tasks provide an alternate way for teachers to assess students' mastery of concepts. This method of assessment requires the student to create answers by using critical thinking skills.

Through observation or analysis of students' responses, teachers can determine what the students do and do not know, and whether the students have any misconceptions.

### Assigning Performance Tasks

Discuss with students what is expected before they start the Performance Task. Provide the *Scoring Rubric for Students* to help them understand the scoring criteria.

- Encourage discussion of new ideas and viability of other students' reasoning and work.

- Encourage multiple approaches and emphasize that not just one answer is correct.

- Encourage students to initiate a plan.

- Encourage students to manage, analyze, and synthesize information.

- Encourage students to use appropriate tools and math models to solve the problems, and remind students to attend to precision.

Use the *Teacher's Guide Scoring Rubric* to help assess the complex learning outcomes.

# Performance Tasks

## Scoring Rubric for Students

### What you are expected to do.

- ☐ Make a plan. If the plan does not work, change it until it does work.
- ☐ Use accurate reasoning to represent the problem.
- ☐ Fully explain the steps that you used to find the solution.
- ☐ Use different methods and models to help you find the solution.
- ☐ Use appropriate tools such as rulers, geometry tools, and calculators.
- ☐ Use clear language to explain your answers. Check that your answers are accurate.
- ☐ Look for patterns and explain your reasoning using different representations such as symbols, words, or graphs.
- ☐ Find efficient ways to solve the problems and explain general rules clearly.

### Your teacher will need to see all your work. Be sure to include the following:

- ☐ Drawings, tables, and graphs to support your answers
- ☐ Clearly written sentences to explain your reasoning
- ☐ All the steps in your solution
- ☐ The answer. Check that it is reasonable and answers the question.

# Performance Tasks

## Teacher's Guide Scoring Rubric

| Mathematical Practices | Level 4 | Level 3 | Level 2 | Level 1 |
|---|---|---|---|---|
| Make sense of problems and persevere in solving them. | Student makes a plan and follows it or adjusts it to obtain a solution. | Student makes a viable plan, but implementation has minor flaws. | Student makes a plan, but it has major flaws that the student is unable to address. | Student shows no evidence of making a plan. |
| Reason abstractly and quantitatively. | Student uses accurate reasoning to represent the problem. | Student reasoning shows a minor flaw. | Student reasoning is missing a critical step. | Student shows little evidence of mathematical reasoning. |
| Construct viable arguments and critique the reasoning of others. | Student fully explains the steps that lead to the conclusion. | Student skips a step in the explanation. | Student has missing or out-of-sequence steps in the explanation. | Student makes no attempt to explain the steps used. |
| Model mathematics [using graphs, diagrams, tables, formulas]. | Student uses appropriate models and implements them correctly. | Student chooses an appropriate model but makes minor error(s) in implementation. | Student chooses a model but is unable to relate it effectively to the problem. | Student is unable to model the relationship. |
| Use appropriate tools [e.g., ruler, paper/pencil, technology] strategically. | Student chooses appropriate tools and uses them effectively. | Student chooses an appropriate tool but makes minor error(s) in its use. | Student chooses an appropriate tool but cannot apply it properly to the problem. | Student chooses an inappropriate tool or none at all. |
| Attend to precision. | Student uses clear language and accurate calculations. | Student uses some vocabulary incorrectly and/or makes minor error(s) in calculations. | Student use of language is confusing and/or student makes errors in calculations. | Student does not provide an explanation; calculations are inaccurate. |
| Look for and make use of structure. | Student finds and uses patterns and processes and expresses them accurately. | Student finds and uses patterns and processes but makes minor error(s) in expressing them. | Student finds patterns and processes but cannot apply them successfully. | Student is unable to find patterns and processes that are appropriate. |
| Look for and express regularity in repeated reasoning. | Student finds shortcuts and/or generalizations and expresses them clearly. | Student finds shortcuts and/or generalizations but makes minor errors. | Student finds a shortcut or generalization but does not represent it effectively. | Student is unable to find shortcuts and/or generalizations. |

# Placement Test

1. Between which two integers does the value of $\sqrt{88}$ lie?

   A  1 and 2        C  9 and 10

   B  8 and 9        D  87 and 89

2. The lengths in centimeters of four line segments are shown below.

   $$3.12, \; 3.24, \; 3\frac{1}{4}, \; \sqrt{10}$$

   Which list shows the lengths in order from **least** to **greatest**?

   A  $3.12, \; 3\frac{1}{4}, \; 3.24, \; \sqrt{10}$

   B  $3.12, \; \sqrt{10}, \; 3.24, \; 3\frac{1}{4}$

   C  $\sqrt{10}, \; 3.12, \; 3.24, \; 3\frac{1}{4}$

   D  $3.12, \; 3.24, \; 3\frac{1}{4}, \; \sqrt{10}$

3. James wrote the number 8,980,000 in scientific notation. Which number did he write?

   A  $8.98 \times 10^{-6}$        C  $89.8 \times 10^{5}$

   B  $8.98 \times 10^{-5}$        D  $8.98 \times 10^{6}$

4. Erica wrote the number $3.24 \times 10^{-3}$ in standard form. Which number did she write?

   A  0.00324        C  0.324

   B  0.0324         D  3,240

5. What is the slope of the line described by the data in the table below?

   | x | −1 | 1 | 3 | 5 |
   |---|----|---|---|---|
   | y | 3 | 8 | 13 | 18 |

   A  $\dfrac{2}{5}$        C  $\dfrac{5}{4}$

   B  $\dfrac{2}{3}$        D  $\dfrac{5}{2}$

6. Which of the following equations represents a proportional relationship?

   A  $y = 3x$        C  $y = \dfrac{3}{x}$

   B  $y = \dfrac{1}{2}x + 1$        D  $y = x + \dfrac{1}{2}$

7. The points $A(0, 0)$, $B(2, 2)$, $C(3, 3)$ and $D(5, 5)$ all lie on the line $y = x$. Ana calculated the slopes of $\overline{AB}$ and $\overline{CD}$. What can she conclude?

   A  The slopes are the same.

   B  The slope of $\overline{AB}$ is greater than the slope of $\overline{CD}$.

   C  The slope of $\overline{CD}$ is greater than the slope of $\overline{AB}$.

   D  The slopes of $\overline{AB}$ and $\overline{CD}$ are negative.

8. Annabelle's total pay varies directly with the number of hours she works. If she works 4 hours, she earns $100. How much does Annabelle earn if she works 6 hours?

   A  $90         C  $150

   B  $120        D  $300

9. Which of the following is the equation of the line graphed below?

   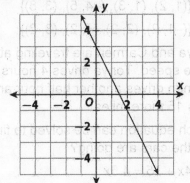

   A  $y = -2x + 3$        C  $y = -3x + 3$

   B  $y = -2x + 5$        D  $y = -3x + 2$

# Placement Test

10. Which equation shows the relationship in the table below?

| x | 5 | 8 | 9 | 11 |
|---|---|---|---|---|
| y | 10 | 16 | 18 | 22 |

  A  $y = 2x$            C  $y = 2x + 1$

  B  $y = 3x$            D  $y = 3x + 3$

11. Which of the following tables represents a function?

  A

| x | 1 | 1 | 4 | 5 |
|---|---|---|---|---|
| y | 2 | 5 | 2 | 6 |

  B

| x | 1 | −1 | 4 | 5 |
|---|---|---|---|---|
| y | 2 | 3 | 4 | −3 |

  C

| x | 0 | 1 | 2 | 2 |
|---|---|---|---|---|
| y | 2 | 3 | 3 | 4 |

  D

| x | 0 | 1 | 2 | 1 |
|---|---|---|---|---|
| y | −1 | 0 | 1 | 3 |

12. Which of the following sets of ordered pairs does **not** represent a function?

  A  {(1, 2), (2, 3), (4, 5), (3, 3)}

  B  {(−1, 3), (2, 3), (6, 5), (7, 3)}

  C  {(1, 2), (1, 3), (−4, 5), (3, 8)}

  D  {(−1, 2), (2, 2), (4, 2), (3, 2)}

13. Tonya and Carmen are traveling at the same speed. Tonya drives 4 hours. Carmen drives another half hour and goes 15 more miles.

Which equation can be solved to find how fast the cars are going?

  A  $4x + 15 = 4.5x$

  B  $4x + 15 = 3.5x$

  C  $2.5x + 15 = 4x$

  D  $4.5x + 25 = 4x$

14. What is the solution of the system of equations graphed below?

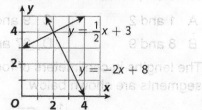

  A  (−1, 1)           C  (2, 2)

  B  (2, 4)            D  (0, 3)

15. What is the solution to the system of equations shown below?

$$\begin{cases} y = -\dfrac{1}{2}x - 6 \\ 2y - 3x = -8 \end{cases}$$

  A  (−1, −5.5)      C  (0, 3)

  B  (−1, 5.5)       D  (0, 8)

16. Ben's Bikes charges $15.50 per hour to rent a bicycle and helmet. Cathie's Bike Shop charges $9.25 per hour for the bike and a flat fee of $12.50 for the helmet rental. For what number of hours are the total charges at both shops the same?

  A  1 h           C  3 h

  B  2 h           D  4 h

17. The vertices of a triangle are located at the points $A(1, 1)$, $B(2, -3)$ and $C(5, 0)$. The triangle is translated 4 units down, then reflected across the x-axis to obtain triangle $A'B'C'$. What are the coordinates of the vertices of triangle $A'B'C'$?

  A  $A'(-1, 3)$, $B'(-2, 7)$, $C'(-5, 4)$

  B  $A'(-1, -3)$, $B'(-2, -7)$, $C'(-5, -4)$

  C  $A'(1, -3)$, $B'(2, -7)$, $C'(5, -4)$

  D  $A'(1, 3)$, $B'(2, 7)$, $C'(5, 4)$

# Placement Test

18. The gray figure is the image of the black figure after a dilation.

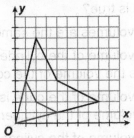

    Which represents the dilation?

    A  $(x, y) \to \left(\dfrac{1}{4}x, \dfrac{1}{4}y\right)$

    B  $(x, y) \to \left(\dfrac{1}{2}x, \dfrac{1}{2}y\right)$

    C  $(x, y) \to (2x, 2y)$

    D  $(x, y) \to (4x, 4y)$

19. Jerlyn applied a sequence of transformations to obtain triangle $X'Y'Z'$ from triangle $XYZ$ as shown below.

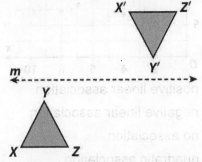

    Which of the following describes the sequence of transformations?

    A  a translation followed by a reflection across line $m$

    B  a translation followed by a 180° counterclockwise rotation

    C  a dilation with scale factor 2

    D  a reflection across line $m$ followed by a 180° counterclockwise rotation

20. Daria applied a transformation to triangle $ABC$ to obtain triangle $A'B'C'$. The two triangles are **not** congruent. Which of the following could be the transformation Daria applied?

    A  translation          C  dilation

    B  rotation             D  reflection

21. In the diagram below, lines $l$ and $m$ are parallel. Both are intersected by transversal $t$. What is the value of $x$?

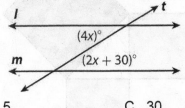

    A  5                    C  30

    B  15                   D  45

22. The measures of three angles of a triangle are $(2x)°$, $(3x)°$ and $(x + 60)°$. What is the value of $x$?

    A  20                   C  40

    B  30                   D  50

23. On the grid below, what is the distance between points $A$ and $B$? Round to the nearest tenth.

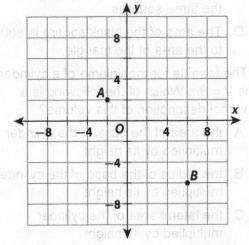

    A  8.2 units           C  10.8 units

    B  9.9 units           D  11.3 units

# Placement Test

24. A diagonal shortcut across a rectangular lot is 130 feet. The lot is 50 feet long. What is the other dimension of the lot?

   A  60 ft          C  120 ft

   B  90 ft          D  150 ft

25. How can the diagram below be used to explain the Pythagorean theorem?

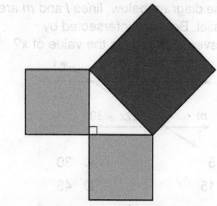

   A  The area of the black square is equal to the sum of the areas of the gray squares.

   B  The sum of the areas of the gray squares is less than the area of the black square.

   C  The perimeter of the triangle is equal to one-fourth of the total perimeter of the three squares.

   D  The area of the black square is equal to the area of the triangle.

26. The formula for the volume of a cylinder is $V = Bh$. Which of the following is a verbal description of this volume?

   A  the area of the base of the cylinder multiplied by its height

   B  the radius of the base of the cylinder multiplied by its height

   C  the lateral area of the cylinder multiplied by its height

   D  the circumference of the base of the cylinder multiplied by its height

27. Ryan drew a cylinder and a cone with identical bases and heights. Which of the following is true?

   A  The volumes are the same.

   B  The volume of the cylinder is three times the volume of the cone.

   C  The volume of the cone is three times the volume of the cylinder.

   D  The volume of the cylinder is four-thirds the volume of the cone.

28. Which of the following best describes the relationship between the data displayed in the scatter plot below?

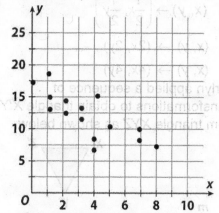

   A  positive linear association

   B  negative linear association

   C  no association

   D  quadratic association

29. Tania analyzed the relationship between student test scores and the number of hours studied. She calculated the trend line to be $y = 6.8x + 60$, where $x$ is the number of hours studied and $y$ is the score. Which is closest to the score for a student who studied 3 hours?

   A  80          C  90

   B  85          D  95

# Beginning-of-Year Diagnostic Test

1. Which measurement is the most precise?

   A  20 in.          C  21 in.

   B  21.3 in.        D  21.25 in.

2. How many significant digits does the measurement 2,000 feet have?

   A  1               C  3

   B  2               D  4

3. What is the perimeter of the rectangle modeled below with the correct number of significant digits?

   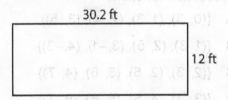

   30.2 ft

   12 ft

   A  42.2 ft         C  84.4 ft

   B  84 ft           D  360 ft

4. Salina is 63 inches tall. Approximately how tall is she in centimeters?

   A  16 cm           C  160 cm

   B  25 cm           D  250 cm

5. Daniel is driving at a speed of 1 kilometer per minute. Approximately how fast is he traveling in miles per hour?

   A  0.62 $\dfrac{\text{mi}}{\text{h}}$     C  37 $\dfrac{\text{mi}}{\text{h}}$

   B  1.6 $\dfrac{\text{mi}}{\text{h}}$      D  96 $\dfrac{\text{mi}}{\text{h}}$

6. Which of the following expressions is equivalent to $x^6 \times x^2$ ?

   A  $x^3$           C  $x^8$

   B  $x^4$           D  $x^{12}$

7. Which of the following expressions is equivalent to $y^{\frac{1}{3}}$ ?

   A  $y^{-3}$        C  $y^3$

   B  $\sqrt[3]{y}$   D  $\dfrac{1}{\sqrt[3]{y}}$

8. Which set is **not** closed under multiplication?

   A  {0}             C  {–1, 0, 1}

   B  {0, 1}          D  {–1, 0}

9. Which set does **not** contain any irrational numbers?

   A  $\left\{-\dfrac{2}{5}, \sqrt{16}\right\}$     C  $\{1.7, \sqrt{11}\}$

   B  $\{-11, \pi\}$     D  $\left\{\sqrt{81}, \sqrt{20}\right\}$

10. What is $12 - 2x$ evaluated for $x = -8$ ?

    A  –80            C  28

    B  –4             D  80

11. What is $8u - \dfrac{v}{2}$ evaluated for $u = -3$ and $v = 16$ ?

    A  –88            C  –24

    B  –32            D  –20

12. Which expression is equivalent to $14x - 21y$?

    A  $7(2x - 21y)$

    B  $7(2x - 3y)$

    C  $7x(2 - 3y)$

    D  $7y(2x - 3)$

# Beginning-of-Year Diagnostic Test

13. Wednesday, Diana made $y$ dollars per hour for 8 hours of work. Thursday she made $y$ dollars per hour for 4 hours of work. She also got a $45 bonus. Which expression best represents the total amount of money Diana earned?

    A  $12y + 45$

    B  $12t - 45$

    C  $8m + 4t + 45$

    D  $4y + 45$

14. Solve $4x + 25 = 51$. What is the solution?

    A  $x = -12.25$

    B  $x = 6.5$

    C  $x = 19$

    D  $x = 37.75$

15. Which is the solution to $2x - 8 = 2(x - 4)$?

    A  $x = -4$

    B  $x = 4$

    C  no solution

    D  $x$ is all real numbers

16. Which graph best represents the solutions of $8x \le -48$?

    A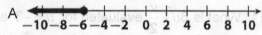

    B

    C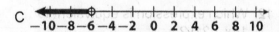

    D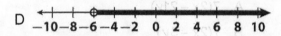

17. Which ordered pair is a solution to the equation $y = 8x - 12$?

    A  $(-1, -4)$

    B  $(3, 12)$

    C  $(4, 2)$

    D  $(12, 3)$

18.

| $x$ | 0 | 1 | 2 | 3 |
|-----|---|---|---|---|
| $y$ | 3 | 5 | 7 | 9 |

Which equation matches the solutions on the table of values above?

A  $y = 2x + 3$

B  $y = x + 3$

C  $y = x - 3$

D  $y = \frac{1}{2}x + 3$

19. Which set of ordered pairs do **not** represent a function?

    A  $\{(0,\ 3),\ (1,\ 3),\ (2,\ 4),\ (3,\ 5)\}$

    B  $\{(1,\ 3),\ (2,\ 5),\ (3, -1),\ (4, -3)\}$

    C  $\{(2,\ 3),\ (2,\ 5),\ (3,\ 6),\ (4,\ 7)\}$

    D  $\{(3,\ 3),\ (4,\ 5),\ (5,\ 6),\ (6,\ 7)\}$

20. Which function is graphed below?

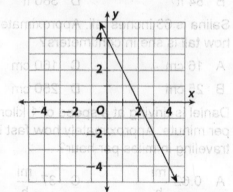

A  $f(x) = 2x + 4$

B  $f(x) = -2x + 4$

C  $f(x) = -\dfrac{x - 4}{2}$

D  $y = \dfrac{x - 4}{2}$

# Beginning-of-Year Diagnostic Test

21. What is the fourth term of a sequence with the recursive rule $f(n) = 2f(n-1)$; $f(1) = -3$?

    A  −78          C  −32

    B  −48          D  −24

22. What are the $x$ and $y$-intercepts of $-12x + 3y = 48$?

    A  $x$-intercept: −4; $y$-intercept: 16

    B  $x$-intercept: 4; $y$-intercept: −16

    C  $x$-intercept: 16; $y$-intercept: −4

    D  $x$-intercept: −16; $y$-intercept: 4

23. Which equation is graphed below?

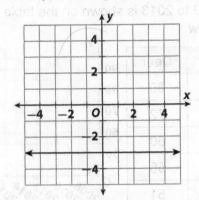

    A  $x = -3$          C  $y = -3$

    B  $x = y - 3$       D  $y = x - 3$

24. What is the slope of a line that contains the points $(-6, -4)$ and $(-2, 4)$?

    A  −2          C  1

    B  $\dfrac{1}{2}$          D  2

25. $f(x) = -\dfrac{2}{3}x + 6$ and $g(x) = \dfrac{1}{2}x - 1$ are graphed below. For what values does $f(x) = g(x)$?

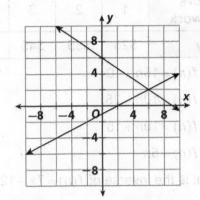

    A  (6, 2)          C  (2, 6)

    B  (2, 0)          D  (0, 6)

26. $f(x) = 2x + 5$, and $g(x) = 2x - 3$. Which statement is true?

    A  $f(x)$ has a steeper slope than $g(x)$.

    B  $g(x)$ has a steeper slope than $f(x)$.

    C  $f(x)$ has a greater $y$-intercept than $g(x)$.

    D  $g(x)$ has a greater $y$-intercept than $f(x)$.

27. $r(x) = x + 5$, and $s(x) = -7$. What is $p(x) = r(x) \times s(x)$?

    A  $-7x + 5$          C  $-7x + 35$

    B  $-7x - 35$          D  $x - 35$

28. Which of the following rules for an arithmetic sequence match the pay scale represented on the table below?

| Hours of work | 1 | 2 | 3 | 4 |
|---|---|---|---|---|
| Pay | $25 | $35 | $45 | $55 |

A  $f(n) = 15n + 10$

B  $f(n) = 10n + 25$

C  $f(n) = 10n + 15$

D  $f(n) = 5n$

29. What is the inverse of $f(n) = 7x - 12$?

A  $f^{-1}(x) = \dfrac{x + 12}{7}$

B  $f^{-1}(x) = \dfrac{x}{7} + 12$

C  $f^{-1}(x) = -7x + 12$

D  $f^{-1}(x) = \dfrac{x}{7} - 12$

30. Which ordered pair is a solution of $y > -8x + 32$?

A  $(-2, 45)$        C  $(2, 18)$

B  $(0, 32)$         D  $(4, -2)$

31. Which type of correlation best describes the data represented on the table below?

| Price of stock over time | | | | |
|---|---|---|---|---|
| 2010 | 2011 | 2012 | 2013 | 2014 |
| $9 | $15 | $20 | $24 | $30 |

A  Strong positive      C  Weak positive

B  Negative             D  None

32. What is the correlation coefficient based on the data represented on the scatterplot below?

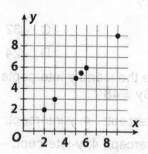

A  −1              C  0.87

B  0               D  1

33. The population of deer on a farm from 2009 to 2013 is shown on the table below.

| Year | Deer |
|---|---|
| '09 | 80 |
| '10 | 72 |
| '11 | 60 |
| '12 | 56 |
| '13 | 51 |

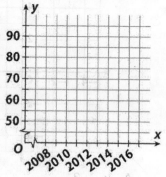

Given that the line of best fit is $y \approx -7.4x + 78.6$, which is the best prediction of the population of deer in 2016?

A  13              C  28

B  21              D  35

# Beginning-of-Year Diagnostic Test

34. Based on the table below, what is the sum of the squared residuals of $y = 15x - 8$?

| x | y observed | y predicted | residual |
|---|---|---|---|
| 0 | -7.5 | -8 | 0.5 |
| 1 | 6 | 7 | -1 |
| 2 | 22 | 22 | 0 |
| 3 | 39 | 37 | 2 |

   A 1.5         C 3.5

   B 3.25        D 5.25

35. How many solutions does the system of equations graphed below have?

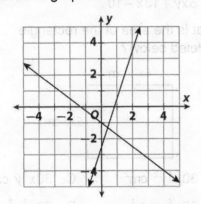

   A None         C Two

   B One          D Infinitely many

36. Which equation would make this system have no solution? $\begin{cases} y = 3x - 12 \\ \underline{\hspace{2cm}} \end{cases}$

   A $y = -3x - 12$     C $y = 3x + 6$

   B $y = 3x - 12$      D $y = \frac{1}{3}x + 1$

37. What is the solution to the system $\begin{cases} 2y = 4x + 20 \\ 4y = 6x + 24 \end{cases}$?

   A $(-8, -6)$       C $(-2, 12)$

   B $(-3, 4)$        D $(8, 52)$

38. Which ordered pair is a solution of the system graphed below?

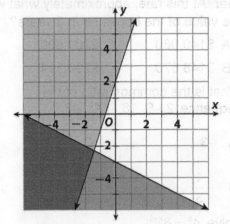

   A $(-4, -2)$      C $(0, 4)$

   B $(-1, -4)$      D $(2, -5)$

39. Which of the following data sets is best described by an exponential model?

   A $\{(-2, 1), (-3, 0), (-4, 1), (-5, 0)\}$

   B $\{(1, 3), (2, 9), (3, 81), (4, 243)\}$

   C $\{(5, 3), (6, 9), (7, 27), (8, 81)\}$

   D $\{(8, 4), (9, 9), (10, 16), (11, 25)\}$

40. A scientist is observing a family of mice. There are four mice which are reproducing and doubling in number every month. Which function best represents the number of mice where $x$ is the number of months that have passed?

   A $f(x) = 2^x$      C $f(x) = 4^x$

   B $f(x) = 2 \times 4^x$    D $f(x) = 4 \times 2^x$

# Beginning-of-Year Diagnostic Test

41. Which exponential equation has a graph that contains the ordered pairs (3, 20) and (5, 80)?

   A $y = 2 \times 2.5^x$     C $y = 2^{x+1} + 4$

   B $y = 2.5 \times 2^x$     D $y = 2^x + 12$

42. A house with an initial value of $140,000 is increasing in value at a rate of 2% each year. At this rate, approximately what will the value of the house be in 3 years?

   A $140,080     C $201,600

   B $148,570     D $290,304

43. What is the common ratio of the sequence 2, −6, 18, −54,... ?

   A −3         C $\dfrac{1}{3}$

   B $-\dfrac{1}{3}$     D 3

44. Solve $4^6 = 8^{x-1}$.

   A $x = 7$         C $x = 4$

   B $x = 5$         D $x = 1$

45. Which regression equation best fits the data shown on the table?

| x | 0 | 1 | 2 | 3 |
|---|---|---|---|---|
| y | 2 | 4.8 | 12.6 | 31 |

   A $y \approx 4.75^x$

   B $y \approx 2.0 \times 2.5^x$

   C $y \approx 2.5 \times 1.9^x$

   D $y \approx 2.5^x + 1.9$

46. The regression equation for a set of data is $y \approx -3.8 \times 5^x$. The observed value of $y$ when $x = 2$ is −93.5. What is the residual?

   A −2.25     C 1.5

   B −1.5      D 2.25

47. Which of the following polynomials is a binomial with a degree of 3?

   A $7x^3y - 13x^4$

   B $-2xy^2 - 19$

   C $2x^3 - 7x - 9y$

   D $-27x^3y + 5x - 18$

48. What is the sum of $(5xy + x - 8)$ and $(13x + 2)$?

   A $5xy + 14x - 6$

   B $5xy + 13x - 6$

   C $5xy + 14x - 10$

   D $5xy + 13x - 10$

49. What is the area of the rectangle modeled below?

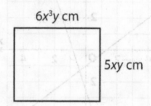

   A $30x^4y^2$ cm$^2$     C $30x^3y$ cm$^2$

   B $30x^4y$ cm$^2$     D $22x^3y^2$ cm$^2$

50. What is the product of $x + 3$ and $x - 9$ ?

   A $x^2 - 27$

   B $x^2 - 6$

   C $x^2 - 6x - 27$

   D $x^2 + 6x - 27$

# Beginning-of-Year Diagnostic Test

51. What is the GCF of $8x^3$ and $12x^2y$ ?

    A  $4x^2$          C  $24x^2$

    B  $4x^5y$         D  $24x^5y$

52. What is the complete factorization of $25x^3 - 75xy$ ?

    A  $5(5x^3 - 15xy)$

    B  $5(5x^2 - 15xy)$

    C  $25(x^3 - 3xy)$

    D  $25x(x^2 - 3y)$

53. What is the complete factorization of $x^2 - 8x + 16$ ?

    A  $(x - 4)^2$

    B  $(x + 4)^2$

    C  $(x - 8)(x - 2)$

    D  $(x - 4)(x + 4)$

54. Which of the following expressions is a difference of perfect squares?

    A  $2x^2 - 16$

    B  $9x^4 - 1$

    C  $x^2 - 9x + 9$

    D  $x^2 + 10x + 25$

55. What is the vertex of the graph of $y = \dfrac{1}{2}x^2 + 2$ ?

    A  $(0, -2)$        C  $(2, 0)$

    B  $(0, 2)$         D  $(-2, 0)$

56. Which function is graphed below?

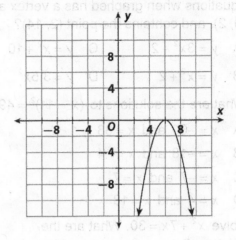

    A  $f(x) = -(x - 6)^2$      C  $f(x) = (x - 6)^2$

    B  $f(x) = -(x + 6)^2$      D  $f(x) = (x + 6)^2$

57. $f(x)$ is $g(x)$ translated up 6 units. Based on the graph of $g(x)$ shown below, what is $f(x)$?

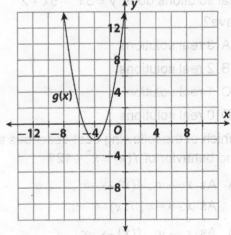

    A  $f(x) = (x + 4)^2 - 2$

    B  $f(x) = (x + 4)^2 + 4$

    C  $f(x) = (x + 10)^2 - 2$

    D  $f(x) = (x + 4)^2 - 8$

# Beginning-of-Year Diagnostic Test

58. Which of the following quadratic equations when graphed has a vertex at $(0, 2)$ and contains the point $(2, 14)$?

   A $y = 3x^2 + 2$    C $y = x^2 + 10$

   B $y = x^2 + 2$    D $y = 3.5x^2$

59. What are the solutions to $(x - 11)^2 = 49$?

   A $x = -60$ and $x = 38$

   B $x = -18$ and $x = -4$

   C $x = -7$ and $x = 7$

   D $x = 4$ and $x = 18$

60. Solve $x^2 + 7x = 30$. What are the solutions?

   A $x = -10$ and $x = 3$

   B $x = -6$ and $x = 5$

   C $x = -6$ and $x = -5$

   D $x = -3$ and $x = 10$

61. Based on the discriminant, how many real solutions does $y = 3x^2 - 5x + 2$ have?

   A 3 real solutions

   B 2 real solutions

   C 1 real solution

   D 0 real solutions

62. Which of the following best describes the end behavior of $f(x) = x^2 - 12$?

   A As $x \to \infty$, $f(x) \to -\infty$;
   As $x \to -\infty$, $f(x) \to -\infty$

   B As $x \to \infty$, $f(x) \to -\infty$;
   As $x \to -\infty$, $f(x) \to \infty$

   C As $x \to \infty$, $f(x) \to \infty$;
   As $x \to -\infty$, $f(x) \to -\infty$

   D As $x \to \infty$, $f(x) \to \infty$;
   As $x \to -\infty$, $f(x) \to \infty$

63. Which ordered pair is the solution to the system: $\begin{cases} y = 3(x - 2)^2 + 6 \\ y = 6 \end{cases}$?

   A $(0, 6)$

   B $(2, 6)$

   C $(6, -2)$

   D $(6, 0)$

64. The following is a frequency table from a survey of 40 elementary school students.

| Preferred Color | | | | |
|---|---|---|---|---|
| Gender | Red | Blue | Black | Total |
| Male | 5 | 3 | 8 | 16 |
| Female | 7 | 9 | 8 | 24 |
| Total | 12 | 12 | 16 | 40 |

   How many more female students than male students preferred blue?

   A 2    C 6

   B 3    D 9

65. The frequency table below shows the results of a survey of 50 people about whether they like cats.

| | Do you like cats? | |
|---|---|---|
| Age in years | Yes | No |
| 21–35 | 6 | 14 |
| 36–50 | 4 | 9 |
| 51–65 | 12 | 5 |

   What was the joint relative frequency that a person surveyed was 51–65 years old and likes cats?

   A 0.12    C 0.24

   B 0.17    D 0.34

# Beginning-of-Year Diagnostic Test

66. What are the mean and range of the set: 21, 25, 18, 23, 26, and 16?

    A  The mean is 21.5. The range is 10.

    B  The mean is 20.5. The range is 26.

    C  The mean is 21.5. The range is 26.

    D  The mean is 20.5. The range is 10.

67. The histogram below shows the ages of teachers at Clarion Community College.

    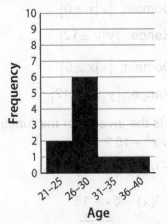

    Age

    Which data set matches the data represented on the histogram?

    A  27, 26, 28, 39, 26, 32, 21, 28, 24, 26

    B  32, 26, 28, 39, 26, 32, 26, 28, 24, 26

    C  21, 26, 22, 39, 38, 26, 32, 21, 24, 26

    D  27, 26, 28, 39, 38, 31, 32, 21, 34, 24

68. What is the interquartile range of the box-and-whisker plot shown below?

    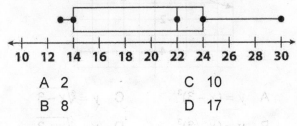

    A  2              C  10

    B  8              D  17

69. The box-and-whisker plot shows the annual salaries of the employees at Alpha Testing in thousands of dollars. The data on the table shows the annual salaries of employees at Beta Testing in thousands of dollars.

    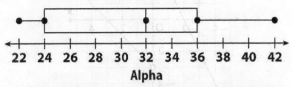

    Alpha

    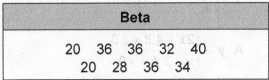

    | Beta |
    |------|
    | 20   36   36   32   40 |
    | 20   28   36   34 |

    Which statement is true based on the data presented above?

    A  The mean of the salaries at Alpha is higher than the mean of the salaries at Beta.

    B  The median salary at Alpha is lower than the median salary of at Beta.

    C  The interquartile range of the salaries at Alpha is greater than the interquartile range of the range of the salaries at Beta.

    D  The range of the salaries at Beta is greater than the range of the salaries at Alpha.

70. What is $y = \lceil x \rceil$ evaluated for $x = -7.2$?

    A  −8              C  −7

    B  −7.2            D  7.2

# Beginning-of-Year Diagnostic Test

71. Which equation is graphed below?

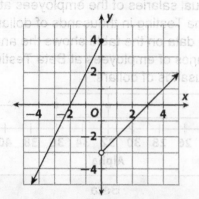

A  $y = \begin{cases} 2x + 4 \text{ if } x \leq 0 \\ x - 3 \text{ if } x > 0 \end{cases}$

B  $y = \begin{cases} 2x + 4 \text{ if } x < 0 \\ x - 3 \text{ if } x \geq 0 \end{cases}$

C  $y = \begin{cases} x + 4 \text{ if } x < 0 \\ x - 3 \text{ if } x > 0 \end{cases}$

D  $y = \begin{cases} x + 4 \text{ if } x \leq 0 \\ 2x - 3 \text{ if } x > 0 \end{cases}$

72. What is the vertex of the graph of $y = |x + 5| - 15$, and is it a maximum or a minimum?

   A  (–5, –15); minimum

   B  (–5, –15); maximum

   C  (5, –15); minimum

   D  (5, –15); maximum

73. Which is not a one-to-one function?

   A  $f(x) = -\sqrt{x}$

   B  $f(x) = \sqrt[3]{x}$

   C  $f(x) = x^2 - 13$

   D  $f(x) = x + 4$

74. What is the domain and range of the function $y = 3\sqrt{x + 12}$ ?

   A  Domain: $\{x \mid x \geq 12\}$

      Range: $\{y \mid y \geq 0\}$

   B  Domain: $\{x \mid x \geq -12\}$

      Range: $\{y \mid y \geq 0\}$

   C  Domain: $\{x \mid x \geq 0\}$

      Range: $\{y \mid y \geq 12\}$

   D  Domain: $\{x \mid x \geq 0\}$

      Range: $\{y \mid y \geq -12\}$

75. What is the inverse of the function $f(x) = x^3 + 15$ ?

   A  $f^{-1}(x) = \sqrt{x - 15}$

   B  $f^{-1}(x) = \sqrt[3]{x} - 15$

   C  $f^{-1}(x) = \sqrt[3]{x + 15}$

   D  $f^{-1}(x) = \sqrt[3]{x - 15}$

76. Which equation is graphed below?

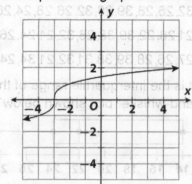

   A  $y = (x - 3)^3$          C  $y = \sqrt[3]{x - 3}$

   B  $y = (x + 3)^3$          D  $y = \sqrt[3]{x + 3}$

## MODULE 1 Relationships Between Quantities
### Module Quiz: B

1. Which of the following is the most precise measurement?

    A  13 in.          C  13.615 in.

    B  13.6 in.        D  13.62 in.

2. What are the minimum and maximum possible measures of 31 centimeters?

    _____

3. How many significant digits are in 17.090?

    _____

4. Does each of the following numbers have 3 significant digits?

    A  0.091          ○ Yes   ○ No

    B  0.910          ○ Yes   ○ No

    C  910            ○ Yes   ○ No

    D  9100           ○ Yes   ○ No

5. How many significant digits should the product of 11,435 meters and 19.35 meters have?

    A  2              C  4

    B  3              D  5

6. A room has a length of 12.62 feet and a width of 10.2 feet. Find the perimeter of the room with the correct number of significant digits.

    _____

7. To the nearest tenth, how many inches equal 12.55 centimeters?

    _____

8. The length of a dollar bill is 6.14 inches. What is the approximate length of a dollar bill to the nearest centimeter?

    _____

9. A bottle can hold 2.75 liters of water. About how many gallons can the bottle hold?

    A  0.73 gal        C  7.3 gal

    B  1.1 gal         D  11 gal

10. At 60°F, water weighs 8.33 pounds per gallon. What is the approximate weight of water to the nearest kilogram per liter?

    _____

11. A train travels 125.5 miles in 150 minutes. One mile is about 1.61 kilometers. Which of the following is closest to the train's speed in kilometers per hour?

    A  $31.2 \frac{km}{h}$        C  $80.8 \frac{km}{h}$

    B  $78.0 \frac{km}{h}$        D  $202 \frac{km}{h}$

12. A computer screen has a length of 16 inches and a width of 10 inches. What is the area of the screen to the nearest square centimeter?

    _____

| MODULE 1 | **Relationships Between Quantities** |
|---|---|

*Module Quiz: B*

**For 13–17, use the table.**

| Tonya's age (yr) | Tonya's height (in.) |
|---|---|
| 3 | 36.8 |
| 4 | 40 |
| 5 | 41.25 |
| 6 | 45 |
| 7 | 48.0 |
| 8 | 51.5 |

13. Were more precise measurements taken when Tonya was 6 years old or 8 years old?

_____

14. a. Which height has the greatest number of significant digits?

_____

    b. How many significant digits are in the number?

_____

15. a. Which height has the least number of significant digits?

_____

    b. How many significant digits are in the number?

_____

16. Tonya grew 2.25 more inches before her 9 year height was recorded. What is her height at age 9 written with the correct number of significant digits?

_____

17. Tonya's mother is 1.5 times as tall as Tonya was when she was 6. How tall is Tonya's mother? Use the correct number of significant digits.

_____

18. Laura's pet snake is 4.3 meters long. To the nearest foot, how long is the snake?

_____

19. A cistern can hold 25 gallons of water. To the nearest liter, how much water can the cistern hold?

_____

20. On average, Sam's truck will travel 57 miles per 2.5 gallons of gas. How many kilometers per liter of gas will the truck travel? Round to the nearest tenth.

_____

21. Tim walked 2.5 miles in 32.5 minutes. Find Tim's walking speed in kilometers per hour. Round to the nearest tenth.

_____

22. A square tile has side lengths of 4.5 centimeters. To the nearest inch, what is the perimeter of the tile?

_____

23. A cubic inch of gold weighs approximately 316 grams. To the nearest gram, how much does a cubic centimeter of gold weigh?

_____

Name _____ Date _____ Class _____

*Module Quiz: D*

1. Which of the following is the most precise measurement?
   A  8 m
   B  8.25 m
   C  8.3 m

2. What are the minimum and maximum possible measures of 5 inches?
   A  4.5 in. to 5.4 in.
   B  5 in. to 6 in.
   C  5.5 in. to 6.4 in.

3. How many significant digits are in 8.70?
   A  2
   B  3
   C  4

4. Which number has 2 significant digits?
   A  0.03
   B  3.40
   C  4.5

5. 9.85 km × 2.80 km = 27.6 km$^2$
   How many significant digits does the product have?
   A  2
   B  3
   C  4

6. How many significant digits should the sum of 5.6 inches and 1.03 inches have?
   A  2
   B  3
   C  4

7. Approximately how many feet are equal to 3 meters?
   A  1 ft
   B  6 ft
   C  10 ft

8. The side length of a square tile is 6.5 centimeters. What is the approximate length of the tile in inches?
   A  2.6 in.
   B  6.1 in.
   C  17 in.

9. About how many liters are in 7.3 gallons?
   A  1.9 L
   B  9.9 L
   C  28 L

10. Water weighs about 8.3 pounds per gallon. Which of the following is closest to the weight of water in kilograms per liter?
    A  1 $\frac{kg}{L}$
    B  5 $\frac{kg}{L}$
    C  15 $\frac{kg}{L}$

11. A marathon runner runs 26.2 miles in 3.5 hours. One mile is about 1.61 kilometers. What is the runner's approximate speed in kilometers per hour?
    A  4.6 $\frac{km}{h}$
    B  12 $\frac{km}{h}$
    C  42 $\frac{km}{h}$

12. The area of a carpet is 45 square feet. What is the approximate area of the carpet in square meters?
    A  4.2 m$^2$
    B  14 m$^2$
    C  148 m$^2$

**MODULE 1**

# Relationships Between Quantities

*Module Quiz: D*

**For 13–15, use the table.**

| Avis's age (yr) | Avis's height (in.) |
|---|---|
| 3 | 37.25 |
| 4 | 43 |
| 5 | 44.0 |
| 6 | 46.5 |

13. Were more precise measurements taken when Avis was 3 years old or 5 years old?

_____

14. a. Which height has the greatest number of significant digits?

_____

   b. How many significant digits are in the number?

_____

15. a. Which height has the least number of significant digits?

_____

   b. How many significant digits are in the number?

_____

16. Find 10.5 inches + 7.35 inches and use the correct number of significant digits.

_____

17. Find the area of a rectangle with a width of 5.5 meters and a length of 12.1 meters. Write your answer using the correct number of significant digits.

_____

18. To the nearest centimeter, how many centimeters are equivalent to 16 inches?

_____

19. To the nearest liter, how many liters are in 19 gallons?

_____

20. On average, Tyrone's truck will travel 19 miles per gallon of gas. How many kilometers per liter of gas will the truck travel? Round to the nearest tenth.

_____

21. Nita ran 7.5 kilometers in 42 minutes. Find Nita's speed in kilometers per hour. Round to the nearest whole number.

_____

22. A can has a circumference of 38.5 centimeters. To the nearest tenth of an inch, what is the circumference of the can?

_____

23. The area of Jami's yard is 250 square feet. Find the area of Jami's yard to the nearest square meter.

_____

**MODULE 2**

# Exponents and Real Numbers
*Module Quiz: B*

1. Which of the following is equal to $\dfrac{a^{\frac{1}{2}}}{a^{\frac{1}{4}}}$?

   A $a^2$    C $a^8$

   B 2    D $a^{\frac{1}{4}}$

2. $343^{\frac{1}{3}}$ is equal to which of the following?

   A 4    C 6

   B 5    D 7

3. Does each expression equal 4 when simplified?

   A $16^{\frac{1}{2}}$    ○ Yes    ○ No

   B $81^{\frac{1}{3}}$    ○ Yes    ○ No

   C $256^{\frac{1}{4}}$    ○ Yes    ○ No

   D $1024^{\frac{1}{5}}$    ○ Yes    ○ No

4. What is $81^{\frac{1}{4}} - 121^{\frac{1}{2}}$ simplified?

   _____

5. $64^{\frac{2}{3}}$ is equal to which of the following?

   A 2    C 96

   B 16    D 512

6. Simplify $8^{\frac{2}{3}} \times 25^{\frac{3}{2}}$.

   _____

7. Which expression is equivalent to $b^{-e}$?

   A $b^{\frac{1}{-e}}$    C $\dfrac{1}{b^{-e}}$

   B $\dfrac{1}{b^e}$    D $b^e$

8. What is $\dfrac{a^4 \times a^3}{a^7}$ simplified?

   _____

9. Does each of the following belong to the set of integers?

   A $81^{\frac{1}{3}}$    ○ Yes    ○ No

   B $64^{\frac{1}{3}}$    ○ Yes    ○ No

   C $16^{\frac{1}{3}}$    ○ Yes    ○ No

   D $1^{\frac{1}{8}}$    ○ Yes    ○ No

10. Determine if $3^{\frac{1}{2}}$ belongs to each set. Choose True or False.

    A Integers    ○ True    ○ False

    B Rational numbers    ○ True    ○ False

    C Irrational numbers    ○ True    ○ False

11. Does each set include only irrational numbers?

    A $\{7\sqrt{7},\ \sqrt{11},\ 4\pi\}$    ○ Yes    ○ No

    B $\{\sqrt{7},\ \sqrt{17},\ \pi\}$    ○ Yes    ○ No

    C $\left\{\pi,\ \dfrac{5}{9},\ \sqrt{144}\right\}$    ○ Yes    ○ No

12. Which set is **not** closed under multiplication?

    A $\{0, 1\}$    C $\{-1, 0, 1\}$

    B $\{0\}$    D $\{-2, 0, 2\}$

13. Which statement shows that the set of irrational numbers is **not** closed under multiplication?

    A $\sqrt{2} \cdot \sqrt{2} = \sqrt{4}$

    B $\sqrt{3} \cdot 3 = 3\sqrt{3}$

    C $\sqrt{5} \cdot \sqrt{2} = \sqrt{10}$

    D $\dfrac{1}{7} \cdot \sqrt{7} = \dfrac{\sqrt{7}}{7}$

**MODULE 2**

# Exponents and Real Numbers

*Module Quiz: B*

14. A rectangular mat has a length of 12.5 inches and a width of 10.2 inches. What is the area of the rug to the nearest square centimeter?

_____

15. Rewrite the expression $\sqrt[3]{18}$ with an exponent.

_____

16. Rewrite the equation $10 = 1000^?$ with an exponent that makes it true.

_____

17. Simplify the expression $400^{\frac{1}{2}} - 1^{\frac{1}{4}}$.

_____

18. Simplify the expression using the Properties of Exponents: $\left(64^{\frac{2}{6}}\right)^3$.

_____

19. The interest Mallory's savings account earned can be found with the formula $T = p(0.09)^{\frac{3}{2}}$, where $p$ is the original amount in the account. If the original amount is $2750, what is her current balance?

_____

20. List the sets that each number belongs to: whole numbers, integers, rational numbers, irrational numbers, and real numbers.

a. $\sqrt{7}$

_____

b. $-2$

_____

c. $-\dfrac{4}{9}$

_____

d. $5\sqrt{2}$

_____

21. Determine whether the set $\{-1, 0, 1\}$ is closed under each operation. Explain why the set is or it is not closed. Give an example.

a. Subtraction

_____

_____

b. Multiplication

_____

_____

Name _____ Date _____ Class _____

**MODULE 2**

# Exponents and Real Numbers
*Module Quiz: D*

1. Which of the following is equal to $a^{\frac{1}{2}} \cdot a^{\frac{1}{2}}$ ?

  A  $a$

  B  $a^{\frac{1}{4}}$

  C  1

2. Which is equal to $144^{\frac{1}{2}}$ ?

  A  10

  B  11

  C  12

3. Which expression equals 3?

  A  $16^{\frac{1}{2}}$

  B  $27^{\frac{1}{3}}$

  C  $125^{\frac{1}{3}}$

4. What is $81^{\frac{1}{2}} + 64^{\frac{1}{3}}$ simplified?

  A  13

  B  17

  C  145

5. $343^{\frac{2}{3}}$ is equivalent to which of the following?

  A  7

  B  49

  C  686

6. What is $25^{\frac{1}{2}} \times 4^{\frac{3}{2}}$ simplified?

  A  20

  B  40

  C  100

7. Which is equivalent to $\sqrt[2]{36} + 16^{\frac{1}{2}}$ ?

  A  10

  B  14

  C  22

8. Which expression is equivalent to $b^p \cdot b^e$ ?

  A  $b^{pe}$

  B  $b^p + b^e$

  C  $b^{p+e}$

9. In which set does $\sqrt{2}$ belong?

  A  Whole numbers

  B  Rational numbers

  C  Irrational numbers

10. Which set includes only rational numbers?

  A  $\left\{0, \frac{3}{5}, -5\right\}$

  B  $\{3, \pi, 4\}$

  C  $\{-1, 0, \sqrt{5}\}$

11. The set $\{0, 1\}$ is closed under which operation?

  A  Addition

  B  Subtraction

  C  Multiplication

12. Which statement shows that the set of irrational numbers is **not** closed under multiplication?

  A  $\sqrt{7} \cdot 7 = 7\sqrt{7}$

  B  $\sqrt{2} \cdot \sqrt{2} = 2$

  C  $\sqrt{3} \cdot \sqrt{2} = \sqrt{6}$

**MODULE 2**

# Exponents and Real Numbers
*Module Quiz: D*

13. Tai is 180 centimeters tall. To the nearest tenth of an inch, how tall is he?

_____

14. Rewrite the expression $\sqrt[3]{11}$ with an exponent.

_____

15. What exponent makes the statement $9^{?} = 3$ true?

_____

16. Simplify $49^{\frac{1}{2}} \times 8^{\frac{1}{3}}$.

_____

17. Simplify $\dfrac{2^5}{2^3}$ with the Properties of Exponents.

_____

18. Orange Computers' stock can be represented by $s = 3t^{\frac{1}{2}}$ where $t$ is the number of months the stock has been on the market. Find the predicted price of the stock after 64 months.

_____

19. List the sets that each number belongs to: whole numbers, integers, rational numbers, irrational numbers, and real numbers.

a. 15

_____

_____

b. $\pi$

_____

_____

_____

c. −6

_____

_____

d. $\dfrac{1}{7}$

_____

_____

20. Determine whether the set $\{-1, 1\}$ is closed under each operation. Explain why the set is or is not closed. Give an example.

a. Addition

_____

_____

b. Division

_____

_____

Name _____ Date _____ Class _____

# Expressions
## *Module Quiz: B*

1. Does $-\sqrt{25}$ belong to each of the following sets?

   A  Whole numbers          ○ Yes    ○ No

   B  Rational numbers       ○ Yes    ○ No

   C  Irrational numbers     ○ Yes    ○ No

   D  Real numbers           ○ Yes    ○ No

2. How many coefficients are in the expression $\frac{1}{3}y^2 - 18y + 9 - 2y^{-2}$?

   _____

3. Which of the following is a term in the expression $-9x^3 + 12p + 6$?

   A  $p$                C  3

   B  $-9$               D  6

4. What is $7 + y(3 + y)^2$ when evaluated for $y = -5$?

   _____

5. Evaluate $-10z + 2y \div z$ for $z = -2$ and $y = 6$.

   _____

6. Find $-3(x - 2) \div y^2$ evaluated for $x = 4$ and $y = \frac{1}{2}$.

   _____

7. Kurt works at a cafe and earns \$16 per hour. On Wednesday, he worked $t$ hours, and his neighbor paid him \$5 per hour to babysit for $b$ hours. Which expression best represents the amount Kurt earned?

   A  $16t + 5$          C  $16t + 5b$

   B  $16t - 5b$         D  $16b + 5t$

8. Which of the following is equivalent to $6(2y - 4) + p$?

   A  $p + 12y - 24$     C  $p - 6(2y - 4)$

   B  $6y + p - 24$      D  $24 + 12y + p$

9. Is each of the following a list of unlike terms, or terms that cannot be combined?

   A  $x, \frac{1}{2}x, 6x$            ○ Yes    ○ No

   B  $-2\frac{2}{5}, 1, 12$           ○ Yes    ○ No

   C  $-3t, 2.5, 4x$                   ○ Yes    ○ No

   D  $0.5x, 6y, 21$                   ○ Yes    ○ No

10. The expression $7z - 9p + 9z - z$ is equivalent to which of the following?

    A  $-2z + 8p$        C  $15z + 9p$

    B  $8z$              D  $-9p + 15z$

11. What is $3(2x + 7y) - 6x$ equivalent to after being simplified?

    _____

12. Les bought 6 pairs of shorts for $s$ dollars each and 2 pairs of pants that cost $p$ dollars each. He also bought a blazer that cost three times as much as a pair of shorts. Write an expression that represents the total amount Les spent.

    _____

| MODULE | # Expressions |
|---|---|
| **3** | *Module Quiz: B* |

13. Simplify $81^{\frac{3}{2}} \div 27^{\frac{5}{3}}$.

_____

14. Write the coefficient(s) in the expression $7x^2 - y + 9$.

_____

15. Evaluate $x \div 4 + 3y^2$ for $x = 8$ and $y = 3$.

_____

16. Evaluate the algebraic expression $-6r + 3s + \dfrac{1}{2}$ for $r = \dfrac{1}{4}$ and $s = 1$.

_____

17. Monday, Nita earned $85 for $h$ hours of babysitting. Wednesday, she earned the same rate for 8 hours of babysitting and got a $12 tip.

   a. Write an expression to represent how much Nita earned on Wednesday.

_____

   b. If Nita worked for 5 hours on Monday, how much did she earn on Wednesday?

_____

18. Selena's family took a road trip. The first day, they traveled 462 miles in 7 hours. They continued at the same rate on the second day and traveled for 4 hours. How far did they travel in all?

_____

19. Write two expressions that are equivalent to $-2(4 - y)$.

_____

20. Simplify $-18x + 5 + 22x$.

_____

21. Simplify $6(7z + y) - 5y$.

_____

22. Simplify $7x^2 + 3(6 + x^2)$.

_____

23. Penelope buys $x$ pounds of bananas for $0.42 per pound and $y$ pounds of apples for $1.19 per pound.

   a. Write an expression that represents the total amount Penelope spent on bananas.

_____

   b. Write an expression that represents the total amount she spent on bananas and apples.

_____

**MODULE 3**

# Expressions
## *Module Quiz: D*

1. In which set does −7 belong?
   A  Whole numbers
   B  Integers
   C  Irrational numbers

2. Which of the following is a coefficient in $8x + 7y$?
   A  $8x$
   B  8
   C  $y$

3. What is $7 + 6x$ evaluated for $x = 3$?
   A  13
   B  15
   C  25

4. Which of the following is $r^2 + 4s$ evaluated for $r = 4$ and $s = 1.5$?
   A  14
   B  22
   C  30

5. Christian works at a library and earns $16 per hour. On Wednesday, he worked $t$ hours and his neighbor paid him $13 to walk her dog. Which expression represents the total amount Christian earned?
   A  $16 + 13t$
   B  $16 − 13t$
   C  $16t + 13$

6. Which of the following is equivalent to $5(7 − p)$?
   A  $−5p + 35$
   B  $35 + 5p$
   C  $−35 + 5p$

7. Which of the following is a list of unlike terms, or terms that cannot be combined?
   A  $x, \frac{1}{2}x, 6x$
   B  $−3t, 2.5, 4x$
   C  $−2\frac{2}{5}, 1, 12$

8. $7z − 9z$ is equivalent to which of the following?
   A  $−2$
   B  $−2z$
   C  $−2z^2$

9. What is $8x − 7 + 12x$ after being simplified?
   A  $13x$
   B  $−4x + 7$
   C  $20x − 7$

10. Hye Sun bought 4 skirts for $s$ dollars each, 3 pairs of pants for $p$ dollars each, and a jacket that cost 4 times as much as each skirt. The total amount she spent is represented by $4s + 3p + 4s$. What is the expression in simplest terms?
    A  $3p + 8s^2$
    B  $3p + 8s$
    C  $11sp$

**MODULE 3**

# Expressions

*Module Quiz: D*

11. Simplify $9^{\frac{3}{2}} - 25^{\frac{1}{2}}$.

_____

12. Write the term(s) in the expression $3t^2 + 5t$.

_____

13. Evaluate $q \div 4 + 8q$ for $q = 8$.

_____

14. Evaluate $11r + 2(s - 5)$ for $r = 4$ and $s = -2$.

_____

15. Ross had $c$ number of coin collections with 15 coins in each collection. His aunt gave him 8 more coins. Write an expression that represents the total number of coins Ross has now.

_____

16. Rosalinda's family is taking a road trip. They drove at a rate of 45 miles per hour. If they drove for 5 hours on the first day and 4 hours on the second day, how far did they go?

_____

17. Write an expression equivalent to $7(3p - 4)$.

_____

18. Simplify $-10x + 7x$.

_____

19. Simplify $6r - 5s + 14r$.

_____

20. Simplify $6x - 7x^2 + 2x^2 + 4$.

_____

21. Jen buys $b$ boxes of cereal for $2.50 each and $c$ cartons of milk for $3.25 each.

a. Write an expression that represents the total amount Jen spent.

_____

b. Jen bought the same number of boxes of cereal as cartons of milk. Write a new expression in simplest terms that represents the amount Jen spent.

_____

c. If Jen bought 3 boxes of cereal, how much did she spend on cereal and milk?

_____

**MODULE 4**

# Equations and Inequalities in One Variable
## *Module Quiz: B*

1. What is $\dfrac{7(5+2x)}{y^2}$ evaluated for $x = -\dfrac{1}{2}$ and $y = 2$?

   _____

2. Solve $7 + \dfrac{x}{4} = 5$ for $x$.

   _____

3. What is the best first step for solving the equation $-1.8 = \dfrac{2z-18}{5}$?

   A  Add 18 to both sides of the equation.

   B  Subtract 18 from both sides of the equation.

   C  Multiply both sides of the equation by 5.

   D  Divide both sides of the equation by 1.8.

4. What is the solution for the equation $0.7m - 3.2 = 2.5 + 1.2m$?

   _____

5.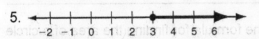

   Does each inequality have solutions that match those graphed on the number line above?

   A  $45 \le 15x$        ○ Yes   ○ No

   B  $\dfrac{x}{3} < 1$        ○ Yes   ○ No

   C  $\dfrac{x}{6} \ge \dfrac{1}{2}$        ○ Yes   ○ No

6. Graph the solutions of $\dfrac{x}{4} + \dfrac{25}{4} > \dfrac{15}{4}$.

7. Choose True or False for each statement about the solutions of $6 - 5x > -9$.

   A  The solutions are all less than −3.

   ○ True   ○ False

   B  The solutions are all less than 3.

   ○ True   ○ False

   C  The solution set includes 0.

   ○ True   ○ False

   D  The solution set includes −6.

   ○ True   ○ False

8. What are the solutions of $7(4 - y) \le 9y + 20$?

   _____

9. The equation for finding the area of a trapezoid is $A = \dfrac{1}{2}(b_1 + b_2)h$. What is the equation solved for $h$?

   A  $h = \dfrac{A}{b_1 + b_2}$

   B  $h = \dfrac{2A}{b_1 + b_2}$

   C  $h = \dfrac{1}{2}(b_1 + b_2)$

   D  $h = 2A - b_1 - b_2$

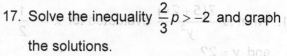

# Equations and Inequalities in One Variable
## *Module Quiz: B*

10. What is $5r = \dfrac{s+2}{3}$ solved for $s$?

_____

11. Simplify $12x - 3(2x + y) - 5y$.

_____

12. Solve $2.5 = \dfrac{x}{6}$.

_____

13. Solve $5z - 12z - 10 = 18 + 7z$.

_____

14. Solve the equation $21p - 4 = \dfrac{12p+7}{2}$.

_____

15. Solve $5x + 2(3x - 7) = -20 + 11x + 6$.

_____

16. A cell phone company charges $45 per month for unlimited calls and $0.25 per text message. Another cell phone company charges $0.15 per text message and $70 per month for unlimited calls.

   a. Write an equation to represent when the cost from both companies will be the same.

   _____

   b. Solve the equation and interpret the solution.

   _____

   _____

   _____

17. Solve the inequality $\dfrac{2}{3}p > -2$ and graph the solutions.

   ```
   ←+—+—+—+—+—+—+—+—+→
    -4 -3 -2 -1  0  1  2  3  4
   ```

18. Solve and graph the solutions for $8 - d \geq -3d + 4$.

   ```
   ←+—+—+—+—+—+—+—+—+→
    -4 -3 -2 -1  0  1  2  3  4
   ```

19. Solve the inequality $2(3x - 4) \geq 9x - 10$.

   _____

20. Solve $2x + 3 > \dfrac{6x+7}{3}$.

   _____

21. Juan is making birdhouses to sell at a craft show. The cost of making the birdhouses is $80 plus $6.25 per birdhouse. He will sell them for $16 each. Write and solve an equation to find the minimum number of birdhouses he must sell to make a profit.

   _____

22. The formula for finding the area of a circle is $A = \pi r^2$. Solve the formula for $r$.

   _____

23. Solve $9(t - 7) = u$ for $t$.

   _____

Name _____ Date _____ Class _____

# Equations and Inequalities in One Variable
*Module Quiz: D*

1. Which of the following is $5(r+2)+4s$ evaluated for $r=8$ and $s=2$?

   A  23

   B  50

   C  58

2. Solve $3x-9=12$ for $x$.

   A  1

   B  7

   C  21

3. What is the best first step for solving the equation $-8=2z-18$?

   A  Add 18 to both sides of the equation.

   B  Subtract 8 from both sides of the equation.

   C  Multiply both sides of the equation by 2.

4. Solve $5m+3=3m-7$. What is the value of $m$?

   A  −5

   B  −2

   C  $-\dfrac{1}{2}$

5.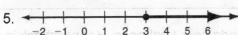

   Which inequality is graphed on the number line above?

   A  $x>3$

   B  $x\le 3$

   C  $x\ge 3$

6. Which graph best represents the solutions of $b+7>-2$?

   A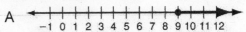

   B

   C

7. Which statement describes the solutions of $-3x>9$?

   A  The solutions are less than −3.

   B  The solutions are less than 3.

   C  The solutions are greater than −3.

8. What are the solutions of $5y\le 9y+16$?

   A  $y\le 4$

   B  $y\ge 4$

   C  $y\ge -4$

9. The equation for finding the area of a rectangle is $A=\ell w$. What is the equation solved for $w$?

   A  $w=\ell A$

   B  $w=\dfrac{\ell}{A}$

   C  $w=\dfrac{A}{\ell}$

10. What is $p=4r+2$ solved for $r$?

    A  $r=\dfrac{p}{4}-2$

    B  $r=\dfrac{p-2}{4}$

    C  $r=\dfrac{2p}{r}$

**MODULE 4**

# Equations and Inequalities in One Variable
## *Module Quiz: D*

11. Simplify $9x + 3y - 2x$.

_____

12. Solve $9 = 4 + x$.

_____

13. Solve $5z = 45 - 4z$.

_____

14. Fill in the blanks to solve the equation.
$$\frac{z}{5} - 7 = -1$$

$$\frac{z}{5} = \underline{\phantom{xx}}$$

$$z = \underline{\phantom{xx}}$$

15. Solve $7x + 3 = 3 + 7x$.

_____

16. Sofia has been saving money to buy a new computer. For her birthday, Sofia's mother gave her twice what she had already saved. Now she has $135.

a. Using $x$ to represent the money Sofia saved before her mother's present, write an equation that represents the situation.

_____

b. How much money did Sofia have before her birthday?

_____

17. Graph the inequality $d \geq 2$.

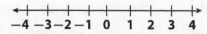

18. $-6p < 12$

a. Solve the inequality.

_____

b. Graph the solutions.

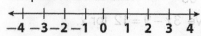

19. Fill in the blanks to solve the inequality.

$$17x + 6 \geq 9x - 10$$

$$\underline{\phantom{xx}} + 6 \geq -10$$

$$8x \geq \underline{\phantom{xx}}$$

$$x \geq \underline{\phantom{xx}}$$

20. Solve $x + 3 > x + 7$.

21. Eric has $115 to spend on back to school clothes. So far, he has spent $90. Write an inequality to show how much more money Eric can spend.

_____

22. Rhonda sells textbooks. Her paycheck is found using the formula $p = 30b + 15$ where $b$ is the number of textbooks she sells. Solve the formula for $b$.

_____

23. Solve $\frac{t}{5} = u$ for $t$.

_____

**MODULE 5**

# Equations in Two Variables and Functions
## *Module Quiz: B*

1. Solve $13 - \dfrac{x}{2} = 0$ for $x$.

_____

2. Does each pair of values make
   $s^2 + 2r = 16$ true?

   A   $s = -2$ and $r = 6$      ○ Yes    ○ No
   B   $s = 3$ and $r = 7$       ○ Yes    ○ No
   C   $s = 4$ and $r = 0$       ○ Yes    ○ No
   D   $s = 8$ and $r = -1$      ○ Yes    ○ No

3. Is $(2.5, 4)$ a solution to each of the
   following equations?

   A   $y = \dfrac{x+1}{2}$       ○ Yes    ○ No

   B   $y = 6x - 11$             ○ Yes    ○ No

   C   $y = x^2 - 13.5$          ○ Yes    ○ No

   D   $y = 4x - 6$              ○ Yes    ○ No

4.

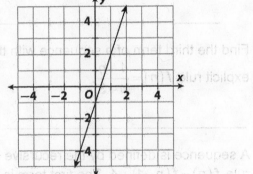

   Which equation matches the graph
   shown?

   A   $y = x - 1$          C   $y = 3x - 1$

   B   $y = 2x - 1$         D   $y = x^2 - 1$

5. What is the value of $f(x) = \dfrac{x}{2} + 8$ for
   $x = 10$?

_____

6.

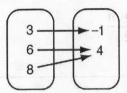

   Find the domain of the relation
   represented on the mapping diagram.

_____

7. Is each of the following a function?
   A   $(2, 1)$, $(4, 3)$, $(6, 5)$, $(8, 7)$

   ○ Yes    ○ No

   B   $(2, 1)$, $(4, 3)$, $(6, 5)$, $(2, 7)$

   ○ Yes    ○ No

   C   $(2, 1)$, $(4, 1)$, $(6, 5)$, $(8, 7)$

   ○ Yes    ○ No

8. What is the fifth term of the sequence
   defined by $f(n) = 3(n - 3)$?

_____

9. The first term of a sequence is 4. What is
   the third term of the sequence with the
   recursive rule $f(n) = 2f(n - 1) + 2$?

_____

10. Which function defines the sequence
    $-8,\ -6,\ -4, \ldots$?

    A   $f(n) = -10 - n$      C   $f(n) = n - 9$

    B   $f(n) = -10 + n^2$    D   $f(n) = 2n - 10$

**MODULE 5** **Equations in Two Variables and Functions**

*Module Quiz: B*

11. Solve $13 - m = \dfrac{-4 + m}{2}$.

_____

12. Determine whether either of the ordered pairs $(3, -2)$ or $(6, 1)$ is a solution to the equation $3x - y^2 = 5$.

_____

13. a. Complete the table.

| $x$ | $3 - 2x = y$ | $y$ |
|-----|--------------|-----|
| $-1$ | $3 - 2(-1) = y$ | $5$ |
| $0$ | | |
| $2$ | | |
| $4$ | | |

   b. Graph the solutions to $3 - 2x = y$.

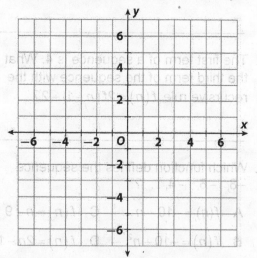

14. Find the value of $f(x) = x^2 + 2x - 5$ for $x = 4$.

_____

15. a. Graph the functions $h(x) = -x + 2$ and $g(x) = x - 8$.

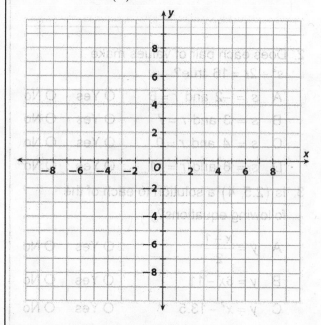

   b. When does $h(x) = g(x)$?

_____

16. Find the third term of a sequence with the explicit rule $f(n) = \dfrac{4 - n}{n + 3}$.

_____

17. A sequence is defined by the recursive rule $f(n) = f(n - 1) + 4$. The first term is 7. Write the first 4 terms of the sequence.

_____

18. Write a recursive function for the sequence 1, $-2$, $-5$, $-8$.

_____

_____

_____

# MODULE 5  Equations in Two Variables and Functions
### *Module Quiz: D*

1. Solve $12 + 2x = 18$ for $x$. What is the value of $x$?

  A  3

  B  6

  C  15

2. For which values is $3r = s$ true?

  A  $r = 3$ and $s = \dfrac{1}{3}$

  B  $r = \dfrac{1}{3}$ and $s = 1$

  C  $r = 18$ and $s = 6$

3. Which ordered pair is a solution to $y = 3 + x$?

  A  $(-4, -1)$

  B  $(2, -1)$

  C  $(2, -5)$

4.

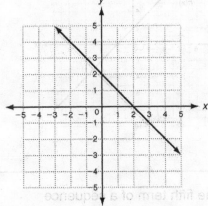

  Which equation matches the graph?

  A  $y = 2x$

  B  $y = 2 - x$

  C  $y = 2 + x$

5. What is the value of $f(x) = 6 + x$ for $x = 10$?

  A  $-4$

  B  4

  C  16

6. What is the range of the following set of points: $\{(3, 4), (7, -2), (11, -8)\}$?

  A  $\{3, 7, 11\}$

  B  $\{-8, -2, 3, 4, 7, 11\}$

  C  $\{-8, -2, 4\}$

7. Which mapping diagram represents a function?

  A

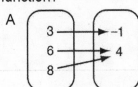

  B

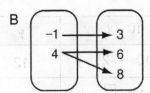

8. What is the fourth term of the sequence 4, 8, 12, 16, 20, 24, . . .?

  A  4

  B  16

  C  24

9. What is the third term of the sequence defined by $f(n) = 2n - 1$?

  A  3

  B  5

  C  7

10. Which function defines the sequence 6, 8, 10, . . .?

  A  $f(n) = 2n + 4$

  B  $f(n) = 3n + 2$

  C  $f(n) = 6n$

## MODULE 5

# Equations in Two Variables and Functions

### Module Quiz: D

11. Solve $5y + 4 = 6y$.

_____

12. Determine if the following are solutions to $y = 5x + 1$.

   a. $(3, 14)$

   _____

   b. $(-1, -4)$

   _____

13. Fill in the table.

| x | $10 - x = y$ | y |
|---|---|---|
| –2 | $10 - (-2) = y$ | 12 |
| 0 | $10 - \square = y$ | |
| 2 | $10 - \square = y$ | |

14. Use the values from the table below to graph the solutions to $y = -x - 1$.

| x | y |
|---|---|
| –2 | 1 |
| 0 | –1 |
| 2 | –3 |

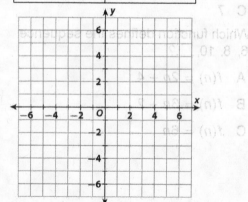

15. Find the value of $f(x) = 6 + 2x$ for $x = 3$.

_____

16. Explain if the graph shown represents a function.

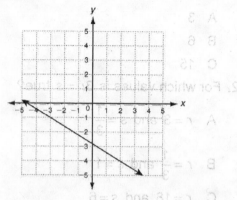

_____

17. Use the graph to determine when the function $h(x)$ equals $g(x)$.

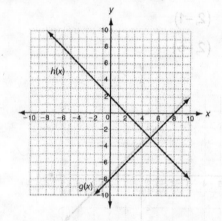

_____

18. Find the fifth term of a sequence represented by $f(n) = 5n - 2$.

_____

19. The terms in a sequence can be found using the recursive rule $f(n) = f(n-1) - 2$. Fill in the missing terms.

   3, ____, –1, ____

20. Write a function that represents the sequence 7, 14, 21, 28, . . .

_____

Name _____     Date _____     Class _____

**MODULE 6**

# Linear Functions

*Module Quiz: B*

1. Is the ordered pair (0.5, 8.5) a solution to the following equations?

   A  $y = 17x$          ○ Yes    ○ No

   B  $y = 5x - 42$      ○ Yes    ○ No

   C  $y = -7x + 12$     ○ Yes    ○ No

   D  $y = x^2 + 15x$    ○ Yes    ○ No

2. Is each of the functions a linear function?

   A  $y = 4x - 7$       ○ Yes    ○ No

   B  $y = 6x^2 - 1$     ○ Yes    ○ No

   C  $y = \dfrac{1}{2x} + 10$   ○ Yes    ○ No

3. What describes the slope of the line shown on the graph below?

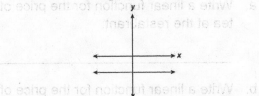

   A  positive          C  0

   B  negative          D  undefined

4. What is the slope of the line below?

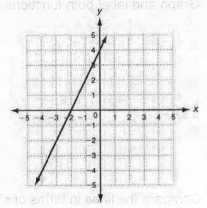

5. What is the slope of a line that contains the point (−0.5, 4) and has a *y*-intercept of −5?

   _____

6. Does each of the following equations describe a line with an *x*-intercept of 7?

   A  $-2x - 7y = -14$   ○ Yes    ○ No

   B  $3x + 2y = 14$     ○ Yes    ○ No

   C  $-4x + 2y = -28$   ○ Yes    ○ No

7. Write an equation that describes the line that passes through (2, 2) and (0, −3).

   _____

8. The table below shows the relationship between the size of a painting by a particular artist and the price the artist charges for the painting.

   | Painting size, in² (*x*) | 48 | 64 | 144 |
   |---|---|---|---|
   | Price, dollars (*y*) | 120 | 152 | 312 |

   Which equation describes the relationship?

   A  $y = 3x - 40$

   B  $y = x + 72$

   C  $y = 2x + 24$

   D  $y = 3x - 24$

**MODULE 6** **Linear Functions**

*Module Quiz: B*

9. Find the value of $f(x) = 3x^2 - x + 23$ for $x = -4$.

_____

10.

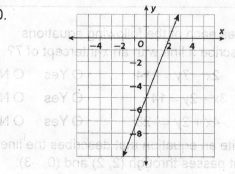

a. What are the x- and y-intercepts of the line graphed above?

_____

b. What is the slope of the line?

_____

c. Write an equation for the line.

_____

11. Graph and label $y = -2$ and $x = 5$ on the graph below.

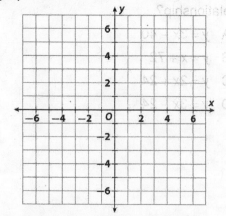

12. What is the domain and range of $y = 3x - 7.25$?

_____

13. Write an equation in slope-intercept form for a line that goes through the points $(-3, 5)$ and $(2, 8)$.

_____

14. Write an equation in standard form for an equation with an x-intercept of 2 and a y-intercept of –6.

_____

15. A restaurant sells tea for $1.50 plus $0.50 per refill.
A gas station store sells tea for $0.50 plus $0.50 per refill.

a. Write a linear function for the price of tea at the restaurant.

_____

b. Write a linear function for the price of tea at the gas station.

_____

c. Graph and label both functions.

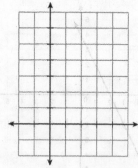

d. Compare the lines in terms of slope and translation.

_____

_____

**MODULE 6**

# Linear Functions

*Module Quiz: D*

1. Which ordered pair is a solution to the equation $y = x - 7$?

   A (−1, −6)

   B (0, −7)

   C (8, −1)

2. Which of the following is a linear function?

   A

   B

   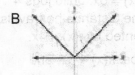

   C

   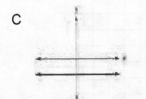

3. What describes the slope of a vertical line?

   A positive

   B 0

   C undefined

4. What is the slope of the line that contains the points (1, −1) and (−2, 8)?

   A −3

   B $-\dfrac{7}{3}$

   C $-\dfrac{1}{3}$

5. What is the slope of the line below?

   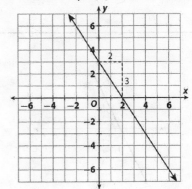

   A $-\dfrac{3}{2}$

   B $-\dfrac{2}{3}$

   C $\dfrac{3}{2}$

6. Which of the following equations describes a line with an x-intercept of 3?

   A $x + y = -3$

   B $y = 3$

   C $x = 3$

7. What is an equation of a linear function with a slope of −5 and y-intercept of 7?

   A $y = \dfrac{-5}{7}x$

   B $y = 7x - 5$

   C $y = -5x + 7$

8. The table shows a relationship between the number of hours Fernando works and his paycheck.

   | Hours (x) | 1 | 2 | 3 | 4 |
   |---|---|---|---|---|
   | Pay (y) | 25 | 40 | 55 | 70 |

   Which equation could represent this relationship?

   A $y = 10x + 15$

   B $y = 15x + 10$

   C $y = x + 25$

# Linear Functions

*Module Quiz: D*

9. Find the value of $f(x) = 3x + 7$ for $x = 8$.

_____

10.

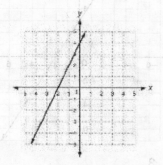

a. What is the *x*-intercept of the line graphed above?

_____

b. What is the *y*-intercept of the line?

_____

c. What is the slope of the line?

_____

d. Write an equation for the line.

_____

11. a. Graph $x = -4$ on the graph below.

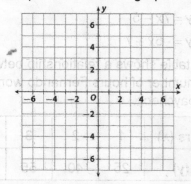

b. What is the domain of $x = -4$?

_____

c. What is the range of $x = -4$?

_____

12. Write an equation in slope-intercept form for a line that goes through the points (0, 6) and (1, −1).

_____

13. Find the *x*-intercept and *y*-intercept of $\frac{1}{2}x = -4y - 8$.

_____

14. Katherine jogs 6 miles per hour. The distance she travels in *x* hours is represented by $k(x) = 6x$. Julio jogs 4 miles per hour. The distance he travels in *x* hours is represented by $j(x) = 4x$.

a. Graph and label $k(x) = 6x$, and $j(x) = 4x$.

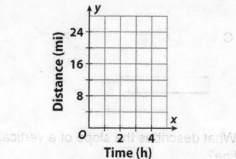

b. Who travels farther in 4 hours, and how far does this person travel?

_____

c. Which function has a greater slope?

_____

Name _____ Date _____ Class _____

# Building Linear Functions
## *Module Quiz: B*

1. What is the slope of a line that contains the point (–5, 4) and has a *x*-intercept of –10?

   _____

2. Is each of the following an arithmetic sequence?

   A  $\frac{1}{3}$, 1, $1\frac{2}{3}$, $2\frac{1}{3}$, ...   ○ Yes   ○ No

   B  –12, –4, 0, 2, ...   ○ Yes   ○ No

   C  –6, 0, 6, 12, ...   ○ Yes   ○ No

3. What is the common difference of the sequence represented in the table?

   | *n* | 2 | 4 | 5 |
   |------|-----|-----|-----|
   | *f(x)* | –4 | 6 | 11 |

   _____

4. Bernice's monthly paycheck can be represented by $p(d) = 210d + 1100$. She also earns money babysitting which can be represented by $b(d) = 36d + 100$. In both functions, *d* represents the number of weekdays. Write a function that represents Bernice's total monthly income.

   _____

5. $f(x) = -2x + 17$; $g(x) = -5x - 10$
   What is $h(x) = f(x) - g(x)$?

   _____

6. Find the inverse of $f(x) = \frac{x}{8} - 5$.

   _____

7. $r(x) = -12x + 3$; $s(x) = 5$
   What is $t(x) = r(x) \times s(x)$?

   _____

8. The solution of which linear inequality is graphed below?

   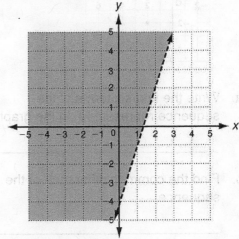

   A  $3x - y > -4$

   B  $3x - y < 4$

   C  $-3x + y \geq -4$

   D  $3x + y \leq 4$

9. Which ordered pair is a solution of $y > 5x - 2$?

   A  (1, 5)          C  (3, 13)

   B  (2, 7)          D  (4, 4)

**MODULE 7**

# Building Linear Functions

*Module Quiz: B*

10. Find the *x*-intercept and *y*-intercept of

$$y = \frac{3}{7}x - 2.$$

_____

11.

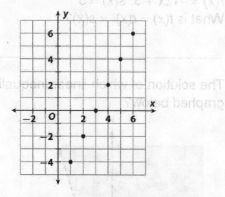

a. Write the first six terms of the sequence represented on the graph.

_____

b. Find the common difference of the sequence.

_____

c. Write a recursive rule for the sequence.

_____

d. Write an explicit rule for the sequence.

_____

**For 12–14, use the functions**

$$f(x) = -3x + \frac{13}{2};\ g(x) = \frac{1}{2}x - 5\ \textbf{and}$$

$$h(x) = -2.$$

12. Find $s(x) = f(x) + g(x)$.

_____

13. Find $d(x) = f(x) - g(x)$.

14. Find $p(x) = f(x) \times h(x)$.

_____

15. a.   Find the inverse of $f(x) = \frac{x}{4} + 2$.

_____

b.   Graph $f(x)$ and $f^{-1}(x)$.

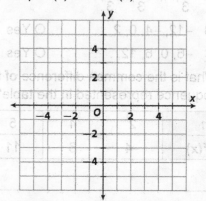

c.   Write the *x*-intercept and *y*-intercept of each line.

_____

16. Determine if $\left(10, -7\frac{1}{2}\right)$ is a solution of

$$y \geq -\frac{1}{4}x - 5.$$

_____

17. Graph the inequality $y > \frac{1}{2}$.

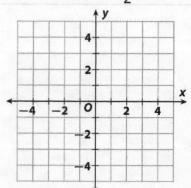

Name _____ Date _____ Class _____

# Building Linear Functions
*Module Quiz: D*

1. What is the slope of the line that contains the points (1, 6) and (2, –2)?

    A  4

    B  –8

    C  $\frac{1}{8}$

2. Which of the following is an arithmetic sequence?

    A  2, 4, 8, 16, …

    B  5, 10, 15, 20, …

    C  7, 8, 10, 13, …

3. What is the common difference of the sequence with the recursive rule

    $f(1) = 4; f(n) = f(n-1) + 5$?

    A  –1

    B  4

    C  5

4. $f(x) = 6x - 7; g(x) = 3x + 10$
   What is the sum of $f(x)$ and $g(x)$?

    A  $3x + 3$

    B  $9x + 3$

    C  $9x - 3$

5. $f(x) = 4x + 13; g(x) = x + 8$
   Which of the following expressions is equal to $h(x)$ if $h(x) = f(x) - g(x)$?

    A  $3x + 21$

    B  $4x + 5$

    C  $3x + 5$

6. What is the inverse of $f(x) = x + 9$?

    A  $f^{-1}(x) = x + 9$

    B  $f^{-1}(x) = x - 9$

    C  $f^{-1}(x) = 9 - x$

7. A pet sitter originally charged clients $4 per hour of sitting plus a set fee of $20, or $T(h) = 4h + 20$. The sitter decided to double the fees. Which of the following functions represents the doubled fees?

    A  $N(h) = 8h + 20$

    B  $N(h) = 4h + 40$

    C  $N(h) = 8h + 40$

8. Which inequality is represented by the graph shown?

    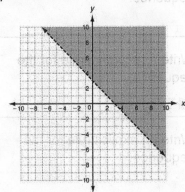

    A  $y \le -x + 3$

    B  $y > -x + 3$

    C  $y \ge -x + 3$

9. Which ordered pair is a solution of the inequality on the graph?

    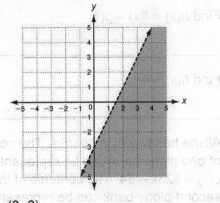

    A  (3, 2)

    B  (0, –2)

    C  (–3, 2)

**MODULE 7**

# Building Linear Functions
### *Module Quiz: D*

10. Find the *x*-intercept and *y*-intercept of $6x - 8y = 24$.

_____

11.

| *n* | 1 | 2 | 3 | 4 |
|-----|---|----|----|----|
| *f(x)* | 7 | 14 | 21 | 28 |

a. Find the common difference of the sequence.

_____

b. Write a recursive rule for the sequence.

_____

c. Write an explicit rule for the sequence.

_____

**For 12–14, use the functions $f(x) = 7x + 6$ and $g(x) = 6x + 8$.**

12. Find $h(x) = f(x) + g(x)$.

_____

13. Find $h(x) = f(x) - g(x)$.

_____

14. Find $h(x) = 4f(x)$.

_____

15. Alisha has two piggy banks. The contents of one piggy bank can be represented by $p(x) = \$23x - \$4$. The contents of the second piggy bank can be represented by $s(x) = \$17x + \$12$. Write a function that represents the total amount of money in the banks.

_____

16. a. Find the inverse of $f(x) = 2x$.

_____

b. Graph $f(x) = 2x$ and the inverse function, $f^{-1}(x)$.

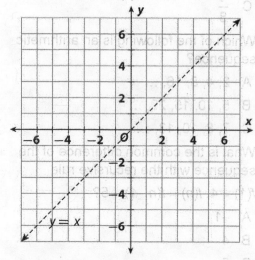

17. Determine whether (4, 3) is a solution of $y \le -2x - 5$.

_____

18. Graph the inequality represented in Exercise 17.

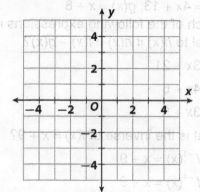

**MODULE 8**
# Modeling with Linear Functions
## *Module Quiz: B*

1. $f(x) = 9x + 11$; $g(x) = -4x + 25$
   What is $h(x) = f(x) - g(x)$?

   _____

2. Based on the graph below, which is the best prediction for the cost of 9 items?

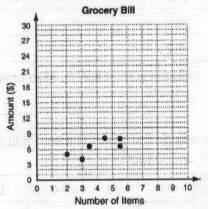

   **Grocery Bill**

   A  about 10          C  about 21

   B  about 14          D  about 28

3. Does each of the following correlation coefficients indicate a weak positive correlation?

   A  $-0.1$          ○ Yes   ○ No

   B  $0$             ○ Yes   ○ No

   C  $0.6$           ○ Yes   ○ No

4. The table shows the ages of several people and how many hours a day they spend playing computer and video games.

| Age (yrs) | 15 | 63 | 33 | 22 | 15 |
|---|---|---|---|---|---|
| Playing (hrs/day) | 5 | 0 | 2 | 8 | 0 |

   Which equation could represent a line of best fit for this data?

   A  $y \approx 53x - 7.9$

   B  $y \approx -7.9x + 53$

   C  $y \approx 5.3x - 0.079$

   D  $y \approx -0.079x + 5.3$

5. Which correlation best describes the data represented in the table below?

| Price of stock over time | | | | |
|---|---|---|---|---|
| 2000 | 2002 | 2004 | 2006 | 2008 |
| $5 | $11 | $4 | $10 | $5 |

   A  Strong positive

   B  Positive

   C  Negative

   D  None

6. What is the sum of the squared residuals based on the data shown on the table?

| $y = 1.6x + 8$ | | |
|---|---|---|
| x | y (actual) | y (predicted) |
| 0 | 9 | 8 |
| 2 | 9.2 | 11.2 |
| 4 | 15 | 14.4 |
| 6 | 19.6 | 17.6 |

   _____

7. The sum of the squared residuals of lines of fit **A** and **B** is calculated. Line **B** better fits the data. Could each of the following be true?

   A  The sum of the squared residuals of **A** is 1.8. The sum of the squared residuals of **B** is 2.5.

   ○ Yes   ○ No

   B  The sum of the squared residuals of **A** is 2.6. The sum of the squared residuals of **B** is 1.1.

   ○ Yes   ○ No

   C  The sum of the squared residuals of **A** is 0.8. The sum of the squared residuals of **B** is 0.09.

   ○ Yes   ○ No

**MODULE**
**8**

# Modeling with Linear Functions

*Module Quiz: B*

8. Find the inverse of $f(x) = -4x + 2.65$.

_____

9. The table shows the percent of students on the honor roll for four years.

| Year | '09 | '10 | '11 | '12 |
|---|---|---|---|---|
| Honor Roll | 35% | 42% | 38% | 48% |

a. Draw a scatter plot and trend line.

**Honor Roll**

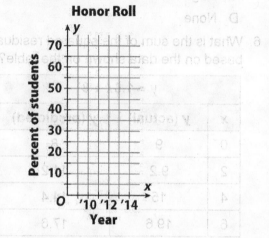

b. Write an equation for the trend line.

_____

c. Make a prediction for the percent of students on the honor roll in 2014.

_____

d. The percent of students on the honor roll in 2013 was 56%. Does this change your prediction for the percent of students on the honor roll in 2014? Explain why or why not.

_____

10. a. Complete the table.

| $p = -1.5x + 4.4$ | | | |
|---|---|---|---|
| x | p (actual) | p (predicted) | residuals |
| -2 | 6 | 7.4 | |
| 0 | 5.5 | | |
| 2 | 1 | | |
| 4 | -1.2 | | |

b. Find the sum of the squared residuals.

_____

11. The line on the graph is a line of fit for the data on the table.

| x | -4 | 0 | 4 | 8 |
|---|---|---|---|---|
| y | -2 | 3 | 6 | 8 |

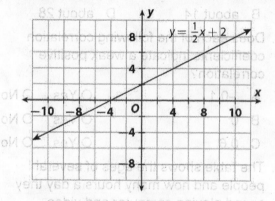

a. Find the sum of the squared residuals.

_____

b. Find the squared residual of the data and the line of fit $y = x + 4$.

_____

c. Which line better fits the data, $y = \frac{1}{2}x + 2$ or $y = x + 4$? Explain why.

_____

# Modeling with Linear Functions

**MODULE 8**

*Module Quiz: D*

1. $f(x) = -10x + 5$; $g(x) = 8x - 5$
   What is the sum of $f(x)$ and $g(x)$?

   A  $-18x - 4$

   B  $-2x$

   C  $2x + 4$

2. Which correlation best describes the scatter plot below?

   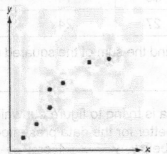

   A  Positive

   B  Negative

   C  No correlation

3. Which of the following correlation coefficients indicates a strong negative correlation?

   A  $-0.8$

   B  $0$

   C  $0.8$

4. Which is the best equation of a line of fit for the data represented on the scatter plot?

   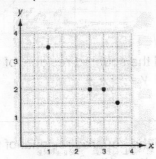

   A  $y = -\dfrac{4}{5}x + 3.6$

   B  $y = -\dfrac{4}{5}x + 4.3$

   C  $y = -\dfrac{4}{5}x + 7.5$

5. The table shows the number of employees in a company over five years.

   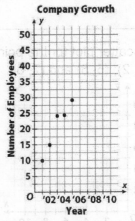

   **Company Growth**

   Which of the following is the best prediction of how many employees the company will have in 2008?

   A  35

   B  40

   C  43

6. What is the sum of the squared residuals shown on the table?

   | $y = 1.6x + 8$ | | | |
   |---|---|---|---|
   | **x** | **y (actual)** | **y (predicted)** | **residuals** |
   | 0 | 9 | 8 | $-1$ |
   | 2 | 9.2 | 11.2 | 2 |
   | 4 | 15 | 14.4 | $-0.6$ |
   | 6 | 17.6 | 17.6 | 0 |

   A  0.16

   B  5.36

   C  12.96

7. The squared residual of line of fit **A** is 2.12. The squared residual of line of fit **B** is 1.94. Which of the following statements best describes the lines?

   A  Line **A** better fits the data.

   B  Line **B** better fits the data.

   C  Not enough information is given to compare the lines of fit.

**MODULE 8**

# Modeling with Linear Functions

*Module Quiz: D*

8. Find the inverse of $f(x) = -\dfrac{x}{11}$.

_____

9. Make a scatter plot for the points (2, 1), (4, 2), (5, 5) and (7, 6).

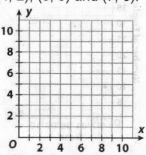

10. The table shows the number of runners in an annual race over four years.

| Year | '08 | '09 | '10 | '11 |
|---|---|---|---|---|
| Number of Runners | 21 | 35 | 46 | 50 |

a. Draw a scatter plot and a trend line.

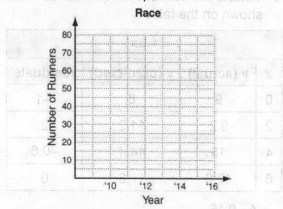

b. Which is the best prediction for the number of runners in 2013, 40 or 72? Explain your answer.

_____

11. a. Complete the table.

| $p = 5x + 4$ | | | |
|---|---|---|---|
| x | p (actual) | p (predicted) | residuals |
| −2 | −5 | −6 | |
| 0 | 6 | 4 | |
| 2 | 13 | 14 | |
| 4 | 27 | 24 | |

b. Find the sum of the squared residuals.

_____

12. Keisha is trying to figure out which line of fit is better for the data presented on the table below, $y = -x + 4$ or $y = -3x - 2$.

| x | −2 | 0 | 2 | 4 |
|---|---|---|---|---|
| y | 4 | 1 | −1 | 0 |

a. Plot the data from the table on the graph below.

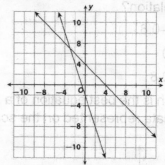

b. Find the squared residual of the line of fit $y = -x + 4$.

_____

c. Find the squared residual of the line of fit $y = -3x - 2$.

_____

d. Which line better fits the data?

_____

**MODULE 9**

# Systems of Equations and Inequalities

*Module Quiz: B*

1. Which correlation coefficient indicates a strong negative correlation?

   A  −4.5          C  −0.21

   B  −0.95        D  0.35

2. Which ordered pair is the solution for the system graphed below?

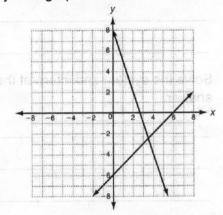

3. A linear system is classified as inconsistent. Choose True or False for each statement about the equations of the system.

   A  Their slopes are the same.
   ○ True    ○ False

   B  Their slopes are different.
   ○ True    ○ False

   C  Their y-intercepts are different.
   ○ True    ○ False

   D  Their y-intercepts are the same.
   ○ True    ○ False

4. Solve $\begin{cases} y = 4x - 1 \\ y = 3x + 6 \end{cases}$ by substitution.

   What is the solution?

   _____

5. How many solutions does the system $\begin{cases} y = 2x + 1 \\ -4x + 2y = 2 \end{cases}$ have?

   _____

6. Does each system of inequalities have at least one solution?

   A  $\begin{cases} y < -2x + 4 \\ y \geq -2x + 6 \end{cases}$       ○ Yes   ○ No

   B  $\begin{cases} y > 3x - 4 \\ y < 3x + 1 \end{cases}$       ○ Yes   ○ No

   C  $\begin{cases} y \geq -\dfrac{1}{2}x + 1 \\ y \leq -\dfrac{1}{2}x \end{cases}$       ○ Yes   ○ No

7. Which of the following is **not** a solution of the system graphed below?

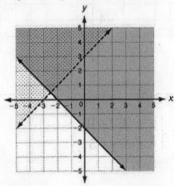

   A  (−1, 4)          C  (1, 4)

   B  (0, 4)            D  (2, 8)

8. Helen spent $7.75 to purchase 23 snacks for the club meeting. Chips are $0.25 and pretzels are $0.50. How many of each type of snack did Helen buy?

   _____

   _____

**MODULE 9**

# Systems of Equations and Inequalities

### Module Quiz: B

9. The line $y = 2.5x - 7$ is a line of fit for the data on the table.

| x | −4 | −2 | 0 | 2 |
|---|---|---|---|---|
| y | −15 | −13 | −6.5 | −2 |

Find the sum of the squared residuals.

_____

10. Graph and solve: $\begin{cases} y - 3x = 2 \\ y = -2x - 8 \end{cases}$

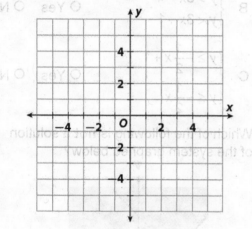

_____

11. Solve: $\begin{cases} y = -6x + 10 \\ y = -6x + 3 \end{cases}$

_____

12. Solve: $\begin{cases} x - 2y = -7 \\ 4x + 2y = 22 \end{cases}$

13. At Healthy Hair, the cost of a children's haircut $x$ is \$4 and the cost of an adult haircut $y$ is \$14. The sales from Friday were \$588. There were 42 haircuts in all.

a. Write a system to represent this situation.

_____

_____

b. Solve the system and interpret the answer.

_____

_____

_____

14. a. Graph $\begin{cases} y \geq -\dfrac{1}{2}x - 4 \\ y \leq x + 1 \end{cases}$

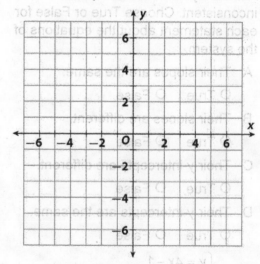

b. Give two ordered pairs that are solutions and two ordered pairs that are not solutions to the system.

_____

_____

_____

**MODULE 9**

# Systems of Equations and Inequalities

*Module Quiz: D*

1. Which correlation coefficient indicates a weak positive correlation?

   A −0.2

   B 0.03

   C 0.8

2. Which ordered pair is the solution of the system graphed below?

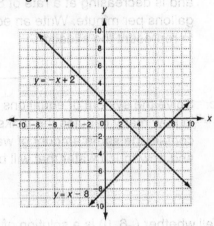

   A (−3, 5)

   B (2, 0)

   C (5, −3)

3. What does it mean if (3, 2) is a solution of $\begin{cases} y = x - 1 \\ y = -x + 5 \end{cases}$ ?

   A (3, 2) makes at least one of the equations true.

   B (3, 2) makes both equations true.

   C (3, 2) makes exactly one of the equations true.

4. Solve $\begin{cases} y = x + 3 \\ 2x + y = -6 \end{cases}$ by substitution.

   What is the solution?

   A (−9, −6)

   B (−3, 0)

   C (−1, 2)

5. How many solutions does the system $\begin{cases} y = 3x - 12 \\ y = 6x - 24 \end{cases}$ have?

   A none

   B exactly one

   C infinitely many

6. For which would you draw a dashed boundary line and shade to the left?

   A $x > -4$

   B $x < -4$

   C $x \leq 4$

7. Which of the following is a solution of the system graphed below?

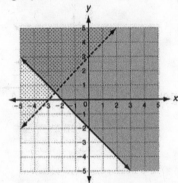

   A (−1, 3)

   B (−4, 1)

   C (0, 1)

8. The drama club is having a car wash as a fundraiser. They wash *x* cars at $5 each and *y* trucks at $8 each. They need to make at least $250. They will wash at least 15 trucks. Which system describes this situation?

   A $\begin{cases} y \geq 15 \\ 5x + 8y \geq 250 \end{cases}$

   B $\begin{cases} x > 15 \\ 5x + 8y > 250 \end{cases}$

   C $\begin{cases} y > 15 \\ 5x + 8y \leq 250 \end{cases}$

# Systems of Equations and Inequalities

**MODULE 9**

*Module Quiz: D*

9. a. Complete the table.

| $y = -2x + 9$ | | | |
| --- | --- | --- | --- |
| x | p (actual) | p (predicted) | residuals |
| -2 | 14 | 13 | |
| 0 | 9 | | |
| 2 | 3 | | |

   b. Find the sum of the squared residuals.

   _____

10. The graph of a system of linear equations is shown below. What is the solution of the system?

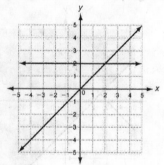

   _____

11. Solve by graphing: $\begin{cases} y = x - 3 \\ y = -x + 5 \end{cases}$

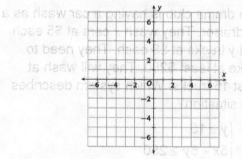

12. Solve by elimination: $\begin{cases} x + y = -10 \\ 2x - y = -8 \end{cases}$

   _____

13. a. Tank A contains 35 gallons of water and is increasing at a rate of 5 gallons per minute. Write an equation to represent the situation.

   _____

   b. Tank B contains 100 gallons of water and is decreasing at a rate of 8 gallons per minute. Write an equation to represent the situation.

   _____

   c. Solve the system of equations to find in how many minutes the tanks contain the same amount of water and how much water that will be.

   _____

14. Tell whether (−6, 0) is a solution of $\begin{cases} y > x + 4 \\ y < -2x \end{cases}$.

   _____

15. Use the graph below to give 2 ordered pairs that are solutions and 2 ordered pairs that are not solutions of the system.

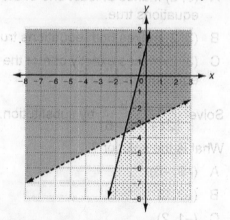

   a. Solutions: _____

   b. Not solutions: _____

| MODULE 10 |
|---|

# Exponential Functions and Equations
## *Module Quiz: B*

1. Which system of equations has no solution?

   A $\begin{cases} y = -3x + 6 \\ y = -2x + 6 \end{cases}$   C $\begin{cases} y = -\dfrac{1}{2}x \\ y = -\dfrac{1}{5}x \end{cases}$

   B $\begin{cases} y = 5x - 4 \\ y = 5x + 1 \end{cases}$   D $\begin{cases} y = 2x + 1 \\ y = -2x + 4 \end{cases}$

2. What is $\dfrac{1}{2^{-3}}$ simplified?

   _____

3. What is $f(x) = -5(-2)^x$ evaluated for $x = 2$?

   _____

4. Which of these sets of ordered pairs satisfies an exponential equation?

   A $\{(1, -1), (2, -8), (3, -27), (4, -64)\}$

   B $\{(1, -1), (2, -4), (3, -9), (4, -16)\}$

   C $\{(1, -2), (3, -8), (5, -32), (7, -128)\}$

   D $\{(1, -2), (3, 2), (5, 6), (7, 10)\}$

5. If a ball is dropped from a height of 18 feet, the function $f(x) = 18(0.75)^x$ gives the height in feet of each bounce, where $x$ is the bounce number. What will be the height of the third bounce to the nearest tenth of a foot?

   _____

6. A population of deer in an area is 2000 and is decreasing at a rate of 15% per year. At this rate, approximately what will the deer population be in 5 years?

   A 887       C 1925

   B 1500      D 4023

7. Is each of the following a geometric sequence?

   A  $-1, 3, -9, 27, \ldots$     ○ Yes   ○ No

   B  $-1, -3, 5, 7, \ldots$      ○ Yes   ○ No

   C  $-1, 4, -9, 16, \ldots$     ○ Yes   ○ No

   D  $-1, 2, -4, 8, \ldots$      ○ Yes   ○ No

8. Which is the tenth term of the geometric sequence $\dfrac{1}{27}, \dfrac{1}{9}, \dfrac{1}{3}, 1, \ldots$?

   _____

9. Compared to the graph of $f(x) = 5^x$, is each statement true about the graph of $f(x) = 2(5)^x - 2$?

   A  It is vertically stretched.
      ○ True   ○ False

   B  It is vertically shrunk.
      ○ True   ○ False

   C  It is translated down.
      ○ True   ○ False

   D  It is translated up.
      ○ True   ○ False

10. Solve $\left(\dfrac{1}{3}\right)^{x-2} = \left(\dfrac{1}{3}\right)^2$. What is the value of $x$?

    _____

11. Solve $4^{x+30} = 64^{2x}$. What is the value of $x$?

    _____

**MODULE 10**

# Exponential Functions and Equations

### Module Quiz: B

12. Solve: $\begin{cases} y = 3x + 12 \\ 2x - 2y = -4 \end{cases}$.

_____

13. a. Complete the table to find the values of the exponential equation

$y = -2 \times \left(\dfrac{1}{2}\right)^x$.

| $x$ | $-2 \times \left(\dfrac{1}{2}\right)^x = y$ | $y$ |
|---|---|---|
| $-2$ | $-2 \times \left(\dfrac{1}{2}\right)^{-2} = -2\left(\dfrac{4}{1}\right)$ | |
| $-1$ | | |
| $0$ | | |
| $1$ | | |
| $2$ | | |

b. Graph $y = -2 \times \left(\dfrac{1}{2}\right)^x$.

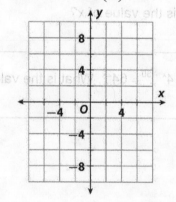

14. The ordered pairs (1, 15) and (2, 45) are solutions to an exponential equation. Write the equation.

_____

15. A car with an initial value of $23,000 is decreasing in value at a rate of 8% each year. At this rate, what will the value of the car be in 3 years? Round to the nearest dollar.

_____

16. $-5, 20, -80, 320, \ldots$ is a geometric sequence.

 a. Find the common ratio.

_____

 b. Write its recursive rule.

_____

 c. Write its explicit rule.

_____

17. Compare the graphs of $y = 3(2)^x - 4$ and $y = 2^x$.

_____

_____

_____

18. Solve $\dfrac{1}{4} \times 10^x = 2500$.

_____

19. Solve $0.5y^3 = 13.5$.

_____

## MODULE 10
# Exponential Functions and Equations
*Module Quiz: D*

1. How many solutions does the following system have?
$$\begin{cases} y = 2x - 12 \\ y = 3x + 12 \end{cases}$$

   A  none

   B  exactly one

   C  infinitely many

2. What is $9^{-2}$ simplified?

   A  −81

   B  $-\dfrac{1}{81}$

   C  $\dfrac{1}{81}$

3. What is $f(x) = 4^x$ evaluated for $x = 3$?

   A  12

   B  16

   C  64

4. Which of these sets of ordered pairs satisfies an exponential equation?

   A  {(1, 3), (2, 9), (3, 27)}

   B  {(1, 7), (2, 14), (3, 21)}

   C  {(1, 10), (2, 20), (3, 30)}

5. An insect population doubles every week. The function $f(x) = 10(2)^x$ models the insect population after $x$ weeks. To the nearest whole number, what will the population be after 4 weeks?

   A  80

   B  160

   C  20,000

6. Jeffrey's savings account earns 3% interest each year. To find the amount Jeffrey has in his account after 2 years, evaluate the equation $f(x) = 350(1 + 0.03)^x$ for $x = 2$. Round to the nearest dollar.

   A  $361

   B  $371

   C  $721

7. Which of the following is a geometric sequence?

   A  3, 6, 12, 24, …

   B  4, 8, 12, 16, …

   C  2, 4, 16, 256, …

8. What is the sixth term of the geometric sequence 1024, 512, 256,…?

   A  64

   B  32

   C  16

9. Compare the graph of $g(x) = 6x^2$ with the graph of $f(x) = x^2$. Which of the following statements is true?

   A  $g(x)$ is vertically stretched.

   B  $g(x)$ is translated up.

   C  $g(x)$ is vertically compressed.

10. Solve $2^5 = 2^x$ for $x$. What is the value of $x$?

   A  5

   B  10

   C  32

11. Solve $36^7 = 6^y$ for $y$. What is the value of $y$?

   A  7

   B  14

   C  49

# Exponential Functions and Equations
*Module Quiz: D*

12. Solve: $\begin{cases} y = x + 10 \\ 2x + y = 28 \end{cases}$

_____

13. a. Complete the table to find the values of the exponential equation $y = 4 \times 2^x$.

| $x$ | $4 \times 2^x = y$ | $y$ |
|---|---|---|
| –2 | $4 \times 2^{-2} = 4\left(\dfrac{1}{4}\right)$ | 1 |
| –1 | $4 \times 2^{-1} = 4\left(\dfrac{1}{2}\right)$ | |
| 0 | | |
| 1 | | |
| 2 | | |

b. Graph $y = 4(2)^x$.

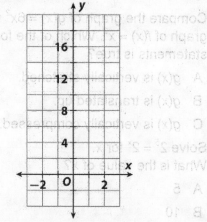

14. The following ordered pairs are solutions to an exponential equation:
(0, 1), (1, 3), (2, 9), (3, 27).
Write the equation.

_____

15. A population of 200 animals has a growth rate of 13% each year. At this growth rate, the function $f(x) = 200(1.13)^x$ gives the population in $x$ years. What is the population in 3 years?

_____

16. 6, 18, 54, 162, … is a geometric sequence.
    a. Find the common ratio of the sequence.

_____

    b. Write a recursive rule for the sequence.

_____

    c. Write an explicit rule for the sequence.

_____

17. Compare the graphs of $y = 2^x$ and $y = 3 \times 2^x - 2$.

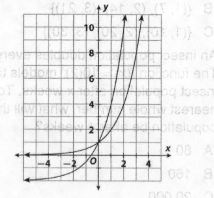

_____

_____

_____

18. Solve $81^2 = y^4$.

_____

**MODULE 11**

# Modeling with Exponential Functions

*Module Quiz: B*

1. The population of a town is 6,500 and is increasing at a rate of 4% per year. At this rate, approximately what will the town's population be in 4 years?

_____

2. Which regression equation best fits the data shown in the table?

| x | 0 | 2 | 4 | 6 |
|---|---|---|---|---|
| y | 1 | 8 | 22 | 90 |

A  $y = 1.3 \times 2^x$

B  $y = 3^x$

C  $y = 3.3^x$

D  $y = 3 \times 2^x$

3. Regression equation **A** is $y = 3x + 4$.
Regression equation **B** is $y = 2^x$.
Which of the following describes a situation in which the exponential regression equation better fits the data?

A  **A**: $r = 0.87$; **B**: $r = 0.93$

B  **A**: $r = 0.89$; **B**: $r = 0.88$

C  **A**: $r = 0.97$; **B**: $r = 0.97$

D  **A**: $r = 0.97$; **B**: $r = 0.96$

4. Martin has $200 in his savings account. He is looking at two investment plans. Under plan A, he will increase his account balance by $40 a year. Under plan B, he will increase his account balance by 15% each year. To the nearest dollar, how much more will he save with plan B after 10 years?

_____

5. Do the ordered pairs satisfy an exponential function?

A

| x | −4 | −3 | −2 | −1 |
|---|---|---|---|---|
| y | 0 | 5 | 0 | −25 |

○ Yes  ○ No

B

| x | −4 | −3 | −2 | −1 |
|---|---|---|---|---|
| y | 81 | 27 | 9 | 3 |

○ Yes  ○ No

C

| x | −4 | −3 | −2 | −1 |
|---|---|---|---|---|
| y | 64 | 27 | 8 | 1 |

○ Yes  ○ No

D

| x | −4 | −3 | −2 | −1 |
|---|---|---|---|---|
| Y | 16 | 8 | 4 | 2 |

○ Yes  ○ No

6. What is the average rate of change for each equation over the interval [2, 3]?

Equation **A**

| x | 0 | 1 | 2 | 3 |
|---|---|---|---|---|
| y | 0 | 4 | 16 | 64 |

Equation **B**

$f(x) = 7x + 2$

_____

7. Is each of the following data sets best described by a linear model?

A  {(2, 4), (3, 9), (4, 16), (5, 25)}
○ Yes  ○ No

B  {(−2, −1), (−3, 0), (−4, 1), (−5, 0)}
○ Yes  ○ No

C  {(2, 12), (3, 6), (4, 0), (5, −6)}
○ Yes  ○ No

D  {(2, 0), (3, 0), (4, 0), (5, 0)}
○ Yes  ○ No

# MODULE 11
## Modeling with Exponential Functions
### Module Quiz: B

8. a. Complete the table to find the values of $y = \frac{1}{4} \times 3^x$.

| $x$ | $\frac{1}{4} \times 3^x = y$ | $y$ |
|---|---|---|
| $-2$ | $\frac{1}{4} \times 3^{-2} = \frac{1}{4}\left(\frac{1}{9}\right)$ | |
| $-1$ | | |
| $0$ | | |
| $1$ | | |
| $2$ | | |

b. Graph $y = \frac{1}{4} \times 3^x$.

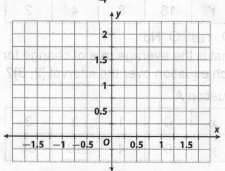

9. The volume of a gas was measured as its temperature was increased from 10°K to 15°K at intervals of 1°K. The volumes were 1.5, 2.2, 3.38, 5.1, and 7.6 cubic centimeters. Would a linear or exponential function better approximate the data described? Explain why.

_____

_____

_____

10. a. Complete the table below to find the residuals of the data shown and the regression equation $y = 4.5^x$.

| $x$ | y observed | y predicted | residual |
|---|---|---|---|
| $-1$ | 0 | | |
| $0$ | 1.2 | | |
| $1$ | 4.4 | | |
| $2$ | 20.4 | | |

b. Describe the accuracy of the regression equation.

_____

_____

11. Neha is trying to decide between two possible jobs. Job A pays $2,000 a month with a 2% annual raise. Job B pays $24,000 a year with a $500 annual raise.

a. Write a function to represent the annual salary for job A.

_____

b. Write a function to represent the annual salary for job B.

_____

c. After how many years would Neha have a higher salary at job A?

_____

**MODULE 11**

# Modeling with Exponential Functions

*Module Quiz: D*

1. The number of fruit flies in a jar triples every week. The function $f(x) = 5(3)^x$ models the insect population after $x$ weeks. To the nearest whole number, what will the population be after 4 weeks?

   A 60

   B 81

   C 405

2. Which regression equation best fits the data shown in the table?

   | x | 0 | 1 | 2 | 3 |
   |---|---|---|---|---|
   | y | 1 | 4 | 22 | 124 |

   A $y = x^5$

   B $y = 5^x$

   C $y = 2 \times 3^x$

3. Which of the following describes a situation in which the linear regression equation best fits the data?

   A exponential equation: $r = 0.92$
   linear equation: $r = 0.45$

   B exponential equation: $r = 0.84$
   linear equation: $r = 0.93$

   C exponential equation: $r = 0.74$
   linear equation: $r = 0.74$

4. Which ordered pairs satisfy an exponential function?

   A
   | x | 0 | 1 | 2 | 3 |
   |---|---|---|---|---|
   | y | 1 | 3 | 9 | 27 |

   B
   | x | 0 | 1 | 2 | 3 |
   |---|---|---|---|---|
   | y | 0 | 2 | 4 | 6 |

   C
   | x | 0 | 1 | 2 | 3 |
   |---|---|---|---|---|
   | y | 1 | 4 | 9 | 16 |

5. Ben has $100 in his savings account. He is looking at two investment plans. Under plan A, he will increase his account balance by $20 a year. Under plan B, he will increase his account balance by 15% each year. Approximately how much will Ben save after 3 years with each plan?

   A Plan A: $160; Plan B: $145

   B Plan A: $160; Plan B: $152

   C Plan A: $173; Plan B: $152

6. What is the average rate of change over the interval [0, 1] for each equation?

   Equation **A**

   | x | 0 | 1 | 2 | 3 |
   |---|---|---|---|---|
   | y | 1 | 5 | 25 | 125 |

   Equation **B**

   $f(x) = 2x$

   A **A**: 5; **B**: 2

   B **A**: 4; **B**: 0

   C **A**: 4; **B**: 2

7. Which kind of model best describes this data set: {(−2, 1), (−1, 3), (0, 5), (1, 7), (2, 9)}?

   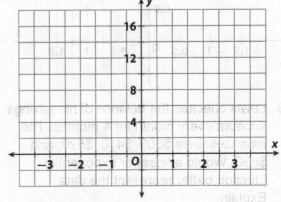

   A linear

   B exponential

   C none of these

# MODULE 11 Modeling with Exponential Functions
### Module Quiz: D

8. a. Complete the table to find the values of $y = \dfrac{1}{2} \times 2^x$.

| $x$ | $\dfrac{1}{2} \times 2^x = y$ | $y$ |
|---|---|---|
| −2 | $\dfrac{1}{2} \times 2^{-2} = \dfrac{1}{2}\left(\dfrac{1}{4}\right)$ | $\dfrac{1}{8}$ |
| −1 | $\dfrac{1}{2} \times 2^{-1} = \dfrac{1}{2}\left(\dfrac{1}{2}\right)$ | |
| 0 | | |
| 1 | | |
| 2 | | |

b. Graph $y = \dfrac{1}{2} \times 2^x$

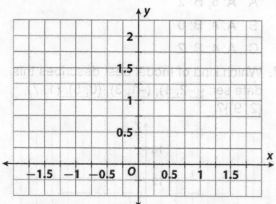

9. Lewis checked the balance of his savings account every month for 4 months. The balances were $300, $410, $520, and $630. Would a linear or exponential function better represent the data? Explain.

_____

_____

10. a. Complete the table below to find the residuals of the data shown and the regression equation $y = 4^x$.

| $x$ | y observed | y predicted | residual |
|---|---|---|---|
| −1 | $\dfrac{1}{4}$ | $\dfrac{1}{4}$ | |
| 0 | 2 | 1 | |
| 1 | 6 | 4 | |
| 2 | 22 | 16 | |

b. Describe the accuracy of the regression equation.

_____

_____

11. Ashley is deciding between two jobs. Job A pays $2000 a month with a monthly raise of $85. Job B pays $2000 a month with a monthly raise of 4%.

a. Write a function to represent the monthly salary for job A.

_____

b. Write a function to represent the monthly salary for job B.

_____

c. After how many months would Ashley have a higher salary at job B?

_____

**MODULE 12**

# Descriptive Statistics
## *Module Quiz: B*

1. Which is an example of qualitative data?

   A  years of education

   B  price of gas

   C  number of pets

   D  type of car

2. Brittany surveyed the 37 students in her math class on whether they liked jogging. Eight girls did not like jogging, and 14 girls liked jogging. How many boys are in Brittany's class?

   _____

3.

|         | Preferred Color | | |
|---------|------|------|-------|
| Gender  | Red  | Blue | Total |
| Male    | 13   | 44   | 57    |
| Female  | 32   | ?    | 46    |
| Total   | 45   | 58   | 103   |

   What is the missing number?

   _____

4.

|             | Like Basketball | | |
|-------------|-----|------|-------|
| Like Soccer | Yes | No   | Total |
| Yes         | 67  | ?    | 109   |
| No          | 8   | ?    | 37    |
| Total       | 75  | ?    | 146   |

   How many surveyed do not like soccer and do not like basketball?

   _____

5. A hiking trail has a paved path and a dirt path. Glenn surveyed 65 hikers, of whom 15 were girls: 3 of the girls preferred the dirt path and the rest of the girls preferred the paved path. What is the conditional relative frequency that a hiker prefers the paved path, given that the hiker is a girl? Write your answer as a fraction and a percent.

   _____

6. The table below shows the results of a survey of students' favorite subjects.

| Science | English | Math |
|---------|---------|------|
| 24      | 48      | 28   |

   What is the relative frequency that a student's favorite subject is not English?

   _____

7. Based on the table below, what is the joint relative frequency of the people surveyed who do not have a job and have a savings account?

| Have a savings account | Have a job | |
|---------|------|------|
|         | Yes  | No   |
| Yes     | 134  | 66   |
| No      | 16   | 84   |

   A  0.22          C  0.44

   B  0.28          D  0.66

8. Ursula interviewed 75 people to see if they liked reading comic books. Of the people surveyed, 15 were males, 32 females liked comic books, and 9 males liked comic books. What is the conditional frequency that a person does not like comic books given that the person is a male?

   _____

## MODULE 12 — Descriptive Statistics
### Module Quiz: B

9. a. Complete the frequency table.

| Gender | Preferred Pet | | | |
|---|---|---|---|---|
| | Dog | Cat | Fish | Total |
| Male | | 208 | 5 | 323 |
| Female | 190 | | 2 | |
| Total | 300 | | | 565 |

b. How many males prefer dogs?

_____

c. How many females do not prefer cats?

_____

10. Brooke conducted a survey to find the eye colors of her neighbors.
Use the following information to complete the frequency table.

– She surveyed 23 children, 14 teenagers, and 36 adults.

– Six adults had blue eyes, and 10 adults had hazel eyes.

– Three teenagers had green eyes.

– No teenagers had hazel eyes.

– The same number of teenagers had green eyes as blue eyes.

– In all 33 people had brown eyes.

| | Blue | Green | Hazel | Brown |
|---|---|---|---|---|
| Child | 5 | 2 | 6 | 10 |
| Teenager | | | | |
| Adult | | | | |

11. In a survey of 300 people, 112 liked only oranges, 120 liked only bananas, some liked both oranges and bananas, and 28 liked neither oranges nor bananas. How many people liked both oranges and bananas?

12.

| Age in years | Do they recycle? | |
|---|---|---|
| | Yes | No |
| 21–35 | 56 | 10 |
| 36–50 | 85 | 21 |
| 51–65 | 45 | 40 |

a. To the nearest hundredth, what is the joint relative frequency that a person was 21–35 and did not recycle?

_____

b. To the nearest hundredth, what is the conditional relative frequency that a person surveyed was 51–65 years old given that they do recycle?

_____

c. Based on this survey, is it more likely that a 21–35 year old recycles or a 51–65 year old recycles? Use conditional frequencies to justify your answer.

_____

_____

_____

# MODULE 12 Descriptive Statistics

## *Module Quiz: D*

1. Which is an example of categorical data?

   A  eye color

   B  age

   C  weight

2. Fernando surveyed his classmates to see who liked tennis. Six males did not like tennis, and 32 males liked tennis. Four females did not like tennis, and 13 females liked tennis.
   How many females did Fernando survey?

   A  17

   B  38

   C  55

3.

|  | Preferred Color | | |
|---|---|---|---|
| Gender | Red | Blue | Total |
| Male | 13 | 44 | 57 |
| Female | 32 | 14 | ? |
| Total | 45 | 58 | 103 |

   What number is missing from the table?

   A  18

   B  46

   C  117

4.

|  | Like Basketball | | |
|---|---|---|---|
| Like Soccer | Yes | No | Total |
| Yes | 67 | 42 | 109 |
| No | 8 | 29 | 37 |
| Total | 75 | 71 | 146 |

   How many people were surveyed in all?

   A  67

   B  109

   C  146

5. Which is an example of quantitative data?

   A  north, south, east, west

   B  aces, kings, queens

   C  6 days, 4 minutes, 9 years

6. The table below shows the results of the survey of students' favorite subjects.

| Science | English | Math | Total |
|---|---|---|---|
| 24 | 48 | 28 | 100 |

   What is the relative frequency that the student's favorite subject is English?

   A  0.29

   B  0.48

   C  0.52

7. What is the joint relative frequency of the people surveyed who do not have a job and have a savings account?

| Have a savings account | Have a job | | |
|---|---|---|---|
|  | Yes | No | Total |
| Yes | 134 | 66 | 200 |
| No | 16 | 84 | 100 |
| Total | 150 | 150 | 300 |

   A  0.22

   B  0.28

   C  0.44

8. Sam interviewed 100 people to find out how many had a garden. Of the people he interviewed, 48 were females, and 12 of the females had a garden.
   What is the conditional relative frequency that a female from the survey had a garden?

   A  0.25

   B  0.28

   C  0.52

## MODULE 12 Descriptive Statistics
### Module Quiz: D

9. a. Complete the frequency table.

| | Preferred Pet | | | |
|---|---|---|---|---|
| Gender | Dog | Cat | Fish | Total |
| Male | 16 | 12 | 3 | |
| Female | 19 | 25 | 7 | |
| Total | | | | 82 |

b. How many males prefer dogs?

_____

c. How many females do not prefer cats?

_____

10. Amber conducted a survey to find the eye colors of her neighbors. Use the following information to complete the frequency table.

– She surveyed 30 children, 15 teenagers, and 52 adults.

– Ten adults had blue eyes, and ten adults had green eyes.

– No teenagers had green eyes.

– Six teenagers had hazel eyes.

– The same number of teenagers had brown eyes as hazel eyes.

– In all, 45 people had brown eyes.

| | Blue | Green | Hazel | Brown |
|---|---|---|---|---|
| Child | 3 | 4 | 9 | 14 |
| Teenager | | | | |
| Adult | | | | |

11. Maggie surveyed 42 girls and 48 boys, and found that 15 girls and 13 boys watch her favorite TV show. To the nearest hundredth, what is the joint relative frequency that a person who watches Maggie's favorite TV show is a girl?

_____

12.

| | Do they recycle? | | |
|---|---|---|---|
| Age in years | Yes | No | Total |
| 21–35 | 60 | 5 | 65 |
| 36–50 | 80 | 20 | 100 |
| 51–65 | 45 | 40 | 85 |
| Total | 180 | 70 | 250 |

a. To the nearest hundredth, what is the joint relative frequency that a person was 21–35 and did not recycle?

_____

b. To the nearest hundredth, what is the conditional relative frequency that a person surveyed was 51–65 years old given that they recycle?

_____

c. To the nearest hundredth, what is the conditional relative frequency that a person surveyed was 21–35 years old given that they recycle?

_____

d. Based on this survey, is it more likely that a 21–35 year old recycles or a 51–65 year old recycles?

_____

## MODULE 13

# Data Displays

### Module Quiz: B

1. The table below shows the results of a survey in which teachers were asked the color of their car.

| Blue | White | Red | Black |
|------|-------|-----|-------|
| 4 | 2 | 11 | 3 |

What is the relative frequency that a teacher surveyed had a red or black car?

_____

2. The ages of the U.S. Presidents that were inaugurated during the 1900's are given below.

| Ages at Inauguration |
|----------------------|
| 42 51 56 55 51 54 51 60 62 |
| 43 55 56 61 52 69 64 46 |

What are the mean, median, and mode of the data?

_____

3. For the set {1, 1, 2, 4, 5, 6, 7, 8, 10} would each of the following measures be affected if another value of 10 was included?

A  range          ○ Yes   ○ No

B  mean          ○ Yes   ○ No

C  median        ○ Yes   ○ No

4. How does the outlier in the following set of data affect the mean and range of the set: 5, 9, 60, 13, 4, 11? Choose True or False.

A  increases the range by 56
   ○ True   ○ False

B  increases the mean by 12
   ○ True   ○ False

C  increases the range by 47
   ○ True   ○ False

D  increases the mean by 8.6
   ○ True   ○ False

5. Which statement best describes the data distribution shown on the dot plots below?

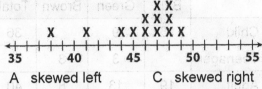

A  skewed left          C  skewed right

B  symmetric           D  bimodal

6. Which of the following could be intervals for the same histogram?

A  70–80 and 80–90

B  70–79 and 80–84

C  70–79 and 80–89

D  70–80 and 81–90

7. The box–and–whisker plot is based on the data from the table below.

| miles per gallon |
|------------------|
| 15.8  26.5  19.1  19.5  25.3  20.2 |
| 19.2  20.0  18.0  27.8  27.3  28.9 |

What, if anything, is wrong with this box–and–whisker plot?

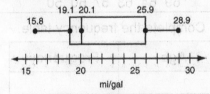

A  The maximum is incorrect.

B  The value of the median is incorrect.

C  The value of Q3 is incorrect.

D  The boxplot is correct.

8. Suppose the heights of 18-year-old males in the U.S. are normally distributed with a mean of 70.1 inches and a standard deviation of 2.7 inches What is the probability that a randomly chosen 18-year-old male is less than 72.8 inches tall?

_____

# MODULE 13 Data Displays
## Module Quiz: B

9. Complete the frequency table.

| Eye Color | | | |
|---|---|---|---|
| | Blue | Green | Brown | Total |
| Child | 15 | 9 | X | 36 |
| Teenager | | 3 | 8 | |
| Adult | 19 | 13 | 8 | 40 |
| Total | 37 | | 28 | |

10. April's test scores in Physics are 78, 85, 65, 82, 90, and 95.
Find the mean and standard deviation of the data. If necessary, round to the nearest hundredth.

_____

11. The ages of the Board of Directors of an insurance company are given below.

| Ages of Board of Directors |
|---|
| 67 52 54 57 61 56 61 |
| 69 64 63 57 60 50 |

a. Complete the frequency table.

| Age | Frequency |
|---|---|
| | |
| | |
| | |
| | |

b. Use the frequency table to make a histogram.

12. The fuel economy in miles per gallon of several vehicles are given below.

| Data set A |
|---|
| miles per gallon |
| 28.5  18.0  19.6  21.1  22.0  24.0  16.9 |
| 27.2  15.2  18.0  21.5  29.0  18.0  28.0 |

a. Use this data to make a box-and-whisker plot.

b. Compare data set A to data set B which is represented on the box-and-whisker plot below.

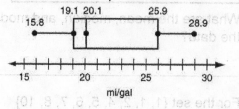

13. The results of a standardized test are normally distributed. The mean test score is 312, and 16% of the scores are under 307.

a. What is the standard deviation?

_____

b. What is the probability that a student scored higher than 322?

_____

## MODULE 13 Data Displays

### Module Quiz: D

1. The table shows the results of a survey of Mrs. Sus's students' favorite color.

| Blue | White | Red | Black |
|------|-------|-----|-------|
| 44 | 42 | 21 | 33 |

What is the relative frequency that a student's favorite color is red?

A 0.79

B 0.21

C 0.15

2. Ian rolled a die ten times. The results of her rolls were 4, 5, 2, 2, 5, 1, 4, 3, 6, 3. What are the mean, median, and mode of the data?

| | **mean** | **median** | **mode(s)** |
|---|------|--------|---------|
| A | 3.5 | 3 | 4 |
| B | 4 | 4 | no mode |
| C | 3.5 | 3.5 | 2, 3, 4, 5 |

3. What is the range of the set {13, 5, 8, 9, 15, 9}?

A 4

B 5

C 10

4. How does the outlier in the following set of data affect the mean and range: 18, 23, 15, 13, 92, 27?

A increases the mean and increases the range

B decreases the mean and increases the range

C increases the mean and decreases the range

5. Which statement best describes the data distribution shown on the dot plot below?

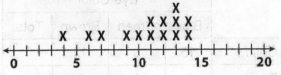

A skewed left

B skewed right

C symmetric

6. Which of the following could be intervals on the same histogram?

A 0–5 and 5–10

B 1–5 and 6–10

C 0–5 and 6–10

7. What is the interquartile range of the data represented by the box–and–whisker plot below?

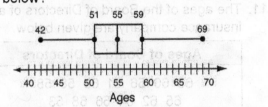

A 4

B 8

C 27

8. What percent of data with a normal distribution is within one standard deviation of the mean?

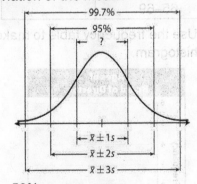

A 50%

B 68%

C 94%

**MODULE 13**

# Data Displays

## Module Quiz: D

9. Complete the frequency table.

| Eye Color | | | |
|---|---|---|---|
| | Blue | Green | Brown | Total |
| Child | 15 | 9 | 12 | |
| Teenager | 3 | 3 | 8 | |
| Adult | 19 | 13 | 8 | |
| Total | | | | 90 |

10. Leema's test scores in Chemistry are 80, 95, 88, 92, and 100. Find the mean and standard deviation of the data. If necessary, round to the nearest tenth.

Mean: _____

Standard deviation: _____

11. The ages of the Board of Directors of an insurance company are given below.

| Ages of Board of Directors |
|---|
| 63  60  56  51  69  58  58 |
| 65  62  64  56  68  53 |

a. Complete the frequency table.

| Age | Frequency |
|---|---|
| 50–54 | |
| 55–59 | |
| 60–64 | |
| 65–69 | |

b. Use the frequency table to make a histogram.

12. The box–and–whisker plot below shows the ages of customers at a car dealership over a week.

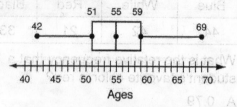

a. What was the median age of the customers at the car dealership?

b. What is the range of ages of the customers at the dealership?

_____

c. The plot below shows the ages of the customers at the same dealership the following week.

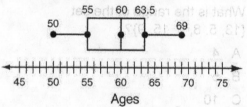

Compare the medians and ranges of the data from week 1 and week 2.

_____

_____

_____

_____

**MODULE 14**

# Polynomials and Operations

*Module Quiz: B*

1. What is $3(5x^2 - 9x)$ evaluated for $x = -3$?

   _____

2. What is the degree of $4xy^2z$?

   A  2              C  4

   B  3              D  5

3. What is the degree of $5x^3 + 2x^2y^3z$?

   _____

4. Is each of the following a cubic binomial?

   A  $2x^3 + 4x$         ○ Yes   ○ No

   B  $3x^2 + x$          ○ Yes   ○ No

   C  $x^3 + 2$           ○ Yes   ○ No

   D  $x^4 + 3x^2 - 11$   ○ Yes   ○ No

5. Which of the following is the correct classification of $3x^3y^2 - 9x + 1$?

   A  binomial with a degree of 3

   B  binomial with a degree of 2

   C  trinomial with a degree of 3

   D  trinomial with a degree of 5

6. Find the sum of $(4x^3 + 2x)$ and $(8x^3 - 5x + 4)$.

   _____

7. Simplify $5mn^2 - 8m + mn^2$.

   _____

8. What is $(2x^2 - 5x - 7) - (7x^2 + 3)$ simplified?

   _____

9. A rectangle has width $w$ and its length is 2 units shorter than 3 times the width. Does each polynomial represent the perimeter of the rectangle?

   A  $2(w^2 - 4)$        ○ Yes   ○ No

   B  $3w^2 - 2w$         ○ Yes   ○ No

   C  $8w - 4$            ○ Yes   ○ No

   D  $2(w - 4)$          ○ Yes   ○ No

10. Find the product of $8xy$ and $3x - 7y$.

    _____

11. What is the product of $(3x + 1)(3x - 4)$?

    _____

12. Which product results in $x^2 - 100$?

    A  $(x - 10)^2$

    B  $(x + 10)^2$

    C  $x(x - 100)$

    D  $(x + 10)(x - 10)$

# Polynomials and Operations
*Module Quiz: B*

13. Evaluate $3.5mn^2 + 6m$ for $m = 4$ and $n = -2$.

_____

14. Identify each expression as a monomial, polynomial, or neither. Classify each polynomial by its number of terms and degree.

  a. $9x^4 - 3x + 6$

  _____

  b. $\dfrac{5}{t^3}$

  _____

  c. $\dfrac{1}{2}rs - 9$

  _____

15. Simplify: $(4x^2 + 21xy - 7y^2) + (10x^2 + 11y^2 - 20)$.

  _____

16.

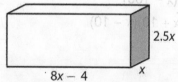

  $8x - 4$   $x$   $2.5x$

  a. Write a polynomial in simplest terms that represents the surface area of the rectangular prism modeled above.

  _____

  b. Write a polynomial to find the volume of the rectangular prism.

  _____

  c. Find the volume if $x = 2$ feet.

  _____

17. Simplify:
  $(32mn^2 + 50m^2n) - (10mn^2 - 16m^2n + 64)$.

  _____

18. Multiply $3x^3 - x^2 + 4$ by $-5$.

  _____

19. Find the opposite of $7x^2 - 5x$, by simplifying $-1(7x^2 - 5x)$.

  _____

20. A trapezoid has height $h$. One base is 2 units longer than the height. The other base is 3 times longer than the height.

  a. Write a polynomial for the area of the trapezoid.
     *Hint:* The formula for finding the area of a trapezoid is $A = \dfrac{1}{2}h(b_1 + b_2)$.

  _____

  b. Find the area if the height is $1\dfrac{2}{3}$ in.

  _____

21. Find the product of $(t + 8)$ and $(3t - 7)$.

  _____

22. Simplify $(rs^3 - 12)(rs^3 + 12)$.

  _____

23. Simplify $(x - y)^3$.

  _____

**MODULE 14**

# Polynomials and Operations
### *Module Quiz: D*

1. What is $r^3 + 3r^2$ evaluated for $r = 3$?

   A 27

   B 54

   C 162

2. What is the degree of $3x^3y^2$?

   A 2

   B 3

   C 5

3. What is the degree of $4xy^2 + 2x^6$?

   A 2

   B 3

   C 6

4. Which of the following best describes $6x^3 - 5y^2$ according to the number of terms?

   A monomial

   B binomial

   C trinomial

5. Which of the following is a binomial with a degree of 3?

   A $2x^3 + 4x$

   B $3x^2 + x$

   C $x^3 + 6x^2 + 2$

6. Add $6p^3 + p^3$. What is the sum?

   A $6p^3$

   B $7p^6$

   C $7p^3$

7. Add $(2x^3 - 5) + (x^3 + 3)$. What is the sum?

   A $2x^3 - 2$

   B $3x^3 - 2$

   C $3x^6 - 2$

8. Subtract $(6a^2 + 3a) - (4a^2 + 2a)$. What is the difference?

   A $2a^2 + a$

   B $2a^2 + 5a$

   C $3a^3$

9. A rectangle has width $w$, and its length is 2 units longer than the width, or $w + 2$. Which polynomial represents the perimeter of the rectangle?

   A $4w + 4$

   B $2w + 2$

   C $w^2 + 2w$

10. Multiply $11x + 3$ by 4. What is the product?

   A $44x^4 + 12$

   B $44x + 12$

   C $44x + 3$

11. Multiply $(x + 2)(x + 3)$. What is the product?

   A $2x + 5x + 6$

   B $x^2 + 6x + 6$

   C $x^2 + 5x + 6$

12. What is the product of $5(5x^2 + 2x - 4)$?

   A $25x^{10} + 10x^5 - 20$

   B $25x^2 + 10x - 20$

   C $10x^2 + 7x - 9$

13. Multiply $(y + 6)(y + 6)$. What is the product?

   A $2y + 12y + 36$

   B $y^2 + 12y + 36$

   C $y^2 + 36$

## MODULE 14  Polynomials and Operations
### Module Quiz: D

14. Evaluate $y^2 + 4x - 2$ for $y = 5$.

_____

15. Simplify $m^2 + 4m - 7m^2$.

_____

16. Classify each expression as a monomial, polynomial, or neither.

a. $7x^7 - y$

_____

b. $5t^{-3}$

_____

c. $\dfrac{1}{2}rs$

_____

17. Find $(mn^2 + 5n) + (7mn^2 + 11n)$.

_____

18. Simplify $(14y + 5) - (29y + 3)$.

_____

19. The polynomial $2b^2 + 4bh$ can be used to find the surface area of a prism with a square base. The side length of the base is $b$, and the height of the prism is $h$.

a. Write a polynomial that represents the surface area of ten congruent prisms by multiplying $2b^2 + 4bh$ by ten.

_____

b. Find the surface area of ten prisms with a base length of 4 inches and a height of 5 inches.

_____

20. Find the product of $5r^3$ and $9r^2$.

_____

21. Find the opposite of $7x^2 - 5x$, by simplifying $-1(7x^2 - 5x)$.

_____

22. Celeste has a garden that has a length of $15x$ and a width of $3x + 5$.

a. Write a polynomial that represents the area of the garden by multiplying $15x(3x + 5)$.

_____

b. Find the area of the garden if $x = 3$ feet.

_____

23. Use the algebra tiles to find the product of $(2x - 1)$ and $(x + 4)$. Write the product below.

_____

24. Find the product of $(t + 8)$ and $(t - 7)$.

_____

25. Simplify $(p - 12)^2$.

_____

**MODULE 15**

# Factoring Polynomials

*Module Quiz: B*

1. Find the product of $3x^2y$ and $12xy - 7y$.

   _____

2. What is the GCF of 54 and 72?

   _____

3. What is the GCF of $36x^2y$ and $18xy^2$?

   _____

4. What is the complete factorization of $108x^2 - 99y + 3$?

   _____

5. What is the correct factorization of $7(x - 3) + y(3 - x)$?

   A  $(7x + 21)(3y - xy)$

   B  $(7 - y)(x - 3)$

   C  $(7 + y)(x - 3)$

   D  $7 + y$

6. The area of a carpet is $36x^2y - 9xy$ square inches. If the width is $3xy$ inches, what is the length of the carpet?

   _____

7. Which of the following is equivalent to $4x - 12$?

   A  $4x + 12$          C  $-2(2x - 6)$

   B  $2(6 - 2x)$        D  $-2(6 - 2x)$

8. What is the correct factorization of $x^2 + 17x + 30$?

   A  $(x + 6)(x + 5)$

   B  $(x + 10)(x + 3)$

   C  $(x + 15)(x + 2)$

   D  $(x + 30)(x + 1)$

9. Factor $2x^2 + 3x - 5$.

   _____

10. Which methods can be used to factor $4x^2 - 16$?

    A  Factor out the GCF
       O Yes    O No

    B  Factor by grouping
       O Yes    O No

    C  Perfect square trinomial
       O Yes    O No

    D  Difference of squares
       O Yes    O No

11. Is each of the following a perfect square trinomial?

    A  $x^2 + 10x + 25$          O Yes   O No

    B  $x^2 + 25x + 25$          O Yes   O No

    C  $x^2 + 7x + 49$           O Yes   O No

    D  $x^2 + 625x + 50$         O Yes   O No

12. What is the complete factorization of $x^4 - 1$?

    A  $(x^2 + 1)(x^2 - 1)$

    B  $(x + 1)^2(x - 1)^2$

    C  $(x^2 + 1)(x - 1)(x + 1)$

    D  $(x + 1)(x + 1)(x - 1)(x + 1)$

## MODULE 15 — Factoring Polynomials
### *Module Quiz: B*

13. Find the product of $(4x - 7y)(2x + 2y)$.

_____

14. Find the greatest common factor of $76rs$ and $57s^2$.

_____

15. Write two monomials with a GCF of $7x^3y$, one of which has a degree of 5.

_____

16. Factor each of the following polynomials. If the polynomial cannot be factored, write *not factorable*.

    a.  $20x^3 - 64x$

    _____

    b.  $17s^2t + 11t$

    _____

    c.  $8x^2 + 3x + 2$

    _____

    d.  $56 - 7x + 8z - xz$

    _____

17. Determine whether each value of $c$ makes $x^2 - 5x + c$ factorable. If so, factor the polynomial.

    a.  $c = 36$

    _____

    b.  $c = -36$

    _____

18. Factor $7x^2 + 29x + 4$.

_____

19. Factor $5x^3 + 40x^2 - 100x$.

_____

20. Factor $m^4 - 16$.

_____

21. The area of a square in square feet is represented by $z^2 + 12z + 36$.

    a.  Find an expression for a side length of the square.

    _____

    b.  Find the perimeter of the square when $z = 12$.

    _____

22. Is $4x^4 - 49$ a difference of two squares? Explain why or why not.

_____

_____

23. Factor $4x^2 - 49$.

_____

24. Factor $9n^2 + 42n + 49$.

_____

25. Factor $15a^3 + 20a^2 - 6a - 8$.

_____

## MODULE 15 Factoring Polynomials
### *Module Quiz: D*

1. What is the product of $11x$ and $(3x - y)$?

    A   $33x^2 - 11xy$

    B   $33x^2 - y$

    C   $33x - 11y$

2. What is the GCF of 10 and 20?

    A   2

    B   5

    C   10

3. What is the GCF of $12x^2$ and $18x$?

    A   6

    B   $3x$

    C   $6x$

4. What is the complete factorization of $16x^2 - 24y$?

    A   $2(8x^2 - 12y)$

    B   $8(2x^2 - 3y)$

    C   $8xy(2x - 3)$

5. What is the correct factorization of $7(x - 3) + y(x - 3)$?

    A   $(7x - 21)(xy - 13y)$

    B   $(7 + y)(x - 3)$

    C   $7 + y$

6. The area of a carpet is $36x - 12$ square inches. If the width of the carpet is $3x - 1$ inches, what is the length?

    A   3 in.

    B   $3x$ in.

    C   12 in.

7. Which of the following is equivalent to $(5 - x)$?

    A   $-1(5 - x)$

    B   $-1(x - 5)$

    C   $x - 5$

8. What is the correct factorization of $x^2 + 6x + 8$?

    A   $(x + 8)(x + 1)$

    B   $(x + 4)(x + 4)$

    C   $(x + 4)(x + 2)$

9. What is the correct factorization of $x^2 - 2x - 15$?

    A   $(x - 5)(x + 3)$

    B   $(x + 5)(x - 3)$

    C   $(x + 5)(x + 3)$

10. What is the correct factorization of $3x^2 + 14x + 8$?

    A   $(3x + 4)(x + 2)$

    B   $(3x + 2)(x + 4)$

    C   $(3x + 8)(x + 1)$

11. Which method could be used to factor $5x^2 - 25$?

    A   Factor out the GCF

    B   Factor by grouping

    C   Difference of squares

12. Which of the following binomials is a difference of squares?

    A   $x^2 - 6$

    B   $5x^2 - 10$

    C   $x^2 - 1$

13. What is the complete factorization of $25x^2 - 36$?

    A   $(5x + 6)(5x + 6)$

    B   $(5x - 6)(5x - 6)$

    C   $(5x + 6)(5x - 6)$

**MODULE 15**

# Factoring Polynomials

## Module Quiz: D

14. Find the product of $(x + 5)$ and $(x - 7)$.

_____

15. Find the greatest common factor of 45 and 60.

_____

16. What is the greatest common factor of $6y$ and $9y^2$?

_____

17. Factor each of the following polynomials. If the polynomial cannot be factored, write *not factorable*.

a. $7x - 77$

_____

b. $6x^2 + 11y$

_____

c. $8x - x^2$

_____

d. $7(8 - x) + z(8 - x)$

_____

18. Determine whether each value of $c$ makes $x^2 - 3x + c$ factorable. If so, factor the polynomial.

a. $c = 10$

_____

b. $c = -10$

_____

19.

| $x^2$ | 10x |
|-------|-----|
| 2x    | 20  |

a. Write the polynomial modeled by this geometric diagram.

_____

b. Factor the polynomial.

_____

20. Factor $x^2 + 4x - 21$.

_____

21. Factor $3x^2 + 7x + 2$.

_____

22. Is $4x^2 + 16$ a difference of two squares? Explain why or why not.

_____

23. Factor $p^2 - 100$.

_____

24. Factor $n^2 + 10n + 25$.

_____

25. Factor $x^2 - 16x + 64$.

_____

MODULE
16

# Solving Quadratic Equations

## *Module Quiz: B*

1. Solve $-x^2 - 2x + 3 = 3$ for *x*. What are the solutions?

_____

2. Simplify $\pm\sqrt{\dfrac{81}{64}}$.

_____

3. Solve $9x^2 - 4 = 0$ for *x*. Which is the correct answer?

   A   $x = \pm\dfrac{9}{4}$       C   $x = \pm\dfrac{4}{9}$

   B   $x = \pm\dfrac{2}{3}$       D   $x = \pm\dfrac{3}{2}$

4. What are the solutions of $(x - 5)^2 = 12$?

_____

5. Are each of the following solutions of $x^2 + 12x - 28 = 0$?

   A  –14          O Yes   O No

   B  –2           O Yes   O No

   C  2            O Yes   O No

   D  7            O Yes   O No

6. Use factorization to solve $16x^2 + 16x + 4 = 0$ for *x*. What is *x*?

_____

7. Solve $x^2 + 10x = 39$ by completing the square. What are the solutions?

_____

8. Solve $2x^2 + 9x - 4 = 0$ for *x* using the quadratic formula. Which is correct?

   A  $x = -4$ or $x = -\dfrac{1}{2}$

   B  $x = \dfrac{-9 \pm \sqrt{113}}{4}$

   C  $x = 4$ or $x = \dfrac{1}{2}$

   D  $x = \dfrac{9 \pm \sqrt{113}}{4}$

9. What is the discriminant of $x^2 + 11x - 10 = 0$, and how many real solutions does the equation have?

_____

_____

**MODULE 16**

# Solving Quadratic Equations

*Module Quiz: B*

10. Solve $0 = (x - 9)^2 - 4$ for $x$. What are the solutions?

   _____

11. What is the product of $\sqrt{\dfrac{1}{2}}$ and $\sqrt{50}$?

   _____

12. Two consecutive numbers can be represented by $x$ and $x + 1$. The product of two consecutive numbers is equal to 35 more than eleven times the sum of the numbers.

   a. Write a quadratic equation to represent the situation.

   _____

   b. What are the solutions to the equation?

   _____

   c. What are the two consecutive numbers?

   _____

13. The height of a ball is modeled by $f(x) = -16x^2 + 128x$, where $x$ is the number of seconds after the ball is hit. How long is the ball in the air?

   _____

14. Solve $4x^2 + 8x = 12$.

15. Solve $3x^2 = 5x + 8$.

   _____

16. Find the discriminant of $x^2 + 6x + 13 = 0$, and determine the number of real solutions of the equation.

   _____

17. Is $n^2 + 10n + 25$ a perfect square trinomial? If so, what is the correct factorization?

   _____

18. Is $x^2 - 16$ a difference of two squares? If so, what is the correct factorization?

   _____

**Find the zeros of each function.**

19. $f(x) = (x - 9)(x + 3)$

   _____

20. $f(x) = \left(x - \dfrac{a}{2}\right)\left(x + \dfrac{2}{b}\right)$

   _____

21. $f(x) = x^2 - 6x - 16$

   _____

22. $f(x) = x^2 - 15x - 34$

   _____

23. $f(x) = 2x^2 + 12x + 10$

   _____

**MODULE 16** **Solving Quadratic Equations**

*Module Quiz: D*

1. Solve $0 = 16 - x^2$ for $x$. What are the solutions?

   A  0 and 16

   B  −2 and 8

   C  −4 and 4

2. Solve $2x^2 = 242$ using square roots. What are the solutions?

   A  2 and 22

   B  −11 and 11

   C  −2 and 121

3. Solve $x^2 - 100 = 0$ for $x$. Which is the correct answer?

   A  $x = \pm 100$

   B  $x = 10$

   C  $x = \pm 10$

4. What are the solutions to $(x + 2)^2 = 36$?

   A  4 and −8

   B  4 and 6

   C  34 and −38

5. What are the solutions of $(x + 2)(x - 3) = 0$?

   A  −2 and −3

   B  −2 and 3

   C  2 and −3

6. Factor and solve $x^2 - 7x - 30 = 0$. What are the solutions?

   A  −10 and 3

   B  10 and −3

   C  10 and 3

7. $x^2 + 12x + \boxed{\phantom{0}}$

   Which number completes the square to form a perfect square trinomial?

   A  12

   B  16

   C  36

8. Carlos is using the quadratic formula to find the solutions of $y = 3x^2 - 5x - 2$. Which of the following will simplify to the correct solutions?

   A  $\dfrac{5 \pm \sqrt{25 - 24}}{6}$

   B  $\dfrac{5 \pm \sqrt{25 + 24}}{6}$

   C  $\dfrac{-5 \pm \sqrt{25 - 24}}{6}$

9. The discriminant of a quadratic equation is 0. Which statement is true?

   A  There are no real solutions.

   B  There is one real solution.

   C  There are two real solutions.

**MODULE 16**

# Solving Quadratic Equations

*Module Quiz: D*

10. Complete the trinomial $x^2 - 34x + c$ so that is a perfect square.

    _____

11. What is $\sqrt{169}$?

    _____

12. The product of two consecutive numbers is equal to six more than six times the sum of the numbers.
    This can be represented with the equation $x^2 - 11x - 12 = 0$.

    a. Factor the equation, and find the possible values of $x$.

       _____

    b. What are the two consecutive numbers?

       _____

13. Solve $x^2 + 8x = 9$.

    _____

14. Solve $3x^2 - 5x - 8 = 0$ using the quadratic formula, $\dfrac{-b \pm \sqrt{b^2 - 4ac}}{2a}$.

    _____

15. Find the discriminant of $x^2 - 6x - 10 = 0$, and determine the number of real solutions of the equation.

    _____

16. Use the graph of $y = x^2 - 2x - 7$ to solve $x^2 - 2x - 7 = 8$.

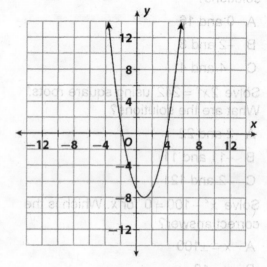

**Solve each quadratic equation.**

17. $9x^2 + 6x + 1 = 0$

    _____

18. $2x^2 - 4x = 70$

    _____

19. $-1 = 16x^2 + 8x$

    _____

20. $3x^2 + 11x + 6 = 0$

    _____

MODULE
17

# Quadratic Functions
*Module Quiz: B*

1. Is each expression equivalent to $2x^2 - 50$?

   A  $2(x-5)(x+5)$    ○ Yes  ○ No

   B  $-2(x+5)(x+5)$    ○ Yes  ○ No

   C  $-2(5-x)(x+5)$    ○ Yes  ○ No

2. Is each of the following a quadratic function?

   A  $3x + y^2 = 5$    ○ Yes  ○ No

   B  $3x^2 + y = 5$    ○ Yes  ○ No

   C  $y = 3x^2 + 5$    ○ Yes  ○ No

3. What is the vertex of the graph of $y = x^2 - 4$?

   _____

4. Given $f(x) = 4x^2$ and $g(x) = -\dfrac{1}{5}x^2$, choose True or False for each statement.

   A  $f(x)$ and $g(x)$ have the same axes of symmetry.

   ○ True  ○ False

   B  $f(x)$ is wider than $g(x)$.

   ○ True  ○ False

   C  $f(x)$ is narrower than $g(x)$.

   ○ True  ○ False

5. Which equation is graphed below?

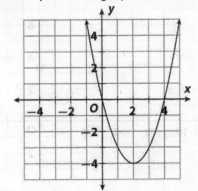

   A  $y = -x^2 - 4x$

   B  $y = x^2 - 4x$

   C  $y = -x^2 + 4x$

   D  $2y = x^2 + 4x$

6. Which functions have the same axis of symmetry?

   A  $f(x) = 2x^2 + 1;\ f(x) = -4x^2$

   B  $f(x) = 3x^2 + 4x;\ f(x) = 3x^2$

   C  $f(x) = (x+1)^2;\ f(x) = (x-3)^2$

   D  $f(x) = x^2 - 3x;\ f(x) = x^2$

7. A ball is dropped off an office building that is 790 feet tall. Apply the function $h(t) = -16t^2 + c$, where $h(t)$ is the height of the ball at time $t$, and $c$ is its initial height. Approximately how long did it take the ball to hit the ground?

   A  6 seconds

   B  7 seconds

   C  36 seconds

   D  49 seconds

8. What are the zeros of $y = x^2 - 5x + 6$?

   _____

9. The zeros of a quadratic function are $-6$ and $-2$. What is a possible vertex of the function?

   A  $(-4, -4)$    C  $(4, 6)$

   B  $(4, -2)$    D  $(8, -4)$

10. What are the zeros of $x^2 - 6x = y$?

    _____

11. Which ordered pairs are solutions to the system: $\begin{cases} y = x^2 + 5x + 4 \\ y = 8x + 8 \end{cases}$?

    A  $(-1, 0), (4, 40)$    C  $(-1, 0), (0, 4)$

    B  $(-1, 0), (-4, 0)$    D  $(1, 16), (4, 40)$

**MODULE 17**

# Quadratic Functions
### *Module Quiz: B*

12. a. Complete the table to find values of $y = -2x^2 + 4$.

| $x$ | $-2x^2 + 4 = y$ | $y$ |
|---|---|---|
| $-2$ | | |
| $-1$ | | |
| $0$ | | |
| $1$ | | |
| $2$ | | |

b. Graph $y = -2x^2 + 4$.

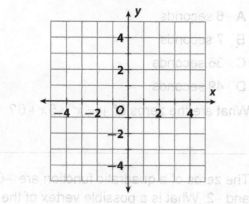

13. Fill in the blanks to describe the end behavior of the function $f(x) = -4x^2 + 6$.

As $x \to \infty$, $f(x) \to \boxed{\phantom{x}}$

As $x \to -\infty$, $f(x) \to \boxed{\phantom{x}}$

14. Does the following set of ordered pairs satisfy a linear, exponential, or quadratic model? Explain why.

$\{(-2, 4), (0, 0), (2, -4), (4, -8)\}$

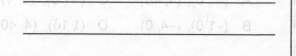

15. Write the equation of a quadratic function with a minimum value of $y = 2$ and an axis of symmetry of $x = 4$.

_____

16. $y = -(x + 5)^2 + 4$

a. Find the vertex, and identify the maximum or minimum value of $y$.

_____

b. Find the axis of symmetry.

_____

c. Find the domain and range.

_____

17. Solve: $\begin{cases} y = x^2 + 8x + 6 \\ 16x - 2y = -44 \end{cases}$.

18. Graph the line $y = 5$ and the quadratic function $y = -x^2 - 6x$ to solve $-x^2 - 6x = 5$. Write the solutions below the graph.

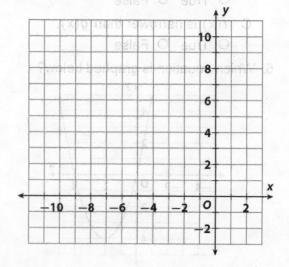

_____

Name _____ Class _____ Date _____ Class _____

# MODULE 17 Quadratic Functions

## *Module Quiz: D*

1. Which is a quadratic function?

    A   $y = x - 9$

    B   $y = x^2 + 9$

    C   $y = x^3 + 2x - 9$

2. What is the vertex of the parabola graphed below?

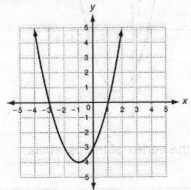

    A   $(-4, -1)$

    B   $(-3, 0)$

    C   $(-1, -4)$

3. Given $f(x) = 4x^2$ and $g(x) = 8x^2$, which statement is true?

    A   $f(x)$ and $g(x)$ have different vertices.

    B   $f(x)$ is wider than $g(x)$.

    C   $f(x)$ is narrower than $g(x)$.

4. Which table of values would you use to graph $y = 3x^2$?

    A

| x | −2 | −1 | 0 | 1 | 2 |
|---|----|----|---|---|---|
| y | 12 | 3  | 0 | 3 | 12 |

    B

| x | −2 | −1 | 0 | 1 | 2 |
|---|----|----|---|---|---|
| y | 36 | 9  | 0 | 9 | 36 |

5. What are the zeros of $y = x^2 + 4x - 45$?

    A   5 and −9

    B   9 and −5

    C   −5 and −9

6. What is the axis of symmetry of the graph of $y = (x - 5)^2$?

    A   $x = -5$

    B   $x = 0$

    C   $x = 5$

7. Use the function $h(t) = -16t^2 + c$, where $t$ is the number of seconds and $c$ is the height of the bridge. How high above the ground is a ball that was dropped off a 260-foot-high bridge after 2 seconds?

    A   0 feet

    B   64 feet

    C   196 feet

8. What are the zeros of the graph below?

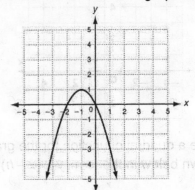

    A   −2 and 0

    B   −1 and 0

    C   0 and 2

9. How many zeros does the function $y = 4x^2 - 36$ have?

    A   0

    B   1

    C   2

**MODULE 17**

# Quadratic Functions

## *Module Quiz: D*

10. a. Complete the table to find values of $y = 2x^2$.

| $x$ | $2x^2 = y$ | $y$ |
|-----|------------|-----|
| $-2$ | $2(-2)^2 = y$ | 8 |
| $-1$ | $2(-1)^2 = y$ | |
| 0 | | |
| 1 | | |
| 2 | | |

b. Graph $y = 2x^2$.

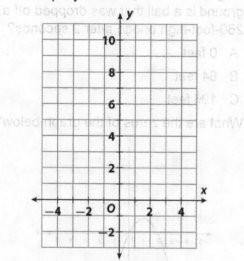

11. Write a quadratic function for the graph shown below in the form $y = (x - h)^2 + k$.

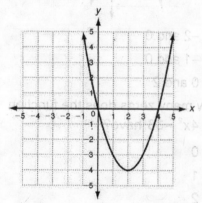

12. What are the zeros of $y = x^2 - 64$?

_____

13.

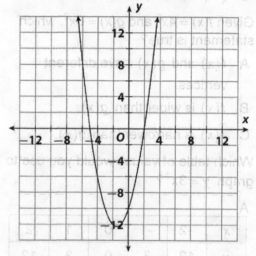

$y = x^2 - 2x - 3$

Find the vertex of the parabola.

_____

14. Use the graph of $f(x) = x^2 + 3x - 10$ to fill in the blanks and describe the end behavior of the parabola.

As $x \to \infty$, $f(x) \to$ ☐

As $x \to -\infty$, $f(x) \to$ ☐

15. Solve: $\begin{cases} y = x^2 + 4 \\ y = -4x \end{cases}$.

**MODULE 18**

# Piecewise and Absolute Value Functions

*Module Quiz: B*

1. What is the interquartile range of the following data: $-9, -12, 3, 5, -13, 2, 9$?

   _____

2. What is $f(x) = [x] - 3$ evaluated for $x = -2.8$?

   _____

3. Which function matches the graph below?

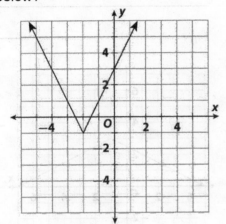

   A  $y = |x + 2| - 1$

   B  $y = 2|x + 2| - 1$

   C  $y = \frac{1}{2}|x - 1| + 2$

   D  $y = 2|x - 1| + 2$

4. Does each function have a domain of all real numbers?

   A  $f(x) = \begin{cases} y = x + 3 \text{ if } x \le -2 \\ y = x^2 \text{ if } x > -2 \end{cases}$

   ○ Yes   ○ No

   B  $f(x) = \begin{cases} y = -9 \text{ if } x < 4 \\ y = x + 2 \text{ if } x > 4 \end{cases}$

   ○ Yes   ○ No

   C  $f(x) = -[x]$

   ○ Yes   ○ No

5. What is the range of the graph shown below?

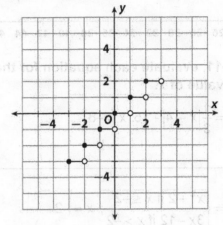

6. An electric company charges $0.018 per kilowatt hour (kWh) for the first 500 kWh, $0.056 for the kWhs over 500 kWh. Which function best represents the amount of a bill based on the total kWh?

   A  $y = \begin{cases} 0.018x \text{ if } 0 < x \le 500 \\ 9 + 0.056(x - 500) \text{ if } x > 500 \end{cases}$

   B  $y = \begin{cases} 0.018x \text{ if } 0 < x < 500 \\ 9 + 0.056x \text{ if } x \ge 500 \end{cases}$

   C  $y = \begin{cases} 0.056x \text{ if } 0 < x \le 500 \\ 9 + 0.018(x - 500) \text{ if } x > 500 \end{cases}$

   D  $y = \begin{cases} 0.018x \text{ if } x < 500 \\ 9 + 0.056(x - 500) \text{ if } x \ge 500 \end{cases}$

7. Is each equation's graph entirely in quadrant III and IV?

   A  $y = -4|x| - 6$     ○ Yes   ○ No

   B  $y = \frac{1}{3}|x| - 6$     ○ Yes   ○ No

8. Solve $3|2x + 5| = 12$.

   _____

**MODULE 18**

# Piecewise and Absolute Value Functions

## Module Quiz: B

9. Make a box–and–whisker plot for the data set $\{25, 28, 30, 32, 40, 42, 45\}$.

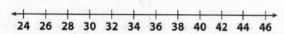

**For 9–11, evaluate each equation for the given value of x.**

10. $y = \dfrac{1}{3}|x - 4| + 15;\ x = -8$

_____

11. $y = \begin{cases} x^2 + 2 \text{ if } x \le -2 \\ 3x - 12 \text{ if } x > -2 \end{cases};\ x = -2$

_____

12. $y = 7[x] - 1;\ x = -3.7$

_____

13. Graph $f(x) = \begin{cases} -3x + 4 \text{ if } x < 2 \\ 3x - 8 \text{ if } x \ge 2 \end{cases}$

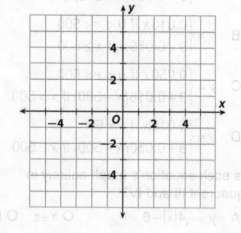

14. $f(x) = 6|x - 9| + 7$

$g(x) = 9|-9 + x| + 7$

a. Compare the vertices of $f(x)$ and $g(x)$.

_____

_____

b. Compare the shape of the two functions.

_____

_____

15.

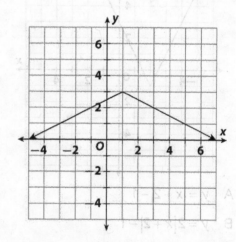

a. Write an equation for the graph shown above.

_____

b. What are the domain and range of the equation?

_____

_____

## MODULE 18 — Piecewise and Absolute Value Functions
### Module Quiz: D

1. What is the mean and the approximate standard deviation of the following set of data: –7, 5, –2, 11, 15, 2?

   A   mean: 4; standard deviation: 7.4

   B   mean: 24; standard deviation: 55.3

   C   mean: 4; standard deviation: 0

2. Which of the following is a greatest integer function?

   A   $f(x) = |x - 6|$

   B   $g(x) = \begin{cases} 5 \text{ if } x < 0 \\ x \text{ if } x \geq 0 \end{cases}$

   C   $h(x) = [x] + 2$

3. What is $f(x) = |x| - 5$ evaluated for $x = -3$?

   A   –8

   B   –2

   C   2

4. Which function matches the graph below?

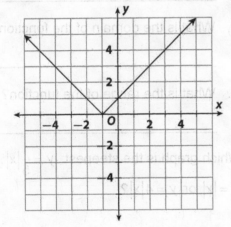

   A   $h(x) = |x + 1|$

   B   $h(x) = |x - 1|$

   C   $h(x) = |x| - 1$

5. What is the domain and range of the graph shown below?

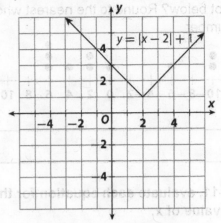

$y = |x - 2| + 1$

   A   Domain: All real numbers
       Range: $y > 1$

   B   Domain: $x \geq 1$
       Range: All real numbers

   C   Domain: All real numbers
       Range: $y \geq 1$

6. A cashier at Giorgio's Grocery Store gets paid $8 an hour for shifts of six hours or less and $12 an hour for working shifts over six hours long. Which function best represents this situation?

   A   $f(x) = \begin{cases} 8x \text{ if } 0 < x \leq 6 \\ 12x \text{ if } x > 6 \end{cases}$

   B   $f(x) = \begin{cases} 12x \text{ if } x < 6 \\ 8x \text{ if } x \geq 6 \end{cases}$

   C   $f(x) = \begin{cases} 8x \text{ if } x \leq 8 \\ 12x \text{ if } x > 8 \end{cases}$

7. Which function has a vertex at (2, –5)?

   A   $y = |x - 2| + 5$

   B   $y = -5|x - 2|$

   C   $y = |x - 2| - 5$

**MODULE 18**

# Piecewise and Absolute Value Functions
*Module Quiz: D*

8. What are the range and interquartile range of the data represented on the dot plot below? Round to the nearest whole number.

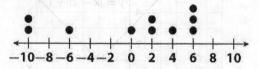

_____

_____

**For 9–11, evaluate each equation for the given value of x.**

9. $y = 5|x + 4|$; $x = -1$

_____

10. $y = [x]$; $x = 4.2$

_____

11. $y = \begin{cases} -x \text{ if } x < 2 \\ x + 3 \text{ if } x \geq 2 \end{cases}$; $x = 3$

_____

12. Graph $f(x) = \begin{cases} 3 \text{ if } x < 0 \\ x - 4 \text{ if } x \geq 0 \end{cases}$.

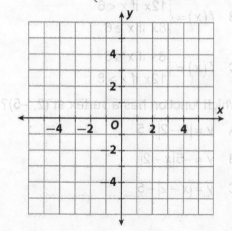

13. Find the vertex and both slopes of $f(x) = |x + 7| - 12$.

_____

_____

14.

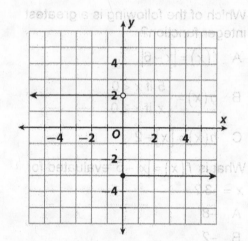

a. Write a function for the graph shown above.

_____

b. What is the domain of the function?

_____

c. What is the range of the function?

_____

15. Which graph is the steepest: $y = \frac{1}{5}|x|$, $y = |x|$ or $y = 4|x|$?

_____

16. Solve $8 = |2x|$.

Name _____ Date _____ Class _____

1. Which function matches the graph shown below?

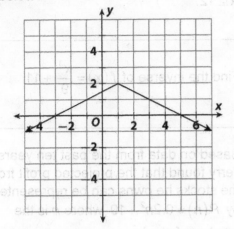

A  $f(x) = -\dfrac{1}{2}|x + 2| - 1$

B  $f(x) = -2|x - 1| + 2$

C  $f(x) = -\dfrac{1}{2}|x - 1| + 2$

D  $f(x) = -2|x + 1| + 2$

2. Is each function one-to-one?

A  $f(x) = -4x$       ○ Yes ○ No

B  $f(x) = (x + 1)^3$    ○ Yes ○ No

C  $f(x) = x^2 + 2$      ○ Yes ○ No

D  $f(x) = \sqrt{x} + 9$      ○ Yes ○ No

3. What is the domain and range of $y = \sqrt{x + 14} - 7$?

_____

4. Write an equation that is the square root function that has been shrunk vertically by a factor of $\dfrac{1}{3}$ and translated down $8\dfrac{1}{2}$ units.

_____

5. The volume $V$ of a sphere is given by $V(r) = \dfrac{4}{3}\pi r^3$ where $r$ is the length of the radius. Write a function that gives the radius in terms of the volume.

_____

6. What is $y = 5\sqrt[3]{x} - 2$ evaluated for $x = -64$?

_____

7. Which equation is graphed below?

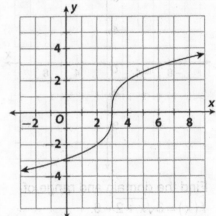

A  $y = 2(x - 3)^3$      C  $y = 2\sqrt[3]{x} - 3$

B  $y = \dfrac{1}{2}(x - 3)^3$      D  $y = \dfrac{1}{2}\sqrt[3]{x} - 3$

**MODULE 19**

# Square Root and Cube Root Functions

*Module Quiz: B*

8. Evaluate $y = \begin{cases} -x+13 \text{ if } x \le -2 \\ x^2 \text{ if } x > -2 \end{cases}$

for $x = -2.2$.

_____

9. a. Fill in the table of values for
$f(x) = 3\sqrt{x+2} - 6$.

| x | f(x) |
|---|---|
| −2 | |
| −1 | |
| 2 | |
| 7 | |

b. Graph $f(x) = 3\sqrt{x+2} - 6$.

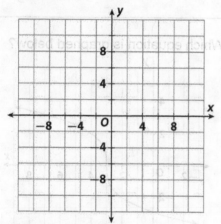

c. Find the domain and range of
$f(x) = 3\sqrt{x+2} - 6$.

_____

_____

10. Write a square root function with a
domain of $x \ge 4$, a range of $y \le 0$, and a
vertical stretch factor of 5.

_____

11. Find the inverse of $f(x) = 6(x-12)^2$ for
$x \ge 12$.

_____

12. Find the inverse of $f(x) = \dfrac{x^3}{9} + 11$.

_____

13. Based on data from the past ten years,
Jerry found that the projected profit from
the stocks he owns can be represented
by $P(n) = 0.2n^2 + 10$ where $n$ is the
number of stocks.

a. Write an inverse function to find the
number of stocks based on the profit,
or $N(p)$.

_____

b. How many stocks does Jerry need to
own to make a projected profit of
$90?

_____

14. Graph $f(x) = \sqrt[3]{x} + 4$ and its inverse
$f^{-1}(x) = (x-4)^3$.

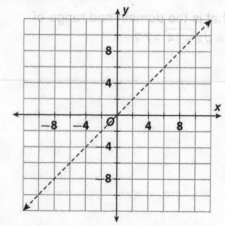

Name _____ Date _____ Class_____

Square Root and Cube Root Functions
*Module Quiz: D*

1. Evaluate $y = \begin{cases} x+4 \text{ if } x < 0 \\ 13 \text{ if } x \geq 0 \end{cases}$ for $x = 0$?

    A  0

    B  4

    C  13

2. Which of the following is **not** a one–to–one function?

    A  $f(x) = x$

    B  $f(x) = x^2$

    C  $f(x) = x^3$

3. What is the domain of $y = \sqrt{x+2}$?

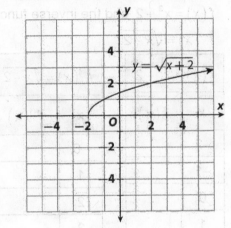

    A  $x > -2$

    B  $x \geq -2$

    C  $y \geq 0$

4. Which of the following square root functions has been vertically stretched by a factor of 2?

    A  $f(x) = \sqrt{x-2} + 4$

    B  $f(x) = \sqrt{x} + 2$

    C  $f(x) = 2\sqrt{x+5}$

5. The surface area $SA$ of a cube is given by $SA(s) = 6s^2$ where $s$ is a side length of the cube. What is the inverse function?

    A  $s(SA) = \sqrt{\dfrac{s}{6}}$

    B  $s(SA) = \dfrac{1}{6s^2}$

    C  $s(SA) = 6\sqrt{s}$

6. What is $y = \sqrt[3]{x} + 2$ evaluated for $x = 64$?

    A  6

    B  10

    C  14

7. Which equation is shown on the graph below?

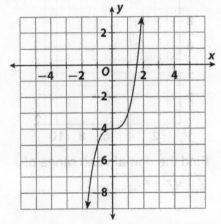

    A  $y = x^3 - 4$

    B  $y = (x-4)^3$

    C  $y = 4x^3$

8. Evaluate $y = 2|x + 5|$ for $x = -10$.

_____

9. a. Complete the table of values for $y = \sqrt{x} + 4$.

| x | y |
|---|---|
| 0 | |
| 1 | |
| 4 | |
| 9 | |

b. Graph $y = \sqrt{x} + 4$.

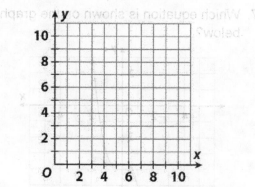

c. Find the domain and range of $y = \sqrt{x} + 4$.

_____

_____

10. Find the inverse of $f(x) = x^2 + 11$ for $x \geq 0$.

_____

11. Find the inverse of $f(x) = (x - 2)^3$.

_____

12. Tracy, a pet sitter, charges a daily fee of $R(p) = p^3 + 10$ where $p$ is the number of pets the client has.

a. Write an inverse function to find the number of pets based on the daily fee, or $P(r)$.

_____

b. How many pets does Tracy need to watch to earn a daily fee of $74?

_____

13. a. Complete the table of values of $f(x) = x^3 + 2$ and the inverse function $f^{-1}(x) = \sqrt[3]{x - 2}$.

| $f(x) = x^3 + 2$ | | $f^{-1}(x) = \sqrt[3]{x - 2}$ | |
|---|---|---|---|
| x | f(x) | x | $f^{-1}(x)$ |
| -2 | | -6 | |
| -1 | | 1 | |
| 0 | | 2 | |
| 1 | | 3 | |
| 2 | | 10 | |

b. Graph $f(x)$ and $f^{-1}(x)$.

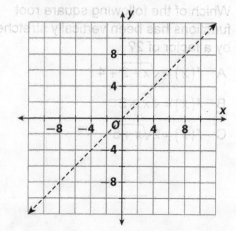

# Numbers and Expressions

## *Unit Test: A*

1. What is the most precise measurement?

   A  120 cm  C  128.77 cm

   B  128 cm  D  128.8 cm

2. Okamura's garden has a perimeter of 20.05 meters. How many significant digits does the perimeter have?

   _____

3. Approximately how many gallons are in 7 liters?

   A  1.8 gal  C  7.3 gal

   B  6.7 gal  D  46 gal

4. $36^{\frac{1}{2}}$ is equal to which of the following?

   A  6  C  18

   B  9  D  1296

5. Simplify $y^6 \times y^{-2}$.

   _____

6. The area of a face of a cube can be found by evaluating the expression $v^{\frac{2}{3}}$ where $v$ is the volume of the cube. What is the area of a face of a cube with a volume of 8 cubic meters?

   _____

7. Does $\pi$ belong to each of the following sets?

   A  Whole numbers  ○ Yes  ○ No

   B  Integers  ○ Yes  ○ No

   C  Rational numbers  ○ Yes  ○ No

8. Does each number belong to all of the following sets: integers, rational numbers, and real numbers?

   A  $\dfrac{9}{3}$  ○ Yes  ○ No

   B  2.5  ○ Yes  ○ No

   C  $-7$  ○ Yes  ○ No

9. What is $24 - 3x$ evaluated for $x = 6$?

   _____

10. What is $\dfrac{6x - 6y}{y}$ evaluated for $x = 5$ and $y = 2$?

    _____

11. The expression $7(y - 5)$ is equivalent to which of the following expressions?

    A  $y - 35$  C  $-35 + 7y$

    B  $2y$  D  $7y - 5$

12. What is $8y - 5x + 13y$ equivalent to after being simplified?

    A  $21y - 5x$  C  $5x + 21y$

    B  $16y$  D  $8y + 8x$

**UNIT 1A**

# Numbers and Expressions
### *Unit Test: A*

13.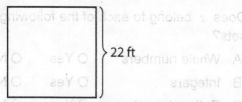
22 ft

To the nearest tenth, what is the length of one side of the square shown above in meters?

_____

14. Guy ran at a rate of 11.5 kilometers per hours. To the nearest tenth, what was Guy's speed in miles per hour?

_____

15. A piece of paper has an area of 88 square inches. Find the area of the paper to the nearest square centimeter.

_____

16. Simplify the expression $64^{\frac{1}{3}} \times 100^{\frac{1}{2}}$.

_____

17. Simplify the expression $27^{\frac{2}{3}} - 4^{\frac{1}{2}}$.

_____

18. Use the Properties of Exponents to simplify the expression $\left(8^{\frac{2}{3}}\right)^{\frac{6}{2}}$.

_____

19. Determine if the set $\{-1, 0\}$ is closed under multiplication. Explain why the set is or is not closed.

_____

20. Find $-10z + 2y$ evaluated for $z = -3$ and $y = 4$.

_____

**For 21–22, use the table.**

| School Supplies | |
|---|---|
| Pencils | $0.25 each |
| Notebooks | $2.50 each |
| Backpacks | $32.00 each |

21. Hugh bought $x$ notebooks. Write an expression for the cost of the notebooks.

_____

22. Julio bought a backpack and $y$ pencils.

a. Write an expression for the total amount Julio spent.

_____

b. Evaluate the expression if Julio bought 6 pencils.

_____

## UNIT 1A  Numbers and Expressions
### Unit Test: B

1. Which measurement has 3 significant digits?

   A  340 in.

   B  232.0 in.

   C  3.42 in.

   D  0.04 in.

2. Clinton's garden is 32.55 meters long and 12.50 meters wide. Write the perimeter of Clinton's garden with the correct number of significant digits.

   _____

3. A water bottle contains 1.5 liters of water. Approximately how many gallons of water does the bottle contain?

   A  0.4 gal

   B  1.2 gal

   C  1.8 gal

   D  5.8 gal

4. Which of the following is equal to $196^{\frac{1}{2}}$?

   A  11

   B  12

   C  13

   D  14

5. Simplify $7y\left(y^{-8} \times y^{-2}\right)$.

   _____

6. The equation $s = 12t^{\frac{2}{5}}$ represents the value of a share of Computer Solutions' stock where $t$ is the number of months the stock has been sold. What is the price of the stock after 243 months?

   _____

7. Does −3.5 belong to each of the following sets?

   A  Whole numbers          ○ Yes    ○ No

   B  Integers               ○ Yes    ○ No

   C  Rational numbers       ○ Yes    ○ No

   D  Real numbers           ○ Yes    ○ No

8. Which statement shows that the set of irrational numbers is **not** closed under division?

   A  $\dfrac{7}{14} = \dfrac{1}{2}$

   B  $\dfrac{\sqrt{2}}{\sqrt{2}} = 1$

   C  $\dfrac{\pi}{1} = \pi$

   D  $\dfrac{4}{2\sqrt{3}} = \dfrac{2}{\sqrt{3}}$

9. What is $(z-3)^2 + 5$ evaluated for $z = -2$?

   _____

10. What is $xy - 12x^2$ evaluated for $x = -2$ and $y = -6$?

    _____

11. Is $3x - 6 + 5 + 17x$ equivalent to each of the following expressions?

    A  $20x + 1$              ○ Yes    ○ No

    B  19                     ○ Yes    ○ No

12. Which of the following is equivalent to $y^2 - 2\left(x + 7y^2\right)$?

    A  $-2x - 13y^2$

    B  $y^2 - 16x^2$

    C  $-6y^2 - 2x$

    D  $-14y^2 - 2x$

13. The driving distance from Jacksonville to Tampa is 199 miles. Find the distance from Jacksonville to Tampa in kilometers. Round the answer to the nearest kilometer.

_____

14. Darryl in-line skated 2.75 kilometers in 90 minutes. Find Darryl's speed in miles per hour. Round the answer to the nearest hundredth.

_____

15.

```
                215 ft
┌─────────────────────────────┐
│                              │⎫
│      Allen's Wrenches        │⎬ 45 ft
│                              │⎭
└─────────────────────────────┘
```

The diagram shows an aerial view of a store. What is the area of Allen's store to the nearest square meter?

_____

16. The side length of a cube can be found with the expression $v^{\frac{1}{3}}$ where $v$ is the volume of the cube. Find the side length of a cube with a volume of 512 cubic centimeters.

_____

17. Simplify the expression $16^{\frac{3}{4}} \times 10{,}000^{\frac{1}{2}}$.

_____

18. Use the Properties of Exponents to simplify $25^{-2}$.

_____

19. Is the set $\{-3, 0, 3\}$ closed under addition, subtraction, multiplication, or division? Explain your answer.

_____

20. Find $-10z + 2y \div z$ evaluated for $z = -2$ and $y = 6$.

_____

**For 21–22, use the table.**

| Pearlie's Produce | |
|---|---|
| Onions | $0.96 per lb |
| Squash | $0.79 per lb |
| Potatoes | $0.45 per lb |
| Corn | $0.75 each |

21. Allie bought 5 pounds of onions, $x$ pounds of squash, and $y$ pieces of corn. Write a simplified expression that represents the amount Allie spent on produce.

_____

22. Serena bought $z$ pounds of squash and twice that weight of potatoes. Write a simplified expression that represents the amount Serena spent on produce.

_____

### UNIT 1A
# Numbers and Expressions
*Unit Test: C*

1. What is the most precise measurement?

   A  0.2 m          C  104 cm

   B  0.45 m          D  31.5 cm

2. Ashlee's garden is 54.75 meters long and 35.50 meters wide. Write the area of Ashlee's garden with the correct number of significant digits.

   _____

3. A cistern is leaking 0.25 liters of water per minute. Approximately how many gallons of water is the cistern losing per hour?

   A  0.25 gal          C  15 gal

   B  3.96 gal          D  58 gal

4. Which of the following is equal to $256^{\frac{1}{4}}$?

   A  4          C  16

   B  8          D  64

5. The amount of money in Clayton's bank account can be found with the formula $T = p(1.21)^{\frac{3}{2}}$ where $p$ is the original amount he put in the account. If he put $1000 in the account, what is his current balance?

   _____

6. Does each set contain only irrational numbers?

   A  $\{\pi, \sqrt{81}\}$          ○ Yes     ○ No

   B  $\{7^{\frac{1}{2}}, 2\pi\}$          ○ Yes     ○ No

   C  $\{3\sqrt{2}, 5^{\frac{1}{2}}\}$          ○ Yes     ○ No

7. Which statement shows that the set of irrational numbers is **not** closed under division?

   A  $\dfrac{2\sqrt{4}}{\sqrt{4}} = 2$          C  $\dfrac{\pi}{3\pi} = \dfrac{1}{3}$

   B  $\dfrac{\sqrt{7}}{\sqrt{25}} = \dfrac{\sqrt{7}}{5}$          D  $\dfrac{4}{2\sqrt{3}} = \dfrac{2}{\sqrt{3}}$

8. What is $3(z-1)^2 + 5z$ evaluated for $z = -4$?

   _____

9. Is $6(2a^2 + 4a) - 2a^2$ equivalent to each of the following expressions?

   A  $5a^2 + 24a + 5a^2$          ○ Yes     ○ No

   B  $10a^2 + 4a$          ○ Yes     ○ No

   C  $24a + 10a^2$          ○ Yes     ○ No

10. Which of the following is equivalent to $x^2 - 6y + 2(x^2 - y)$?

    A  $3x^2 - 8y$          C  $3x^2 - 4y$

    B  $2x^2 - 5y$          D  $x^2 + 4y$

# Numbers and Expressions
*Unit Test: C*

11. A soccer field is 105 meters long and 71 feet wide. Find the perimeter of the field in feet. Round to the nearest foot.

_____

12. Marcie drove 124 miles in 150 minutes. Find Marcie's speed in kilometers per hour. Round to the nearest kilometer.

_____

13.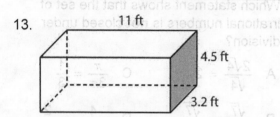

11 ft

4.5 ft

3.2 ft

What is the volume of the box in the diagram above in cubic yards? Round to the nearest tenth.

_____

14. The side length of the base of a square pyramid can be found with the expression $\left(\dfrac{3v}{h}\right)^{\frac{1}{2}}$ where $v$ is the volume of the pyramid and $h$ is the height. Find the side length of a pyramid with a volume of 54 cubic inches and a height of 4.5 inches.

_____

15. Simplify the expression $\dfrac{32^{\frac{6}{5}} \div 64^{\frac{1}{2}}}{256^{\frac{1}{4}}}$.

_____

16. Use the Properties of Exponents to simplify the expression $\left(9^{-2}\right)^{-\frac{1}{4}}$.

_____

17. Write a set that is closed under multiplication but not under subtraction. Explain why the set is closed under one operation and not the other.

_____

_____

_____

18. Find $8z^2 - (2y + z)$ evaluated for $z = 4$ and $y = -3$.

_____

**For 19, use the table.**

| Pearlie's Produce | |
|---|---|
| Onions | $0.96 per lb |
| Squash | $0.79 per lb |
| Potatoes | $0.45 per lb |
| Corn | $0.75 each |

19. Jerri bought $x$ pounds of onions and twice as many pounds of squash. He also bought 7 pieces of corn.

a. Write a simplified expression that represents the amount Jerri spent on produce in simplest terms.

_____

b. If Jerri bought 3 pounds of onions, how much did he spend in all?

_____

UNIT
**1A**

# Numbers and Expressions
*Unit Test: D*

1. What is the most precise measurement?

   A  5.69 cm

   B  5.7 cm

   C  6 cm

2. Allan's bedroom has a perimeter of 110 feet. How many significant digits does 110 have?

   A  1

   B  2

   C  3

3. Approximately how many gallons are in 10 liters?

   A  0.26 gal

   B  2.6 gal

   C  38 gal

4. Which of the following is equal to $9^{\frac{1}{2}}$ ?

   A  3

   B  4.5

   C  18

5. $y^7 \times y^4$ is equal to which of the following?

   A  $y^{28}$

   B  $y^{11}$

   C  $y^3$

6. The length of a side of a cube can be found with the expression $v^{\frac{1}{3}}$. If $v = 27$ cubic centimeters, what is $v^{\frac{1}{3}}$ in centimeters?

   A  3 cm

   B  9 cm

   C  81 cm

7. To which set does $\pi$ belong?

   A  Integers

   B  Rational numbers

   C  Irrational numbers

8. Which number belongs to all of the following sets: integers, rational numbers, and real numbers?

   A  −3

   B  2.5

   C  $\sqrt{2}$

9. What is $4 + 2x$ evaluated for $x = 5$?

   A  11

   B  14

   C  30

10. What is $6x - 5y \times 3$ evaluated for $x = 5$ and $y = 2$?

    A  0

    B  60

    C  75

11. Which of the following is equivalent to $8(y - 5)$?

    A  $8y - 5$

    B  $3y$

    C  $8y - 40$

12. What is $9z + 2z - 8$ equivalent to after being simplified?

    A  $11z - 8$

    B  $3z$

    C  $9z - 6$

Class

**UNIT**
**1A**

# Numbers and Expressions
## *Unit Test: D*

13. Convert 95 meters to feet. Round to the nearest foot.

_____

14. Neil ran at a rate of 0.23 kilometer per minute. What was Neil's speed in kilometers per hour? Round to the nearest kilometer.

_____

15. The area of a computer screen is 160 square inches. Complete the conversion equation to find the area of the screen to the nearest square centimeter.

$$\frac{160 \text{ in}^2}{1} \times \frac{\text{cm}}{\text{in.}} \times \frac{\text{cm}}{\text{in.}}$$

= _____

16. Simplify $8^{\frac{1}{3}} \times 25^{\frac{1}{2}}$.

_____

17. Simplify $4^{\frac{3}{2}} \times 100^{\frac{1}{2}}$.

_____

18. Use the Properties of Exponents to simplify $\left(3^4\right)^{\frac{1}{4}}$.

_____

19. Determine if the set $\{0, 1\}$ is closed under addition. Explain why the set is or is not closed.

_____

_____

_____

20. List all the sets $-\frac{1}{2}$ belongs to from the following list: real numbers, rational numbers, irrational numbers, integers, and whole numbers.

_____

21. Evaluate $5p + p^2$ for $p = 7$.

_____

22. Evaluate $2z + 3y$ for $z = -2$ and $y = 6$.

_____

23. Gabi has 7 bags of apples with $x$ apples each.

   a. Write an expression to represent the total number of apples.

   _____

   b. If there are 14 apples per bag, how many apples does Gabi have in all?

   _____

24. Tia bought $x$ boxes of cereal for $2 each and a can of peanuts for $6.

   a. Write an expression for the total amount Tia spent.

   _____

   b. How much did Tia spend if she bought 3 boxes of cereal?

   _____

# Numbers and Expressions

**UNIT 1A**

*Performance Task*

## That's the Ticket!

**There are 40 rows of seats in the Varsity Theater, with 20 seats in each row. During regular performances, all seats cost $12.**

1. a. A movie rents for $275 per performance. Explain how you could find the theater owner's profit for one performance if you knew the number of tickets sold.

   _____

   b. Write an expression for the theater owner's profit if $n$ people buy tickets for a performance.

   c. Evaluate the expression for $n = 124$.

   _____

**For a special movie premiere, the theater owner decided to charge $20 per ticket for the first $r$ rows of the theater and $15 for the remaining rows.**

2. Explain how you could find the owner's total income if you knew the value of $r$ and you knew that all of the tickets were sold.

   _____

   _____

3. Suppose $r = 16$.
   a. Find the income in the first $r$ rows if all of the tickets were sold.

   _____

   b. Find the income in the remaining $r$ rows if all of the tickets were sold.

   _____

   c. Find the total income if $r = 16$.

   _____

4. Write and simplify an expression for the owner's profit if tickets are priced at $20 per ticket in the first $r$ rows and $15 per ticket in the remaining rows, if all the seats are sold.

   _____

5. Evaluate the expression you wrote in Question 4 for $r = 16$ and show that the result equals your answer for Question 3c.

   _____

Name _____ Date _____ Class _____

1. What is the solution for $2x - 5 = 7$?

   _____

2. Solve $5m - 3 = 2m + 12$. What is the solution?

   _____

3. Does each equation have at least one solution?

   A $\quad 4x - 5 = 2x - x$     ○ Yes    ○ No

   B $\quad 4x - 1 = 4x - 1$     ○ Yes    ○ No

   C $\quad 7x - 2 = 7x + 2$     ○ Yes    ○ No

   D $\quad 12 + 2x = 2x + 10$     ○ Yes    ○ No

4. What best describes the solutions of $2x < 6$?

   A   All real numbers greater than 12

   B   All real numbers less than 12

   C   All real numbers less than 3

   D   All real numbers less than or equal to 3

5. Graph the solutions for $-3x \le -9$ on the number line.

   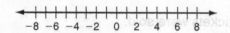

6. Do these values make $4y + 7 = z$ true?

   A $\quad y = -3$ and $z = 5$    ○ Yes    ○ No

   B $\quad y = -1$ and $z = 3$    ○ Yes    ○ No

   C $\quad y = 0$ and $z = 7$    ○ Yes    ○ No

   D $\quad y = 4$ and $z = 22$    ○ Yes    ○ No

7.

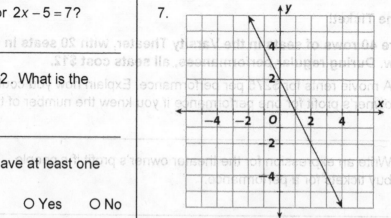

Which equation is represented on the graph?

A $\quad y = -2x + 2$     C $\quad y = -x + 2$

B $\quad y = 2x + 2$     D $\quad y = -3x - 2$

8. What is the $8^{th}$ term of the sequence $f(n) = 2^{n-1}$?

A $\quad 14$            C $\quad 128$

B $\quad 26$            D $\quad 256$

9. What is the range of the relation shown in the table?

| x | 3 | 5 | 7 | 9 |
|---|---|---|---|---|
| y | 4 | -1 | -6 | -11 |

A $\quad \{-11, 9\}$

B $\quad \{3, 5, 7, 9\}$

C $\quad \{-11, -6, -1, 4\}$

D $\quad \{-11, -6, -13, 4, 5, 7, 9\}$

10. What is the third term in a sequence defined by $f(n) = \dfrac{n+1}{2}$?

11. Solve $-14 + 5x = -12$.

_____

12. Solve $3(p-2) = 18$.

_____

13. Harold wants to get an 84 in math class. His grade will be the average of two test scores. He got a 77 on the first test.

 a. Write an equation to represent the situation.

 _____

 b What grade does Harold need to get on his second test to meet his goal?

 _____

14. $12p + 4 \leq 8p - 12$

 a. Solve the inequality.

 _____

 b. Graph the solutions.

 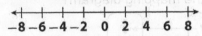

15. Does the inequality $2x + 7 > 2(3 + x)$ have no solution, or can $x$ be all real numbers? Explain.

 _____

 _____

16. Solve the equation $y = 3x - 1$ for $x$.

 _____

17. The equation for finding the volume of a rectangular prism is $V = \ell wh$. Solve the equation for $h$.

 _____

**For 18–19, determine if the ordered pairs are solutions to the given equation.**

18. $y + 9 = 2x$; $(3, -3)$

 _____

19. $x - \dfrac{y}{2} = 4$; $(12, 16)$

 _____

20. a. Complete the table.

| $x$ | $-2x = y$ | $y$ |
|---|---|---|
| $-2$ | $-2(-2) = y$ | 4 |
| 0 | | |
| 2 | | |

 b. Graph the solutions to $-2x = y$.

 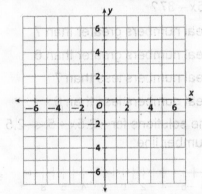

 c. Is $-2x = y$ a function? Explain.

 _____

21. A sequence has the explicit rule $f(n) = 7n - 1$. Find the sixth term in the sequence.

 _____

22. A sequence has the recursive rule $f(n) = 2f(n-1)$. The first term of the sequence is 7. Write the first 3 terms of the sequence.

 _____

## UNIT 1B Equations and Functions
### Unit Test: B

1. What is the solution to $4\left(\dfrac{1}{2}x + 7\right) = 12$?

_____

2. Solve $4(t-7) = 12 - t$. What is the solution?

_____

3. Does each equation have at least one solution?

A $\quad 5r - 5 = 5(r-1)$    ○ Yes    ○ No

B $\quad 6(r+5) = r + 30$    ○ Yes    ○ No

C $\quad 2r - 7 = 3r - 14$    ○ Yes    ○ No

D $\quad 3(8+r) = 3r - 27$    ○ Yes    ○ No

4. What best describes the solutions of $-2 > 5x - 37$?

A   All real numbers greater than 7

B   All real numbers greater than 6

C   All real numbers less than 7

D   All real numbers less than 6

5. Graph the solutions for $-2.5x + 5 < -2.5$ on the number line.

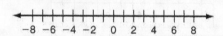

6. Do these values make $6r + 4 = s^2$ true?

A $\quad r = 2$ and $s = -1.5$    ○ Yes    ○ No

B $\quad r = 7.5$ and $s = 7$    ○ Yes    ○ No

C $\quad r = 5$ and $s = 3.5$    ○ Yes    ○ No

D $\quad r = 10$ and $s = -8$    ○ Yes    ○ No

7.

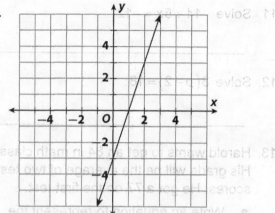

Which equation is represented on the graph?

A $\quad y = x - 3$      C $\quad y = 3x + 1$

B $\quad y = 3(x-1)$      D $\quad y = -3(x + 1)$

8. What is the 10th term of the sequence $f(n) = 1^{n-1}$?

A   0          C   9

B   1          D   10

9. What is the range of the relation shown on the mapping diagram?

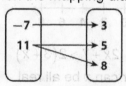

A $\quad \{-7, 11\}$

B $\quad \{3, 5, 8, 11\}$

C $\quad \{3, 5, 8\}$

D $\quad \{-7, 3, 5, 8, 11\}$

10. $f(n) = \dfrac{n^2}{2n}$ is the explicit rule of a function.

What is the sixth term?

_____

**UNIT 1B**

# Equations and Functions
### *Unit Test: B*

11. Solve $\frac{4}{3} - \frac{y}{3} = 9$.

_____

12. Solve $-9(x+5) = 81$.

_____

13. Candice paid her parents $445 for rent and divided the rest of her paycheck evenly into a checking account, a savings account, and a retirement fund. She put $592 into her savings account.

   a.  Write an equation to represent the situation.

_____

   b.  How much was Candice paid?

_____

14. $5z - 14 \le 2(7 - z)$

   a.  Solve the inequality.

_____

   b.  Graph the solutions.

   ```
   ←+──+──+──+──+──+──+──+──+──→
    -8 -6 -4 -2  0  2  4  6  8
   ```

15. Solve $-3x - 13 + 28x \le 5(-2 + 5x) - 3$.

_____

16. Solve $3x + 7y = -9 - 11y$ for y.

_____

17. The formula Selena uses to charge her clients is $t = 25 + 13.5h - 0.25h$. Solve for h.

_____

18. Find whether $(-12.5, 4)$ and $(1, -4)$ are solutions to $-15 = \frac{4x - 10}{y}$.

_____

19. a.  Complete the table.

| $x$ | $-\frac{1}{2}x + 3 = y$ | $y$ |
|-----|------------------------|-----|
|     |                        |     |
| -2  | $-\frac{1}{2}(-2) + 3 = y$ |     |
| 0   |                        |     |
| 2   |                        |     |

   b.  Graph the solutions to $y = -\frac{1}{2}x + 3$.

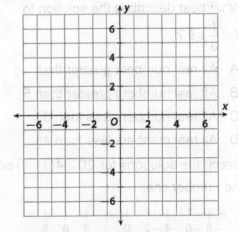

20. A sequence has the explicit rule $f(n) = 2 - n^2$. Find the first three terms of the sequence.

_____

21. Mike wrote the sequence 1, 3, 5, 7,…

   a.  Find the next two terms in the sequence.

_____

   b.  Write a recursive rule for the sequence.

_____

# UNIT 1B Equations and Functions
### *Unit Test: C*

1. What is the solution for $7 + \dfrac{2x}{5} = 13$?

   _____

2. Solve $7p - 4 + 12p = -3(5 + p)$. What is the solution?

   _____

3. Which equation has no solution?

   A  $\dfrac{x}{3} + 6 = 2\left(\dfrac{x}{6} + 5\right)$

   B  $8y + 3y - 6 = 2 + 11y - 8$

   C  $1 - d + 5 = -6(d - 1) + 5d$

   D  $5.5(2 - t) = -2.5t + 11 - 3t$

4. What best describes the solution to $7 < \dfrac{t}{3} + 9$?

   A  All real numbers greater than −6

   B  All real numbers greater than 5

   C  All real numbers less than 6

   D  All real numbers less than 45

5. Graph the solutions for $20 \geq 4(1 - x)$ on the number line.

   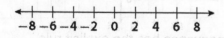

6. Do these values make $3(y - 5) = 2z - 10 + 4y$ true?

   A  $y = -3$; $z = 3$        ○ Yes   ○ No

   B  $y = 0$; $z = -2.5$      ○ Yes   ○ No

   C  $y = -1$; $z = 2$        ○ Yes   ○ No

   D  $y = 3$; $z = -4$        ○ Yes   ○ No

7.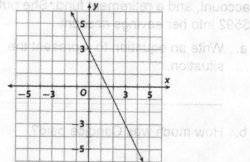

   What equation is represented on the graph?

   _____

8. What is the 12th term of an arithmetic sequence where the 22nd term is −49 and the 25th term is −58?

   _____

9. What is the domain of the relation shown on the graph?

   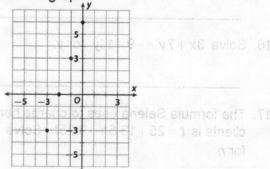

   A  $\{-3, 6\}$              C  $\{-3, -2, -1, 10\}$

   B  $\{-3, 0, 3, 6\}$        D  $\{0, 3, 6\}$

**UNIT 1B**

# Equations and Functions
### Unit Test: C

10. The recursive rule for a sequence is $f(n) = \dfrac{f(n-1)}{2} + 5$. The first term is 4. What is the third term?

   A $6\dfrac{1}{2}$            C 8

   B 7            D $8\dfrac{1}{2}$

11. Solve $-4 = 3\left(\dfrac{x}{2} - 7\right)$.

   _____

12. If $0.5(y + 10) = 4$, find the value of $\dfrac{1}{4}y$.

   _____

13. 

   The squares in the diagram are congruent. The total area of the figure is 168.75 square millimeters.

   a. Write an equation that represents the relationship between the side length of one square and the area of the figure.

   _____

   b. What is the side length of one square?

   _____

14. $5z - 14 \le 2(-14 - z)$

   a. Solve the inequality.

   _____

   b. Graph the solutions.

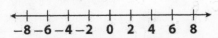

15. Fill in the blank to make the value of $y$ all real numbers.

   $7(2 - 2y) > 5y + \boxed{\phantom{x}} - 19y$

16. Solve $14 = \dfrac{4y - 6x}{3}$ for $y$.

   _____

17. The formula for finding the volume of a sphere is $V = \dfrac{4}{3}\pi r^3$. Solve for $r$.

   _____

18. Determine whether $\left(\dfrac{1}{2}, \dfrac{1}{4}\right)$ and $(-9, 9)$ are solutions to $3y = x^2 + \dfrac{1}{2}$.

   _____

19. a. Graph the solutions to $y = -\dfrac{1}{2}x - 2$.

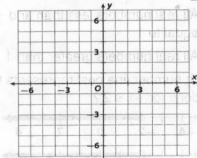

   b. Is $y = -\dfrac{1}{2}x - 2$ a function? Explain.

   _____

20. 1, 4, 7, 10, ...

   a. Find the next two terms in the sequence.

   _____

   b. Write an explicit rule for the sequence.

   _____

   c. Write a recursive rule for the sequence.

   _____

# UNIT 1B   Equations and Functions
## Unit Test: D

1. What is the solution for $21 = 3x$?

   A   $x = 7$

   B   $x = 18$

   C   $x = 63$

2. Solve $8x - 6 = 6x$. What is the solution?

   A   $x = \dfrac{1}{2}$

   B   $x = 3$

   C   $x = 6$

3. Which equation has no solution?

   A   $x + 5 = x + 7$

   B   $x + 7 = 0$

   C   $x - 8 = x - 8$

4. What best describes the solutions of $y < 1$?

   A   All real numbers less than 1

   B   All real numbers less than and equal to 1

   C   All real numbers greater than 1

5. Which number line best represents the solutions for $-x \le 2$?

6. Which inequality best represents the situation "the temperature should be at least 40 degrees"?

   A   $t > 40$

   B   $t < 40$

   C   $t \ge 40$

7. Which values make $y = 4x$ true?

   A   $x = 1$ and $y = 5$

   B   $x = 2$ and $y = 8$

   C   $x = 12$ and $y = 3$

8.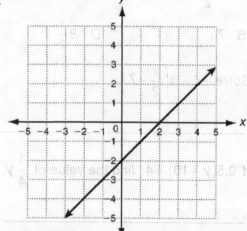

Which equation is represented on the graph?

   A   $y = 2 - x$

   B   $y = x - 2$

   C   $y = -2x$

9. What is the fourth term of the sequence defined by $f(n) = n^2 + n$? Assume that the domain of the function is the set of whole numbers greater than 0.

   A  4           C  64

   B  20

10. What is the domain of the set $\{(-3, 5), (2, 0), (7, -5)\}$?

   A   $\{-5, 7\}$        C   $\{-3, 2, 7\}$

   B   $\{-5, 0, 5\}$

11. What is the fourth term in a sequence defined by $f(n) = 2n$?

   A  2

   B  6

   C  8

**UNIT 1B** **Equations and Functions**

*Unit Test: D*

12. Solve $\dfrac{x}{6} = 12$.

_____

13. Solve $3z + 5 = -13$.

_____

14. Kurt has 26 plants on his porch. His neighbor gives him $p$ more plants. Now he has 31 plants in all.

 a. Write an equation to represent the situation.

 _____

 b. How many plants did Kurt's neighbor give him?

 _____

15. $10s < 2s - 8$

 a. Solve the inequality.

 _____

 b. Graph the solutions.

 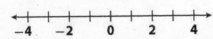

16. Does the inequality $x + 7 > x - 4$ have no solution, or can $x$ be all real numbers?

 _____

17. Solve the equation $y = 2x$ for $x$.

 _____

18. Solve the equation $3y + z = 13$ for $z$.

 _____

19. Determine whether the following ordered pairs are solutions to $x - 5 = y$.

 a. $(-3, -8)$

 _____

 b. $(4, 9)$

 _____

20. a. Fill in a mapping diagram for the points $(2, 3)$, $(2, 5)$, and $(4, 7)$.

 X       Y

 b. Could the points represent a function? Explain why or why not.

21. The sequence 3, 5, 7, 9,... has the explicit rule $f(n) = 2n + 1$.

 a. What is the third term in the sequence?

 _____

 b. Find the next two terms in the sequence.

22. The sequence below has the recursive rule $f(n) = f(n-1) - 3$. Fill in the blanks.

 7, ⬚, 1, ⬚

Name _____ Date _____ Class _____

# Equations and Functions
## *Performance Task*

| | ABC | DEF |
|---|---|---|
| 1 | 2 | 3 |
| GHI 4 | JKL 5 | MNO 6 |
| PQRS 7 | TUV 8 | WXYZ 9 |
| * | space 0 | # |

**Text Messaging**

Look at the standard cell phone keypad shown at right. As you can see, there is a relationship between the letters and numbers.

1. Complete the tables below to show the relationship between letters and numbers.

| Letter | Number |
|---|---|
| A | 2 |
| B | 2 |
| C | 2 |
| D | |
| E | |
| F | |
| G | |

| Letter | Number |
|---|---|
| H | |
| I | |
| | |
| | |
| | |
| | |
| | |

| Letter | Number |
|---|---|
| | |
| | |
| | |
| | |
| | |
| | |
| | |

| Letter | Number |
|---|---|
| | |
| | |
| | |
| | |
| | |
| | |
| | |

2. What is the domain of this relation? _____

3. What is the range of this relation? _____

4. Is the relation from letter to number a function? Explain. _____

_____

5. The phone number for a local bookstore is 555-BOOK. What sequence of numbers would you press to call the store?

**Using the keypad and tables above, consider the relationship between numbers and letters.**

6. What is the domain of this relation? _____

7. What is the range of this relation? _____

8. Is the relation from number to letter a function? Explain. _____

_____

9. List the possible three-letter combinations dialing 3 6 4 could represent. _____

_____

| UNIT 2A | **Linear Relationships** |
|---|---|

*Unit Test: A*

1. What are the *x*- and *y*-intercepts of the line graphed below?

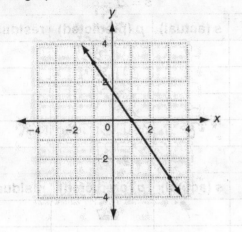

_____

2. What are the slope and *y*-intercept of the line described by $y = 3x - 6$?

_____

3. Which of the following sequences has the recursive rule $f(n) = f(n-1) + 3$?

A  2, 4, 6,...

B  9, 6, 3,...

C  2, 5, 8,...

D  9, 12, 16,...

4. Solve $\begin{cases} x - 8y = 0 \\ 3x + 10y = 17 \end{cases}$

What is the solution?

_____

5. Data set **A** has a correlation coefficient of −0.93, and data set **B** has a correlation coefficient of 0.09. Choose True or False for each statement.

A  The variables from set **A** have a low negative correlation.

   ○ True      ○ False

B  The variables from set **A** have a strong negative correlation.

   ○ True      ○ False

C  The variables from set **B** have a strong positive correlation.

   ○ True      ○ False

6. Which correlation coefficient best matches the data shown on the graph below?

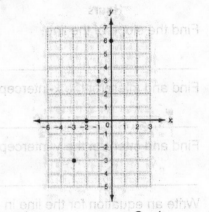

A  −1              C  1

B  0.8             D  3

7. Solve $\begin{cases} x = 2y + 4 \\ y = x - 2 \end{cases}$

What is the solution?

_____

8. Leslie joins a fitness club that has a membership fee of $20 plus $15 per month. Rashad's club has a fee of $40 and charges $10 per month. In how many months will the clubs cost the same?

_____

# Linear Relationships
### *Unit Test: A*

9. Opal walked from school to home, a distance of 12 miles. She walked at a rate of 4 miles per hour. The graph represents the remaining distance Opal had to walk.

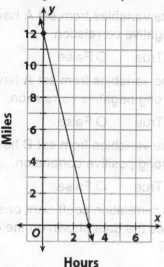

a. Find the slope of the line.

_____

b. Find and interpret the $x$-intercept.

_____

c. Find and interpret the $y$-intercept.

_____

d. Write an equation for the line in slope-intercept form.

_____

**Use the following functions for 10–12:**

$f(x) = -7x + 12$
$g(x) = 10x - 8$

10. Find $s(x) = f(x) + g(x)$.

_____

11. Find $d(x) = g(x) - f(x)$.

_____

12. Find $p(x) = 4g(x)$.

_____

13. a. Complete the tables.

| $s = 2r - 6$ | | | |
|---|---|---|---|
| $r$ | $s$ (actual) | $p$ (predicted) | residuals |
| −1 | −7 | −8 | |
| 0 | −7 | | |
| 1 | −3 | | |
| 2 | 0 | | |

| $s = 2r - 5$ | | | |
|---|---|---|---|
| $r$ | $s$ (actual) | $p$ (predicted) | residuals |
| −1 | −7 | −7 | |
| 0 | −7 | | |
| 1 | −3 | | |
| 2 | 0 | | |

b. Find the sum of the squared residuals for both lines of fit.

_____

c. Which line is a better fit to the data? Explain why.

_____

14. a. Graph the solution to the system of inequalities: $\begin{cases} y \le 1 \\ y \le 2x \end{cases}$.

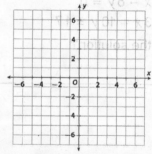

b. List 2 ordered pairs that are solutions to the system and 2 ordered pairs that are not solutions.

Solutions: _____

Not solutions: _____

Name _____  Date _____  Class _____

# Linear Relationships
*Unit Test: B*

1. What are the *x*- and *y*-intercepts of $4x + 2y = 20$?

_____

2. What equation describes the line on the graph below?

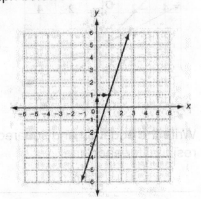

_____

3. Which explicit rule matches the sequence –4, 0, 4,...?

A  $f(n) = n + 4$

B  $f(n) = 4n - 8$

C  $f(n) = n - 4$

D  $f(n) = 4n - 4$

4. Solve $\begin{cases} 2x + 4y = 17 \\ 6x + 12y = 34 \end{cases}$.

What is the solution?

_____

5. The variables in data set **A** have a strong negative correlation. Could each of the following correlation coefficients match set **A**?

A  –3.2        ○ Yes        ○ No

B  –0.92       ○ Yes        ○ No

C  –0.3        ○ Yes        ○ No

D  –0.99       ○ Yes        ○ No

6. Which correlation coefficient best matches the data shown on the scatter plot below?

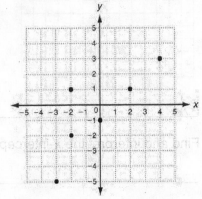

A  –0.4        C  1

B  0.8         D  3

7. Solve $\begin{cases} x - y = -3 \\ 2x + y = 0 \end{cases}$

What is the solution?

_____

8. Sam has a prepaid phone card that charges $1 to connect and $0.50 per minute. He also can use a satellite phone that charges $3 to connect and $0.25 per minute. In how many minutes will the phone card and the cell phone cost the same?

_____

# Linear Relationships
## Unit Test: B

**UNIT 2A**

9. Carla has $200 in her bank account. Each week, she withdraws $20.

 a. Write and graph a linear function that represents the amount of money Carla has left in her account after a certain number of withdraws.

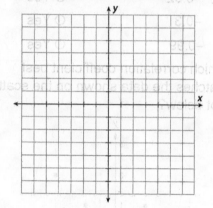

 b. Find and interpret the *x*-intercept.

 c. Find and interpret the *y*-intercept.

 d. Find the appropriate domain and range for this situation.

**Use the following functions for 10–12:**
$f(x) = -2.5x + 12;\ g(x) = 21x - 28$

10. Find $h(x) = f(x) + g(x)$.

11. Find $h(x) = g(x) - f(x)$.

12. Find $h(x) = 4g(x)$.

13. Two possible lines of fit are graphed below for the data: (−5, 0), (−3, −2), (0, −2), (2, −4), (3, −6).

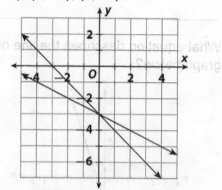

 a. Write the equation and squared residual for each line.

 b. Which line is a better fit to the data? Explain why.

14. Graph $\begin{cases} y \ge -\dfrac{1}{2}x - 4 \\ y \le x + 1 \end{cases}$

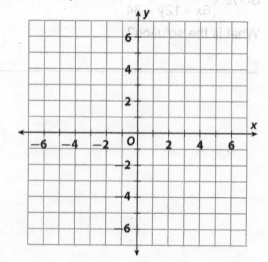

# Linear Relationships

**UNIT 2A**

## Unit Test: C

1. What are the x- and y-intercepts of $y = -4x + 12$?

   _____

2. Write an equation for a line that includes the points $(-3, 2)$ and $(3, 5)$?

   _____

3. Which rule matches the sequence described in the table?

   | n | 1 | 3 | 5 | 7 |
   |---|---|---|---|---|
   | f(n) | -1 | -5 | -9 | -13 |

   A $f(n) = -4n + 1$

   B $f(n) = -2n + 1$

   C $f(n) = -n + 2$

   D $f(n) = -n - 2$

4. Solve $\begin{cases} 0.5x + 0.4y = 1.35 \\ 0.2x + 0.5y = 2.75 \end{cases}$.

   What is the solution?

   _____

5. The variables in data sets **A** and **B** have strong negative correlations. The variables in set **A** have a stronger correlation than the variables in data set **B**. Could each of the following correlation coefficients match the sets?

   A  **A**: -3.1; **B**: -2.2     ○ Yes   ○ No

   B  **A**: -0.93; **B**: -0.91   ○ Yes   ○ No

   C  **A**: -0.88; **B**: -0.95   ○ Yes   ○ No

   D  **A**: -0.90; **B**: -0.89   ○ Yes   ○ No

6. What is the correlation coefficient that best matches the data represented with the ordered pairs: $(-3, -5)$, $(2, -2)$, $(2, 1)$ $(0, -1)$ $(-2, 1)$, and $(-4, 3)$?

   A  -1              C  -0.3

   B  -0.8            D  0

7. Solve $\begin{cases} 3x + 2y = -1 \\ x - 2y = 11 \end{cases}$.

   What is the solution?

   _____

8. The population of Medford High School is 800 students and the population of Westville High School is 1240 students. The population of Medford High is increasing at a rate of 30 students per year, while the population of Westville High has been decreasing by 25 students per year. In about how many years will the population of the two schools be the same?

   _____

UNIT
2A

# Linear Relationships

## Unit Test: C

9. Weasley has 30 bacteria in his petri dish. They are dying at a rate of 4 bacteria per minute.

   a. Write and graph a linear function that represents the situation.

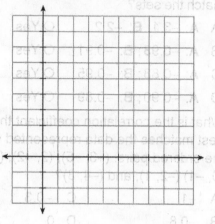

   b. Find and interpret the $x$-intercept.

   _____

   c. Find and interpret the $y$-intercept.

   _____

   d. Find the appropriate domain and range for this situation.

   _____

**Use the following functions for 10–12:**
$f(x) = -7.5 + 32$; $g(x) = 10x - 27$

10. Find $h(x) = f(x) - g(x)$.

   _____

11. Find $h(x) = \dfrac{1}{5}g(x)$.

   _____

12. Find $h(x) = 2f(x) - g(x)$.

   _____

13.

| $x$ | –5 | –2 | 0 | 2 | 5 |
|---|---|---|---|---|---|
| $y$ | 1 | 2 | 2 | 3.5 | 4 |

A line of fit for the data on the table is graphed below.

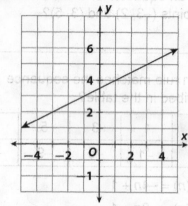

   a. Write the equation and squared residual for the line of fit.

   _____

   b. Write an equation for a line of fit that better fits the data. Explain why the line is a better fit for the data.

   _____

14. Graph $\begin{cases} -4x + y > -6 \\ 5y \le -x - 20 \end{cases}$

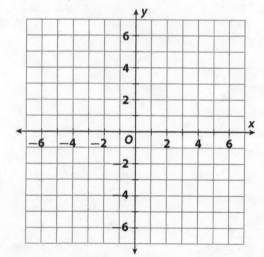

| UNIT 2A | **Linear Relationships** |
|---|---|

*Unit Test: D*

1. What are the *x*- and *y*-intercepts of the line graphed below?

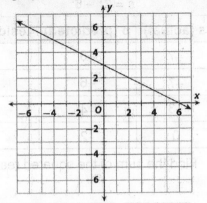

   A   *x*-int: 2, *y*-int: 1

   B   *x*-int: 3, *y*-int: 6

   C   *x*-int: 6, *y*-int: 3

2. Which equation describes the line with slope 6 and *y*-intercept –2?

   A   $y = -2x + 6$

   B   $y = 2x + 6$

   C   $y = 6x - 2$

3. What is the next term of the arithmetic sequence 12, 9, 6, ...?

   A   15                       C   0

   B   3

4. Solve $\begin{cases} x = 4 \\ y = 2x + 5 \end{cases}$.

   What is the solution?

   _____

   _____

5. Data set **A** has a correlation coefficient of –0.9, and data set **B** has a correlation coefficient of 0.3. Which of the following statements is true?

   A   The variables from Set **A** have a low negative correlation.

   B   The variables from Set **A** have a strong negative correlation.

   C   The variables from Set **B** have a strong positive correlation.

6. Which correlation coefficient best matches the data on the scatter plot below?

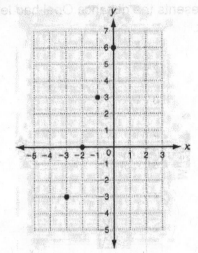

   A   –0.3

   B   0.6

   C   1

7. Solve $\begin{cases} x = 2y + 1 \\ y = x \end{cases}$.

   What is the solution?

   A   $x = -1$ and $y = -1$

   B   $x = 1$ and $y = 1$

   C   $x = -2$ and $y = -2$

8. Leslie joins a fitness club that has a membership fee of $20 plus $15 per month. Rashad's club has a fee of $40 and charges $10 per month. Which system represents the situation?

   A   $\begin{cases} y = 20 + 15x \\ y = 40 + 10x \end{cases}$

   B   $\begin{cases} y = 20x + 15 \\ y = 40x + 10 \end{cases}$

   C   $\begin{cases} y = 20 + 15 \\ y = 40 + 10 \end{cases}$

# Linear Relationships

## UNIT 2A

### Unit Test: D

9. Opal walked from school to home, a distance of 12 miles. She walked at a rate of 4 miles per hour. The graph represents the distance Opal had left to walk.

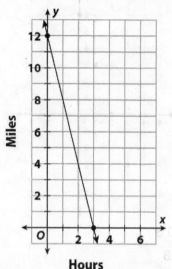

**Hours**

a. Find the slope of the line.

_____

b. Find the x-intercept of the line.

_____

c. Find the y-intercept of the line.

_____

d. Write an equation for the line in slope-intercept form.

_____

**Use the following functions for 10–12:**

$f(x) = 5x + 2$; $g(x) = 7x + 4$

10. Find $s(x) = f(x) + g(x)$.

_____

11. Find $d(x) = f(x) - g(x)$.

_____

12. Find $p(x) = 6g(x)$.

_____

13. a. Complete the table.

| $s = 2r - 6$ | | | |
|---|---|---|---|
| $r$ | $s$ (actual) | $p$ (predicted) | residuals |
| −1 | −7 | −8 | |
| 0 | −7 | −6 | |
| 1 | −3 | −4 | |
| 2 | 0 | −2 | |

b. Find the sum of the squared residuals.

_____

c. A second line of fit has a squared residual of 11. Which line is a better fit to the data?

_____

14. What is the solution for the system of equations graphed below?

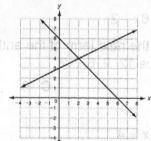

_____

15. Find 2 ordered pairs that are solutions and 2 ordered pairs that are not solutions for the system of inequalities graphed below.

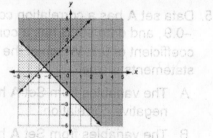

Solutions: _____

Not solutions: _____

**UNIT 2A** **Linear Relationships**
*Performance Task*

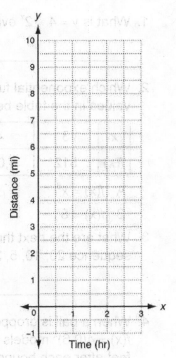

Distance (mi)

Time (hr)

**The Marathon**

Bethany and Calista are sisters who both run marathons. Today they are racing against each other in the same marathon. Because there are thousands of people racing, Bethany and Calista are assigned random starting positions. Bethany starts at the starting line, while Calista starts a half-mile behind the starting line.

Calista runs one mile in 12 minutes, while Bethany runs one mile in 15 minutes. So, although Calista starts behind Bethany, she hopes to pass her sister at some point during the race.

Let *x* represent the amount of time in hours that Bethany or Calista run and let *y* represent distance after the starting line in miles.

1. The rate or speed at which someone runs is frequently stated in miles per hour.

    a. What is Bethany's speed in miles per hour? _____

    b. What is Calista's speed in miles per hour? _____

2. Write a linear equation in slope-intercept form that describes each distance.

    a. Bethany's distance as a function of time _____

    b. Calista's distance as a function of time _____

3. On the grid above, graph the system of equations that you wrote for question 2.

4. Use your graph to estimate each of the following.

    a. the sister in the lead after 15 minutes (0.25 hour) _____

    b. the time when Calista will catch up to Bethany _____

    c. the distance from the starting line where Calista will catch up _____

    d. the sister in the lead after 2 hours assuming each sister keeps running at a steady pace. _____

5. Use substitution or elimination to solve the system of equations that you wrote for Question 2. Interpret the solution in terms of this problem.

    _____

6. A marathon is 26.2 miles. Which sister do you think will cross the finish line first? Explain. _____

    _____

# Exponential Relationships
## *Unit Test: A*

1. What is $y = 4 \times 2^x$ evaluated for $x = 3$?

_____

2. Which exponential function matches the values in the table below?

| x | 3 | 4 | 5 |
|---|---|---|---|
| f(x) | 512 | 4,096 | 32,768 |

A $f(x) = x^8$      C $f(x) = 64 \times 2^x$

B $f(x) = 8^x$      D $f(x) = 8x$

3. What are the next three terms in the sequence 20, 10, 5, 2.5, …?

_____

4. When a ball is dropped, the function $f(x) = 4(0.6)^x$ models the ball's height in feet after each bounce, where $x$ is the bounce number. To the nearest hundredth, what is the height after the third bounce?

A 0.86      C 7.20

B 1.80      D 8.64

5. The first term of a geometric sequence is 8 and the common ratio is 3. What is the fifth term of the sequence?

A 120      C 648

B 512      D 1,944

6. $5 \times 2^x = 40$
What is the value of $x$?

_____

7. The population of a town over the past 10 years can be represented with the regression equation $y = 2450(1.07)^x$. Choose True or False for each statement.

A The initial population was 2450 with a growth rate of 1.07%.

  ○ True     ○ False

B The initial population was 2450 with a growth rate of 7%.

  ○ True     ○ False

C At the end of the first year, the population was about 2622.

  ○ True     ○ False

D At the end of the first year, the population was about 2805.

  ○ True     ○ False

8. Which of these sets of ordered pairs satisfies an exponential equation?

A {(1, 2), (3, 8), (5, 32), (7, 128)}

B {(1, −2), (3, 2), (5, 6), (7, 10)}

C {(1, 1), (2, 8), (3, 27), (4, 64)}

D {(1, −1), (2, −4), (3, −9), (4, −16)}

9. Would each of the following sets of data be best represented by an exponential model?

A

| x | 0 | 1 | 2 | 3 |
|---|---|---|---|---|
| y | 0 | 3 | 6 | 9 |

  ○ Yes     ○ No

B

| x | 0 | 1 | 2 | 3 |
|---|---|---|---|---|
| y | 6 | 3 | 0 | −3 |

  ○ Yes     ○ No

C

| x | 0 | 1 | 2 | 3 |
|---|---|---|---|---|
| y | 0.25 | 0.5 | 1 | 2 |

  ○ Yes     ○ No

**UNIT 2B**

# Exponential Relationships
## *Unit Test: A*

10. Write an explicit rule for the geometric sequence where $a_1 = 6$, $a_2 = 12$, and $a_5 = 96$. Assume that the common ratio $r$ is positive.

_____

11. a. Complete the table.

| $x$ | $4(3)^x = y$ | $y$ |
|---|---|---|
| −2 | $4(3)^{-2} = 4\left(\dfrac{1}{9}\right)$ | $\dfrac{4}{9}$ |
| −1 | | |
| 0 | | |
| 1 | | |
| 2 | | |

b. Graph $y = 4(3)^x$

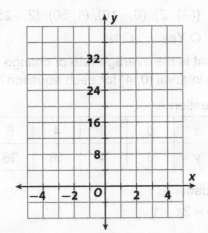

12. A pond has 150 fish, and the population decreases by 8% each day. Find the population after 4 days. Round to the nearest whole number.

13. Emil has $500 in his savings account. He is looking at two savings plans. Under plan A, he will increase his account balance by $150 a year. Under plan B, he will increase his account balance by 25% each year.

   a. Write an equation for the amount Emil will have with plan A.

   _____

   b. Write an equation for the amount Emil will have with plan B.

   _____

   c. To the nearest hundredth, how much more will Emil save with plan B after three years?

   _____

14. Determine whether a linear model or an exponential model best describes the following data set. Explain why.
   $\{(-2, -2), (-1, -1), (0, 2), (1, 7), (2, 14)\}$

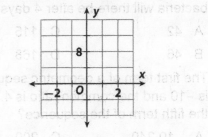

   _____

   _____

# Exponential Relationships
## *Unit Test: B*

1. What is $y = 6 \times 3^x$ evaluated for $x = -3$?

_____

2. Which exponential function matches the values in the table below?

| x | 1 | 2 | 3 |
|---|---|---|---|
| f(x) | −18 | 162 | −1458 |

A $f(x) = \dfrac{1}{2}(-18)^x$

B $f(x) = 2(-9)^x$

C $f(x) = -2(3)^{2x}$

D $f(x) = -18^x$

3. What are the next two terms in the sequence −9, 3, −1, …?

_____

4. The function $f(x) = 30(1.4)^x$ gives the number of bacteria in a science experiment, where $x$ is the number of days after the start of the experiment. To the nearest whole number, how many bacteria will there be after 4 days?

A  42          C  115

B  46          D  168

5. The first term of a geometric sequence is −10 and the common ratio is 4. What is the fifth term of the sequence?

A  −10,240          C  200

B  −2,560          D  2,560

6. Solve $8^x \div 4 = 128$. What is the value of $x$?

_____

7. Which of the following regression equations could represent a town with an initial population of 875 people and an annual growth rate of approximately 2%?

A  $y = 875 \times 1.02x$

B  $y = 875(1.02)^x$

C  $y = 875(2)^x$

D  $y = 875x^{1.02}$

8. Does each set of ordered pairs satisfy an exponential function?

A  {(1, 2), (2, 6), (3, 18), (4, 54)}

○ Yes      ○ No

B  {(1, −2), (2, 4), (3, −6), (4, 8)}

○ Yes      ○ No

C  {(−2, 1), (−8, 2), (−32, 3), (−128, 4)}

○ Yes      ○ No

D  {(−1, 2), (0, −10), (1, 50), (2, −250)}

○ Yes      ○ No

9. What is the average rate of change over the interval [0, 4] for each equation?

Equation A

| x | 0 | 2 | 4 | 6 |
|---|---|---|---|---|
| y | 0 | 4 | 16 | 36 |

Equation B

$f(x) = 2x - 1$

# Exponential Relationships

**Unit Test: B**

10. Write an explicit rule for the geometric sequence where $a_3 = 63$ and $a_5 = 7$. Assume that the common ratio $r$ is positive.

_____

11. a. Graph $y = 3^x$ and $y = 3^x + 4$.

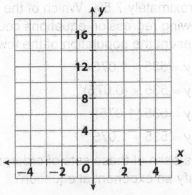

b. Compare the graphs of $y = 3^x$ and $y = 3^x + 4$.

_____

_____

_____

12. A new movie premiered on Friday, September 2, and 1350 people attended. Attendance then decreased by 20% each day. Write an exponential decay function to model this situation. Then find the attendance on September 7. Round to the nearest whole number.

_____

_____

13. Alistair has $900 in his savings account. He is looking at two investment plans. Under plan A, he will increase his account balance by $250 a year. Under plan B, he will increase his account balance by 25% each year.

a. Write equations to represent the money Alistair would have under plan A and plan B.

_____

b. To the nearest hundredth, how much more would Alistair save under plan B after 5 years?

_____

14. $y = 4^x$ is a possible exponential regression model for the data set $\left\{ \left(-2, \dfrac{1}{14}\right), \left(-1, \dfrac{1}{3}\right), (0, 1), (1, 5), (2, 16) \right\}$.

a. Complete the table to find the residuals.

| x | y observed | y predicted | residual |
|---|---|---|---|
| −2 | $\dfrac{1}{14}$ | $\dfrac{1}{16}$ | $\dfrac{1}{112}$ |
| −1 | $\dfrac{1}{3}$ | $\dfrac{1}{4}$ | |
| 0 | 1 | | |
| 1 | 5 | | |
| 2 | 16 | | |

b. Describe how well the model fits the data based on the residuals.

_____

_____

**UNIT 2B**

# Exponential Relationships
*Unit Test: C*

1. What is $y = \dfrac{1}{4}(3)^x$ evaluated for $x = -4$?

_____

2. Which exponential function matches the values in the table below?

| x | −4 | −3 | −2 | −1 |
|---|---|---|---|---|
| f(x) | 81 | −27 | 9 | −3 |

A $f(x) = (-3)^x$

B $f(x) = \left(-\dfrac{1}{3}\right)^x$

C $f(x) = \dfrac{1}{3}^x$

D $f(x) = 3^x$

3. What is the seventh term in the sequence 5120, 1280, 320, 80, …?

_____

4. A population of 200 animals is decreasing by 4% per year. At this rate, in how many years will the population be less than 170?

A 3          C 5

B 4          D 6

5. The first term of a geometric sequence is −2 and the common ratio is 3. What is the sixth term of the sequence?

_____

6. What is the value of $y$ in $\dfrac{1}{2}\left(\dfrac{2}{5}\right)^y = \dfrac{4}{125}$?

_____

7. Ten years ago, the population of a small town was 535. The population has been growing at an annual rate of approximately 7.5%. Which of the following regression equations could represent the population of the town?

A $y = 535 \times 1.075x$

B $y = 535 \times (0.075)^x$

C $y = 535(1.075)^x$

D $y = 535 + 1.075^x$

8. Does each of these sets of ordered pairs satisfy an exponential equation?

A {(1, −2), (3, −8), (5, −32), (7, −128)}

○ Yes     ○ No

B {(1, −2), (3, 2), (5, 6), (7, 10)}

○ Yes     ○ No

C {(1, −1), (2, −8), (3, −27), (4, −64)}

○ Yes     ○ No

D {(1, −1), (2, −4), (3, −9), (4, −16)}

○ Yes     ○ No

9. What is the average rate of change over the interval [0, 4] for each equation?
Equation A

| x | 0 | 2 | 4 | 6 |
|---|---|---|---|---|
| y | 7 | 11 | 15 | 19 |

Equation B
$f(x) = 2x^2 - 1$

_____

**UNIT 2B**

# Exponential Relationships

*Unit Test: C*

10. Write an explicit rule for the geometric sequence where $a_2 = 1$ and $a_4 = 2.25$. Assume that the common ratio $r$ is positive.

_____

11. a. Graph $f(x) = \dfrac{1}{2} \times 4^x$ and $f(x) = 4^x - 2$.

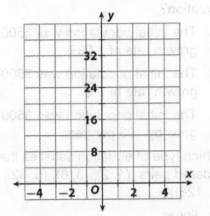

b. Compare the graphs of $f(x) = \dfrac{1}{2} \times 4^x$ and $f(x) = 4^x - 2$ to the parent function $y = 4^x$.

_____

_____

12. The number of students at Bayside High School was 2,400 in 2010, 2,520 in 2011, and 2,778 in 2013. Write an exponential growth equation to model this situation. Use the model to predict the number of students in 2015. Round to the nearest whole number.

_____

_____

13. Ross has $500 in his savings account. He is looking at two investment plans. Under plan A, he will increase his account balance by $150 a year. Under plan B, he will increase his account balance by 25% each year. How much more will he save with plan B after four years? Round your answer to the nearest whole number.

_____

14. $y = 9.4 \times 2.5^x$ is a possible regression model for the data set graphed on the scatterplot below.

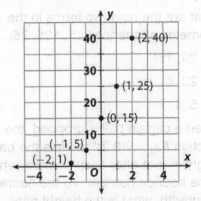

a. Complete the table. Round to the nearest hundredth.

| x | y observed | y predicted | residual |
|---|---|---|---|
| −2 | | | |
| −1 | | | |
| 0 | | | |
| 1 | | | |
| 2 | | | |

b. Describe how well the model fits the data based on the residuals.

_____

_____

**UNIT 2B**

# Exponential Relationships
*Unit Test: D*

1. What is $y = 10 \times 2^x$ evaluated for $x = 3$?

   A  60

   B  80

   C  8000

2. Which exponential function matches the values in the table below?

   | $x$ | 3 | 4 | 5 |
   |---|---|---|---|
   | $y$ | 216 | 1296 | 7776 |

   A  $y = 6^x$

   B  $y = 6^6$

   C  $y = 27 \times 3^x$

3. What are the next two terms in the geometric sequence 625, 125, 25, …?

   A  20, 15

   B  20, 4

   C  5, 1

4. When a certain ball is dropped, the function $f(x) = 9(0.2)^x$ models the ball's height in feet after each bounce, where $x$ is the bounce number. To the nearest hundredth, what is the height after the third bounce?

   A  5.40

   B  0.72

   C  0.07

5. The first term of a geometric sequence is 5 and the common ratio is 2. What is the sixth term of the sequence?

   A  320

   B  160

   C  60

6. $10^x = 10^3$
   What is the value of $x$?

   A  3

   B  10

   C  1000

7. What is the value of $x$ in $5^x = 125$?

   A  3

   B  5

   C  25

8. The population of a town over the past 10 years can be represented with the regression equation $y = 3500(1.03)^x$. What could be an interpretation of this equation?

   A  The initial population was 3500 with a growth rate of 1.03%.

   B  The initial population was 3500 with a growth rate of 3%.

   C  The initial population was 3500 and grew by 103 per year.

9. Which type of equation satisfies the ordered pairs {(1, 2), (3, 8), (5, 32), (7, 128)}?

   A  linear

   B  exponential

   C  none of these

10. Which of the following sets of data would be best represented by a linear model?

    A

    | $x$ | 0 | 1 | 2 | 3 |
    |---|---|---|---|---|
    | $y$ | 4 | 1 | 0 | 1 |

    B

    | $x$ | 0 | 1 | 2 | 3 |
    |---|---|---|---|---|
    | $y$ | 0 | 3 | 6 | 12 |

    C

    | $x$ | 0 | 1 | 2 | 3 |
    |---|---|---|---|---|
    | $y$ | 6 | 3 | 0 | −3 |

# Exponential Relationships
### *Unit Test: D*

11. Write an explicit rule for the geometric sequence where $a_1 = 5$ and $a_2 = 25$. Assume that the common ratio $r$ is positive.

_____

12. a.  Complete the table.

| $x$ | $2(3)^x = y$ | $y$ |
|---|---|---|
| –2 | $2(3)^{-2} = 2\left(\dfrac{1}{9}\right)$ | $\dfrac{2}{9}$ |
| –1 | $2(3)^{-1} = 2\left(\dfrac{1}{3}\right)$ | |
| 0 | | |
| 1 | | |
| 2 | | |

b.  Graph $y = 2(3)^x$

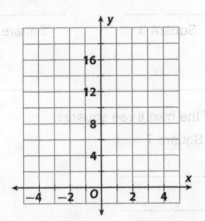

13. A pond has 150 fish, and the population decreases by 8% each day. This situation can be represented with the exponential decay function $f(x) = 150(0.92)^x$. Find the population after 4 days. Round to the nearest whole number.

_____

14. Ira has $100 in his savings account. He is looking at two savings plans. Under plan A, he will increase his account balance by $10 a year. Under plan B, he will increase his account balance by 10% each year.

a.  Write an equation for the amount Ira will have with plan A.

_____

b.  Write an equation for the amount Ira will have with plan B.

_____

c.  To the nearest hundredth, how much would Ira save in 3 years under plan A? How much would he save under plan B?

15. Determine which kind of model—linear or exponential—best describes the data set shown on the graph. Explain why.

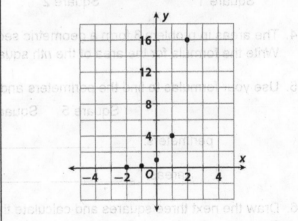

_____

_____

# UNIT 2B Exponential Relationships
## *Performance Task*

**Square Sequence**

**The diagram below shows four squares with increasingly greater side lengths. The smallest square has 1-unit sides.**

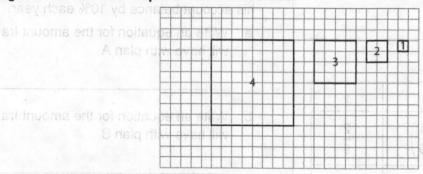

1. Count grid units and find the perimeter of each square.

   Square 1 _____ Square 2 _____ Square 3 _____ Square 4 _____

2. The perimeters in problem 1 form a geometric sequence.
   Write the formula for the perimeter of the *n*th square. _____

3. Find the areas of the first four squares.

   Square 1 _____ Square 2 _____ Square 3 _____ Square 4 _____

4. The areas in problem 3 form a geometric sequence.
   Write the formula for the area of the *n*th square. _____

5. Use your formulas to find the perimeters and areas of the next three squares.

   Square 5   Square 6   Square 7

   perimeters: _____ _____ _____

   areas: _____ _____ _____

6. Draw the next three squares and calculate the perimeters and areas.
   Does your drawing confirm your answers to problem 5?

# Statistics and Data

*Unit Test: A*

**UNIT 3**

1.

| | Do you read more than 30 minutes per day? | |
|---|---|---|
| Gender | Yes | No |
| Male | 107 | 21 |
| Female | 86 | 9 |

How many people surveyed read 30 minutes or less per day?

_____

2.

| | What types of music do you like? | | |
|---|---|---|---|
| | Classical | | |
| Pop | Yes | No | Total |
| Yes | 82 | 42 | 124 |
| No | 15 | 61 | 76 |
| Total | 97 | 103 | 200 |

What is the joint relative frequency that a person surveyed likes Classical music and Pop music?

A  0.41          C  0.76

B  0.82          D  0.97

3. 180 people filled out a survey about their favorite color. 95 of the respondents were female. 21 males responded that their favorite color is red. What is the conditional relative frequency that a person surveyed was a male whose favorite color is red? Round to the nearest hundredth.

A  0.12          C  0.25

B  0.22          D  0.33

4. What is the mean of the data set {−5, −5, 2, 6, 8, 9, 12, 13}?

_____

5. What effect does the outlier have on the range of the data set {20, 27, 19, 24, 102, 24}? Choose True or False for each statement.

A  Increases the range by 19

○ True     ○ False

B  Increases the range by 75

○ True     ○ False

C  Increases the mean by 13.2

○ True     ○ False

D  Increases the mean by 22.8

○ True     ○ False

6. Based on the box–and–whisker plot below, what is the range of the data?

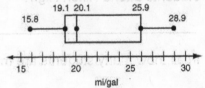

_____

7.

| High Temperatures (°F) |
|---|
| 80 73 72 76 84 86 82 73 |
| 81 84 78 85 87 84 70 |

**High Temperatures for Oct. 1–15, 2013**

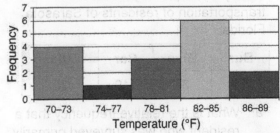

The histogram is supposed to represent the data shown on the table above it. Choose True or False for each statement.

A  The bar for 82–85 is too tall.

○ True     ○ False

B  The bar for 86–89 is too short.

○ True     ○ False

8. The frequency table below shows the age and gender of the students at Hilton High School.

   a. Complete the frequency table.

   | Age | Gender | | |
   |---|---|---|---|
   | | Male | Female | |
   | 13–14 | 61 | 60 | |
   | 15–16 | 62 | 52 | 114 |
   | 17–18 | 45 | | |
   | 19–20 | 15 | 13 | |
   | Total | | 175 | |

   b. How many 15–16 year old female students attend Hilton High?

   _____

   c. In all, how many students are male?

   _____

   d. Are there more 13–14 year old students or 15–16 year old students? How many more?

   _____

9. The table below shows the results of a survey of the primary mode of transportation of residents of Sarasota, Florida.

   | Bus | Bike | Car | Walking |
   |---|---|---|---|
   | 31 | 35 | 119 | 25 |

   a. What is the relative frequency that a resident who was surveyed primarily takes the bus? Round to the nearest hundredth.

   _____

b. Of the residents surveyed who walk to work, 15 are males. What is the relative frequency that a person surveyed is a male, given that they walk to work?

_____

10. The average monthly rainfall in Orlando, Florida for 2012 is given on the table below.

| Monthly rainfall (rounded to the nearest tenth of an inch) |
|---|
| 2.4  2.5  3.8  2.7  3.5  7.6 |
| 7.3  7.1  6.1  3.3  2.2  2.6 |

Complete the histogram based on the data.

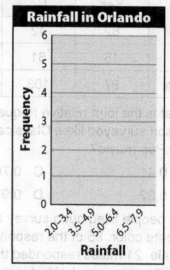

11. The test scores of a standardized test are normally distributed with a mean score of 425 and a standard deviation of 14.

   a. What percent of students scored between 411 and 439?

   _____

   b. What is the probability that a student scored less than 411?

   _____

# UNIT 3 Statistics and Data

## Unit Test: B

1.

| Do you shop for groceries at least once a week? | | | |
|---|---|---|---|
| Gender | Yes | No | Total |
| Male | 78 | 11 | 89 |
| Female | 54 | ? | ? |
| Total | 132 | 45 | 177 |

How many females surveyed grocery shop less than once a week?

_____

2.

| What type of music do you like? | | | |
|---|---|---|---|
| | Blues | | |
| Rock | Yes | No | Total |
| Yes | 75 | 35 | 110 |
| No | 32 | 8 | 40 |
| Total | 107 | 43 | 150 |

Approximately what is the marginal relative frequency that a person surveyed likes Rock music?

A  0.21          C  0.71

B  0.32          D  0.73

3. Taran collected surveys from 540 people about their preferred pet. 312 of the people surveyed were under 18 years old. The conditional relative frequency that a person surveyed prefers dogs given that they are under 18 years old is 0.25. How many people under 18 preferred dogs?

_____

4. For the set {–6, –6, –2, 4, 8, 10}, would each of the following be affected if the value of 3 was included?

A  mode        ○ Yes    ○ No

B  median      ○ Yes    ○ No

C  mean        ○ Yes    ○ No

D  range       ○ Yes    ○ No

5. What is the mean and standard deviation of the data set {32, 35, 35, 45, 46, 48, 49, 50}?

_____

6. What is the interquartile range of the data represented on the plot below?

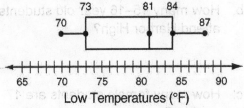

7. The histogram below represents the fuel economy of a company's fleet of vehicles.

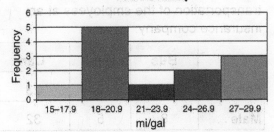

What is the relative frequency that the fuel economy of a car from the fleet is between 24 and 26.9 miles per gallon?

A  $\frac{1}{12}$          C  $\frac{1}{5}$

B  $\frac{1}{10}$          D  $\frac{1}{6}$

**UNIT 3**

# Statistics and Data
## *Unit Test: B*

8. The frequency table below shows the age and gender of the students at Harbor High School. There are a total of 572 students at the high school.

   a. Complete the frequency table.

| Age | Gender | | |
|---|---|---|---|
| | Male | Female | |
| 13–14 | | 108 | 190 |
| 15–16 | | | |
| 17–18 | 63 | | 161 |
| 19–20 | 11 | 23 | 34 |
| Total | 258 | | |

   b. How many 15–16 year old students attend Harbor High?

   _____

   c. How many female students are 17 or older?

   _____

9. The table below displays the results of a survey of the primary mode of transportation of the employees at an insurance company.

| | Bus | Bike | Car |
|---|---|---|---|
| **Female** | 12 | 3 | 23 |
| **Male** | 8 | 5 | 32 |

   a. Find the joint relative frequency that an employee is a female who primarily drives. Round to the nearest hundredth.

   _____

   b. Find the marginal relative frequency that an employee's primary mode of transportation is biking. Write the frequency as a fraction.

   _____

   c. Given that an employee's primary mode of transportation is the bus, what is the conditional relative frequency that the employee is a male?

   _____

10. The ages of the U.S. Presidents that were inaugurated during the 1900s are given below.

| Ages at Inauguration |
|---|
| 42 51 56 55 51 54 51 60 62 |
| 43 55 56 61 52 69 64 46 |

   Create a histogram based on the data.

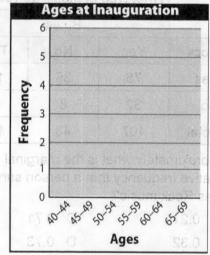

11. The scores on a standardized test are normally distributed. The mean score is 82, and the standard distribution is 7.

   a. What percentage of students scored higher than 68 on the test?

   _____

   b. If a test taker is chosen at random, what is the probability that their score is between 75 and 96?

   _____

# Statistics and Data
## Unit Test: C

1.

| | Gender | | |
|---|---|---|---|
| Eye Color | Male | Female | Total |
| Brown | 12 | 32 | 44 |
| Blue | 25 | 16 | 41 |
| Green | 13 | 4 | 17 |
| Total | 50 | 52 | 102 |

How many females surveyed did not have brown eyes?

_____

2.

| What type of music do you listen to? | | | |
|---|---|---|---|
| | Country | | |
| Rock | Yes | No | Total |
| Yes | 55 | 25 | 80 |
| No | 32 | 38 | 70 |
| Total | 87 | 63 | 150 |

To the nearest hundredth, what is the relative frequency that a person surveyed listens to Rock music or Country music or both?

_____

3. Marion surveyed 55 girls and 25 boys and asked about their preferred sport. 22 girls preferred soccer, and 7 boys preferred soccer. What is the conditional relative frequency that a student's favorite sport is not soccer given that the student is a boy?

_____

4. What are the mean, median, and mode of the data set {80, 73, 72, 76, 84, 86, 82, 73, 81, 84, 78, 85, 87, 84, 70}?

_____

5. What is the mean of the data represented on the dot plot?

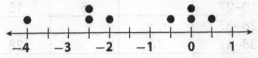

A  $\bar{x} \approx -1.38$

B  $\bar{x} \approx -1.83$

C  $\bar{x} \approx -1.25$

D  $\bar{x} \approx -1.42$

**For 6–7, refer to the histogram below.**

Ages of Board of Directors

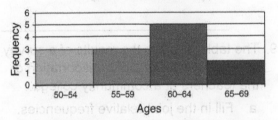

6. Could each of these be a possible median of the data?

A  57          ○ Yes     ○ No

B  60          ○ Yes     ○ No

C  62          ○ Yes     ○ No

7. What is the relative frequency that a member of the board of directors is less than 60 years old? Write the answer as a fraction in simplest form.

_____

# Statistics and Data
## Unit Test: C

**8.** The frequency table below shows the ages of the employees at Marianna's Auto Shop. Marianna has 56 male employees and 34 female employees.

a. Fill in the frequency table.

| | Gender | | |
|---|---|---|---|
| Age | Male | Female | |
| 18–27 | | 5 | 15 |
| 28–37 | | | |
| 38–47 | 18 | | 28 |
| 48–57 | 12 | 17 | |
| Total | | | |

b. How many 38–47 year olds work at the Auto Shop?

_____

c. Does Marianna employ more 18–27 year olds or 48–57 year olds? How many more?

_____

_____

**9.** The table displays the results of a survey of the primary mode of transportation of the teachers at a community college.

a. Fill in the joint relative frequencies.

| | Bus | Bike | Car |
|---|---|---|---|
| **Female** | 20 = 0.16 | 15 = | 30 = |
| **Male** | 12 = | 12 = | 36 = |

b. Find the marginal relative frequency that an employee bikes to work.

_____

c. What is the conditional relative frequency that an employee drives a car, given that it is a male?

_____

d. Is it more likely that a male employee rides the bus or that a female employee rides the bus? Explain.

_____

**10.** The scores on a quiz for ten students in Mrs. Franc's morning math class are given below.

{32, 48, 50, 46, 35, 49, 35, 45, 33, 50}

a. Make a box-and-whisker plot to represent the data.

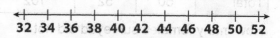

b. The scores for ten students in Mrs. Franc's afternoon math class are represented on the box-and-whisker plot below.

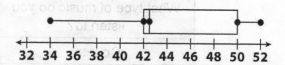

Compare the medians and interquartile ranges of the quiz scores from the morning class and the quiz scores from the afternoon class.

_____

_____

_____

**11.** Dani is analyzing a normal data distribution. She knows that the mean of the data is 12.3 and that 2.5% of the data is less than 10.8.

a. What is the standard deviation of the data?

_____

b. What value will 16% of the data be greater than?

_____

# Statistics and Data

**UNIT 3**

## *Unit Test: D*

1.

| Do you read more than 30 minutes per day? | | |
|---|---|---|
| Gender | Yes | No |
| Male | 67 | 32 |
| Female | 56 | 19 |

How many females surveyed read more than 30 minutes per day?

A  19

B  56

C  123

2.

| What types of music do you like? | | | |
|---|---|---|---|
| | Jazz | | |
| Country | Yes | No | Total |
| Yes | 12 | 9 | 21 |
| No | 14 | 5 | 19 |
| Total | 26 | 14 | 40 |

What is the joint relative frequency that a person surveyed likes Jazz and Country?

A  $\dfrac{12}{100}$

B  $\dfrac{12}{40}$

C  $\dfrac{12}{26}$

3. Suzanne had 100 people fill out a questionnaire about their favorite color. 45 of the respondents were male. Ten males said yellow was their favorite color. What was the conditional relative frequency that a participant's favorite color is yellow, given it is a male?

A  0.10

B  0.22

C  0.45

4. What is the mean of the data set {2, 2, 2, 3, 0, 5, 8, 3, 7, 10}?

A  4.2

B  10

C  42

5. What is the outlier of the following set of data: −8, 1, 6, −4, 0, 45, −3?

A  −8

B  0

C  45

6. What is the median of the data represented on the box–and–whisker plot?

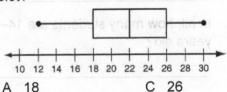

A  18                C  26

B  22

7. Which frequency table reflects the data shown below?

| Miles per gallon |
|---|
| 15.8  26.5  19.1  19.5  25.3  20.2  19.2 |
| 20.0  18.0  27.8  27.3  18.9  28.9  22.5 |

A

| mi/gal | freq. |
|---|---|
| 15–19.9 | 4 |
| 20–24.9 | 5 |

B

| mi/gal | freq. |
|---|---|
| 15–19.9 | 6 |
| 20–24.9 | 4 |
| 25–29.9 | 4 |

C

| mi/gal | freq. |
|---|---|
| 15–19.9 | 6 |
| 20–24.9 | 3 |
| 25–29.9 | 5 |

8. The frequency table below shows the ages and gender of the students at Muddle Middle School.

   a. Complete the table.

| Age | Gender | | |
|---|---|---|---|
| | Male | Female | |
| 10–11 | 105 | 98 | |
| 12–13 | 90 | 102 | |
| 14–15 | 95 | 110 | |
| Total | | | |

   b. How many male students are 12–13 years old?

   _____

   c. In all, how many students are 14–15 years old?

   _____

   d. Are there more males or females at Muddle Middle School? How many more?

   _____

9. The table shows the results of a survey of the primary mode of transportation of residents of East Palatka, Florida.

| Bus | Bike | Car | Walking |
|---|---|---|---|
| 118 | 75 | 147 | 60 |

   a. How many residents were surveyed?

   _____

   b. What is the relative frequency that a resident who was surveyed primarily bikes?

   _____

   c. Of the residents surveyed who ride a bike to work, 30 are males. What is the relative frequency that a person surveyed is a male, given that they ride a bike?

   _____

10. The monthly rainfall in Pensacola, Florida for 2012 is given on the table below.

| Monthly rainfall (rounded to the nearest inch) |
|---|
| 2  5  6  1  4  7 |
| 7  7  6  5  7  8 |

   a. Complete the frequency table.

| Monthly rainfall | Frequency |
|---|---|
| 1–2 | |
| 3–4 | |
| 5–6 | |
| 7–8 | |

   b. Use the frequency table to complete the histogram.

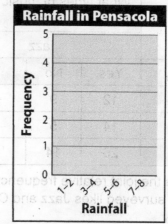

11. The scores from a college chemistry test are normally distributed. The mean grade is 50, and the standard deviation is 15. What percentage of the students scored between 50 and 65?

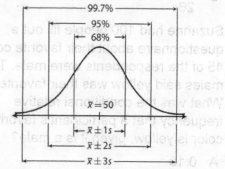

   _____

# Statistics and Data
### *Performance Task*

**UNIT 3**

## Brothers and Sisters

**One hundred students were surveyed. Of those surveyed, 60% said they had a sister. Of that group, 30% also had a brother. Of the students who did not have a sister, 50% had a brother.**

Use the table below for Questions 1–5. Leave room in each box to write a second number.

1. Fill in box ⊙. Explain how you found the number.

   _____

2. Fill in box ◯. Explain how you found the number.

   _____

3. Fill in box ☽. Explain how you found the number.

   _____

4. Fill in box ☾. Explain how you found the number.

   _____

5. Fill in box ♀. Explain how you found the number.

   _____

6. Fill in the rest of the table.

| | Has a brother | Does not have a brother | TOTAL |
|---|---|---|---|
| Has a sister | ◯ | ♀ | ⊙ |
| Does not have a sister | ☾ | | ☽ |
| TOTAL | | | |

7. To the right of the number in each box, write the relative frequency of the number compared to the total for the row the number is in.

8. Explain the meaning of the relative frequency you wrote in box ☾.

   _____

9. What is the marginal relative frequency given that the student has a sister?

   _____

UNIT
4

# Polynomial Expressions and Equations

## Unit Test: A

1. Which of the following terms is **not** a monomial?

   A   $6x$

   B   $\frac{1}{3}x^2$

   C   13

   D   $3x^{-3}$

2. Which best describes the polynomial $7xy - 15y^3$?

   A   monomial with a degree of 2

   B   binomial with a degree of 3

   C   binomial with a degree of 7

   D   trinomial with a degree of 2

3. Add $(2x^3 - 5) + (x^3 + 3)$. What is the sum?

   _____

4. Multiply $(8x^4)(7x^2)$. What is the product?

   _____

5. Multiply $(x + 4)(x - 3)$. What is the product?

   _____

6. Does each of the following result in $x^2 - 100$?

   A   $(x - 90) + (x - 10)$        O Yes        O No

   B   $(x - 9)^2 - 19$             O Yes        O No

   C   $x(x - 100)$                 O Yes        O No

   D   $(x + 10)(x - 10)$           O Yes        O No

7. What is the complete factorization of $16y^2 + 12y$?

   A   $y(16y + 12)$

   B   $2y(8y + 6)$

   C   $4(4y^2 + 3y)$

   D   $4y(4y + 3)$

8. Factor $x^2 + 8x + 12$.

   _____

9. Solve $x^2 - 6x = 40$ by factoring. What is the solution?

   _____

10. Which of the following will simplify to the correct solutions of $y = 2x^2 + 5x - 7$?

    A   $\dfrac{-5 \pm \sqrt{25 - 56}}{4}$        C   $\dfrac{5 \pm \sqrt{25 - 56}}{4}$

    B   $\dfrac{-5 \pm \sqrt{25 + 56}}{4}$        D   $\dfrac{5 \pm \sqrt{25 + 56}}{4}$

11. What is the discriminant of $3x^2 + 14x + 8 = 0$?

    A   −82                C   100

    B   14                 D   292

12. A quadratic equation has a discriminant of 25. Which statement is true?

    A   The equation has no real solutions.

    B   The equation has one real solution.

    C   The equation has two real solutions.

    D   None of the above statements is true.

UNIT
4

# Polynomial Expressions and Equations

### *Unit Test: A*

13. Simplify $5m^2 + 11m - 16m^2 - 7m$.

_____

14. Subtract $(7x^2 - 3x) - (5x^2 - 5x)$.

_____

15. Multiply $6(10p^3 - 8p + 2)$.

_____

16.

$$5x^2 + 1$$

$x^2 + 4$

a. Write a polynomial that represents the perimeter of the rectangle.

_____

b. Find the perimeter of the rectangle if $x = 5$ feet.

_____

c. Write a polynomial that represents the area of the rectangle.

_____

d. Find the area of the rectangle if $x = 2$ inches.

_____

17. Multiply $(2x + 9)(x + 3)$.

_____

18. Multiply $(x - 13)(x + 5)$.

_____

19. Multiply $(5x - 3)^2$.

_____

20. Find the zeros of $y = x^2 - 12x + 32$.

_____

21. Solve by completing the square:
$x^2 + 22x = -104$.

_____

22. Solve $x^2 + 10x + 23 = 0$ using the quadratic equation.

_____

23. Factor $8x + 16 + xy + 2y$ by grouping.

_____

24. Factor $4y^2 - 16y + 16$.

_____

25. Is $x^2 + 20x - 100$ a perfect square trinomial? Explain why or why not.

_____

26. Factor $b^2 - 144$.

_____

27. Factor $125 - 5x^2$.

_____

# Polynomial Expressions and Equations
## *Unit Test: B*

1. What is the degree of $7x^3y$?

   A  1

   B  3

   C  4

   D  7

2. Add $(15x^2 - 10x - 7) + (6x^2 + 8)$. What is the sum?

   _____

3. What is the product of $8a^3b^2$ and $2a^2b$?

   _____

4. Multiply $(2x + 1)(x - 1)$. What is the product?

   A  $3x$

   B  $2x^2 - 1$

   C  $2x^2 - x - 1$

   D  $2x^2 - 3x - 1$

5. Does each of the following result in $4x^2 - 25$?

   A  $(2x - 5)(2x + 5)$  ○ Yes  ○ No

   B  $(4x + 25)(x - 1)$  ○ Yes  ○ No

   C  $(2x + 5)^2 - 20x - 50$  ○ Yes  ○ No

   D  $(2x - 5)^2 + 20x + 50$  ○ Yes  ○ No

6. What is $30y^3 - 6y^2 + 12$ factored completely?

   _____

7. Factor $x^2 + 29x + 210$.

   _____

8. What is the solution to $2x^2 - 24 = -8x$?

   A  $x = -2$ or $x = 6$

   B  $x = -1$ or $x = 3$

   C  $x = 2$ or $x = -6$

   D  $x = 3$ or $x = -4$

9. Solve $2x^2 - 7x = 4$ using the Quadratic Formula. Which is correct?

   A  $x = 4$ or $x = -\dfrac{1}{2}$

   B  $x = \dfrac{7 + \sqrt{17}}{4}$ or $x = \dfrac{7 - \sqrt{17}}{4}$

   C  $x = -4$ or $x = \dfrac{1}{2}$

   D  $x = \dfrac{7 + \sqrt{17}}{2}$ or $x = \dfrac{7 - \sqrt{17}}{2}$

10. What is the discriminant of $y = -16x^2 - 2x + 1$?

    _____

11. A quadratic equation has a discriminant of $-2$. Choose True or False for each statement.

    A  The graph of the equation does not intersect the x-axis.

       ○ True     ○ False

    B  The graph of the equation does not intersect the y-axis.

       ○ True     ○ False

    C  The equation has no real solution.

       ○ True     ○ False

    D  The equation has two real solutions.

       ○ True     ○ False

# Polynomial Expressions and Equations
### *Unit Test: B*

12. Simplify $8m^2 - 15 + m^2 - 10m + 8$.

_____

13. Subtract $(8.5x^2 + 18x - 10) - (5x^2 + 2.5)$.

_____

14. Multiply $7x^2(5x^2 + 11xy)$.

_____

15.
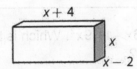

a. Write a polynomial that represents the surface area of the prism.

_____

b. Find the surface area of the prism if $x = 4$ centimeters.

_____

c. Write a polynomial that represents the volume of the prism.

_____

d. Find the volume of the prism if $x = 3$ inch.

_____

16. Multiply $(3x + 9)(2x + 4)$.

_____

17. Multiply $(5x - 13)(x + 5)$.

_____

18. Multiply $(6x - 8)^2$.

_____

**For 19–20, find the GCF.**

19. 144, 240

_____

20. $14xy^2$, $51y$

_____

21. Find the zeros of $y = 4x^2 - 12x - 16$.

_____

22. Solve $-x + 3x^2 - 2 = 0$.

_____

23. Solve $-4x^2 - 5x = -9$.

_____

24. $xp^2 - 4x$
Give a value of $x$ that makes the binomial a difference of perfect squares, and write the factors of the binomial.

_____

_____

25. Factor $144 - b^6$.

_____

**UNIT 4**

# Polynomial Expressions and Equations

*Unit Test: C*

1. Which of the following terms is a monomial with a degree of 5?

   A  $xyz^3$

   B  $3x^5yz$

   C  $5xyz$

   D  $-6x^2yz$

2. Which best describes $7x^2yz + 8xy - 18$?

   A  cubic binomial

   B  cubic trinomial

   C  quadratic trinomial

   D  quartic trinomial

3. What is the sum of $(1.2x^5 - 5x^3 - 0.7) + (3.7x^5 + 3)$?

   _____

4. What is the product of $13x^3yz^2$ and $6x^3y^2z$?

   A  $78xyz$

   B  $78x^3y^2z^2$

   C  $78x^6y^3z^3$

   D  $78x^9y^3z^3$

5. Multiply $(3x - 2)(2x + 6)$. What is the product?

   _____

6. Is each of the following equivalent to $(b + 3)^3$?

   A  $b^3 + 27$

   ○ Yes    ○ No

   B  $(b^3 + 6b^2 + 81) + (3b^2 - 27b)$

   ○ Yes    ○ No

   C  $b^3 + 9b^2 + 27b + 27$

   ○ Yes    ○ No

   D  $(3b^3 + 9b^2) - (2b^3 - 27b - 27)$

   ○ Yes    ○ No

7. What is $-3y^3 - 6y^2 + 6y$ factored completely?

   A  $-3y(y^2 + 2y - 2)$

   B  $-y(3y^2 - 6y + 2)$

   C  $-y(3y^2 + 6y^2 - 2)$

   D  $-3(y^3 - 2y^2 - 2)$

8. What is the solution to $3x^2 + \dfrac{1}{10} = -\dfrac{13}{10}x$?

   _____

9. Solve $6x - 1 = 9x^2$. Which is the correct answer?

   A  $x = \dfrac{1}{3}$ or $x = -\dfrac{1}{3}$    C  $x = 2 \pm 2\sqrt{2}$

   B  $x = \dfrac{1}{3}$    D  $x = \dfrac{3 \pm \sqrt{2}}{9}$

10. What is the discriminant of $-4x^2 + 6 = 2x$ and the number of real solutions of the equation?

    _____

11. The discriminant of a quadratic equation is 0. Choose True or False for each statement.

    A  The graph intersects the y-axis once.

    ○ True    ○ False

    B  The graph intersects the x-axis once.

    ○ True    ○ False

    C  The equation has no solutions.

    ○ True    ○ False

    D  The equation has one solution.

    ○ True    ○ False

# Polynomial Expressions and Equations
## *Unit Test: C*

12. Simplify $9m^2n - 9m^2 + 7n - 14m^2n - m^2$.

_____

13. Subtract $\left(\dfrac{21}{2}x^2 + 9\right) - \left(\dfrac{1}{2}x^2 - 5x - 2\right)$.

_____

14. Multiply $-9xy(9x^2 + 5xy - y^3)$.

_____

15.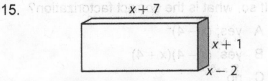

    a. Write a polynomial that represents the surface area of the prism.

    _____

    b. Find the surface area of the prism if $x = 3$ meters.

    _____

    c. Write a polynomial that represents the volume of the prism.

    _____

    d. Find the volume of the prism if $x = 5$ inches.

    _____

16. Multiply $\left(\dfrac{1}{2}x + 9\right)\left(2x + \dfrac{5}{2}\right)$.

17. Multiply $(5t^2 - 13t)(t + 5)$.

_____

18. Multiply $(x - 4)^3$.

_____

19. Find the zeros of $y = 4x^2 - 16x - 20$.

_____

20. What values of $c$ result in $y = 3x^2 - 5x + c$ **not** having real number solutions?

_____

21. Solve $-4 = x^2 - 5x - 19$.

_____

**For 22–24, factor completely.**

22. $2m^3 - 3m^2 - 18m + 27$

_____

23. $5x^3 - 40x^2 - 100x$

_____

24. $9x^2 - 120x + 400$

_____

25. $4p^2 - 20p + c$
    Give the value of $c$ that makes the expression a perfect square trinomial, and write the factorization.

_____

_____

**UNIT 4**

# Polynomial Expressions and Equations
### *Unit Test: D*

1. Which of the following terms is a monomial?

   A  $x - 6$

   B  $3x^2$

   C  $\dfrac{5}{x^3}$

2. Which describes the polynomial $12x^2 - 5$?

   A  monomial with a degree of 5

   B  binomial with a degree of 12

   C  binomial with a degree of 2

3. Add $(5x^2 + 8) + (2x^2 - 9)$. What is the sum?

   A  $7x^2 - 1$

   B  $7x^2 + 1$

   C  $7x^4 + 17$

4. Multiply $(8x^3)(10x^2)$. What is the product?

   A  $80x^3$

   B  $80x^5$

   C  $80x^6$

5. Multiply $(x + 4)(x + 3)$. What is the product?

   A  $x^2 + 12$

   B  $x^2 + 12x + 12$

   C  $x^2 + 7x + 12$

6. Which results in $x^2 - 100$?

   A  $(x + 10)^2$

   B  $x(x - 100)$

   C  $(x + 10)(x - 10)$

7. What is the complete factorization of $16y + 12$?

   A  $2(8y + 6)$

   B  $4(4y + 3)$

   C  $4y(4y + 3)$

8. What is the factorization of $x^2 + 8x + 12$?

   A  $(x + 1)(x + 12)$

   B  $(x + 2)(x + 6)$

   C  $(x + 3)(x + 4)$

9. Factor $3x^2 + 14x + 8$.

   A  $(3x + 4)(x + 2)$

   B  $(3x + 1)(x + 8)$

   C  $(3x + 2)(x + 4)$

10. Is $x^2 + 6x + 9$ a perfect square trinomial? If so, what is the correct factorization?

    A  yes; $(x + 3)^2$

    B  yes; $(x + 6)^2$

    C  no

11. Is $x^2 - 16$ a difference of two squares? If so, what is the correct factorization?

    A  yes; $(x - 4)^2$

    B  yes; $(x - 4)(x + 4)$

    C  no

12. Solve $x^2 - 11x + 18 = 0$ by factoring. What is the solution?

    A  $x = -2$ or $x = -9$

    B  $x = -2$ or $x = 9$

    C  $x = 2$ or $x = 9$

13. Which of the following will simplify to the correct solutions of $y = -4x^2 - 2x + 4$?

    A  $\dfrac{-2 \pm \sqrt{4 + 64}}{-8}$

    B  $\dfrac{2 \pm \sqrt{4 + 64}}{-8}$

    C  $\dfrac{2 \pm \sqrt{4 - 64}}{-8}$

14. What is the discriminant of $y = x^2 + 6x - 6$?

    A  12

    B  36

    C  60

**UNIT 4**

# Polynomial Expressions and Equations

## Unit Test: D

15. Simplify $7m^2 + 12 + 15m^2 + m$.

_____

16. Subtract $(10x^2 + 8) - (3x^2 + 3)$.

_____

17. Multiply $7(7p^3 + 15p)$.

_____

18.

$6x - 8$

$x$

   a.  Write a polynomial that represents the perimeter of the rectangle.

_____

   b.  Find the perimeter of the rectangle if $x = 6$ centimeters.

_____

   c.  Write a polynomial that represents the area of the rectangle.

_____

   d.  Find the area of the rectangle if $x = 4$ inches.

_____

19. Multiply $(x + 8)(x + 7)$.

20. Multiply $(x - 9)(x + 4)$.

_____

21. Multiply $(x - 4)^2$.

_____

22. Solve $x^2 + 6x = 7$.

_____

23. Solve $x^2 + 8x + 16 = 0$.

_____

24. Factor $y^2 - 4y + 4$.

_____

25. Is $x^2 + 10x + 100$ a perfect square trinomial? Explain why or why not.

_____

26. Factor $b^2 - 121$.

_____

27. Factor $4 - x^2$.

_____

# Polynomial Expressions and Equations
## *Performance Task*

**Scale Factors**

The area of rectangle A is given by the polynomial $8x^2 + 2x - 3$.
The area of rectangle B is given by the polynomial $32x^2 + 8x - 12$.

1. Factor the expression for the area of rectangle A.

_____

_____

2. Factor the expression for the area of rectangle B.

_____

_____

3. Each dimension of rectangle A was multiplied by a scale factor to get the dimensions of rectangle B. What was the scale factor? Explain how you know.

_____

_____

The area of circle A is given by the polynomial $4\pi x^2 - 20\pi x + 25\pi$.

4. Factor the expression for the area of circle A. Compare it with the formula for the area of a circle. Then write an expression for the radius of circle A.

_____

_____

5. Circle B has a radius 3 times the radius of Circle A. Express the area of Circle B as a polynomial.

_____

_____

6. How is the scale factor from the area of Circle A to the area of Circle B related to the GCF of the areas of the two circles?

_____

_____

_____

The surface area of sphere A is given by the polynomial $4\pi x^2 + 24\pi x + 36\pi$.

7. Factor the expression for the surface area of sphere A. Compare it with the formula for the area of a sphere, $A = 4\pi r^2$. Then write an expression for the radius of sphere A.

_____

_____

8. Sphere B has a radius 5 times the radius of Sphere A. Express the surface of Sphere B as a polynomial.

_____

_____

9. How is the scale factor from the surface area of Sphere A to the surface area of Sphere B related to the GCF of the surface areas of the two spheres?

_____

_____

Name _____ Date _____ Class _____

# Functions and Modeling
## *Unit Test: A*

1. Which is a quadratic equation?

   A $y = x + 9$

   B $y = 2x - 15$

   C $y = x^2 + 2x - 7$

   D $y = x^3 - x^2$

2. What is the axis of symmetry of the parabola graphed below?

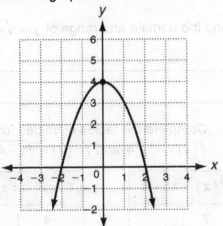

   A $y = 4$      C $y = 2$

   B $x = -2$      D $x = 0$

3. What are the zeros of $y = 4x^2 - 16$?

   _____

4. Given $f(x) = x^2$ and $g(x) = (x - 5)^2$, choose True or False for each statement.

   A $g(x)$ is $f(x)$ translated up 5 units.

      ○ True     ○ False

   B $g(x)$ is $f(x)$ translated right 5 units.

      ○ True     ○ False

   C $g(x)$ is the same shape as $f(x)$.

      ○ True     ○ False

   D $g(x)$ is narrower than $f(x)$.

      ○ True     ○ False

5. What is the inverse of $f(x) = 4x^3$?

   _____

6. What is $y = \begin{cases} 2x + 3 \text{ if } x \le -2 \\ x + 4 \text{ if } x > -2 \end{cases}$ evaluated for $x = 0$?

   _____

7. Which equation is graphed below?

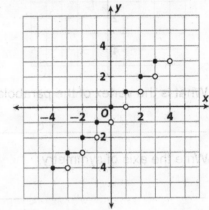

   A $y = [x] + 1$      C $y = |x|$

   B $y = [x]$      D $y = |x| - 1$

8. What is the vertex of the graph of $y = |x + 12| - 10$?

   _____

9. A math tutor charges $10 per hour for 3 hours or less and $9 per hour for over 3 hours of tutoring. Which function represents what the tutor charges for *h* hours of tutoring?

   A $y = \begin{cases} 10h \text{ if } 0 \le h \le 3 \\ 9h \text{ if } h > 3 \end{cases}$

   B $y = \begin{cases} 10h \text{ if } 0 \le h < 3 \\ 9h \text{ if } h \ge 3 \end{cases}$

   C $y = \begin{cases} 9h \text{ if } 0 \le h \le 3 \\ 10h \text{ if } h > 3 \end{cases}$

   D $y = \begin{cases} 9h \text{ if } 0 \le h < 3 \\ 10h \text{ if } h \ge 3 \end{cases}$

# Functions and Modeling
## Unit Test: A

10. a. Graph $y = x^2 - 4$ below.

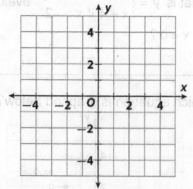

b. What is the vertex of the parabola?

_____

c. Write the axis of symmetry.

_____

d. Find the maximum or minimum value of the parabola.

_____

11. The height of a ball in feet is modeled by $f(x) = -16x^2 + 80x$, which is shown below, where $x$ is the time in seconds after it is hit.

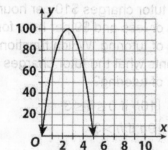

a. How long is the ball in the air?

_____

b. Find and interpret the vertex of the graph.

_____

_____

12. Solve the system by elimination.

$$\begin{cases} y = 16x + 44 \\ y = -x^2 + 8x + 28 \end{cases}$$

_____

13. Solve $|-x + 4| = 7$.

_____

14. Find the domain and range of $y = \sqrt{x + 5}$.

_____

_____

15. a. Complete the tables of values for $f(x) = x^3 + 4$ and $f^{-1}(x) = \sqrt[3]{x - 4}$.

| $f(x) = x^3 + 4$ | |
| --- | --- |
| −2 | |
| −1 | |
| 0 | |
| 1 | |
| 2 | |

| $f^{-1}(x) = \sqrt[3]{x - 4}$ | |
| --- | --- |
| −4 | |
| 3 | |
| 4 | |
| 5 | |
| 12 | |

b. Graph $f(x) = x^3 + 4$ and $f^{-1}(x) = \sqrt[3]{x - 4}$.

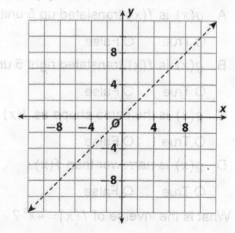

Name _____ Date _____ Class _____

# Functions and Modeling
## *Unit Test: B*

1. Which is a quadratic function?

   A $f(x) = (x + 8)(x - 11)$

   B $f(x) = x^3 + 5x^2 - 9x$

   C $f(x) = x^{-2} + 8$

   D $f(x) = 2x + 24$

2. What is the axis of symmetry of the graph of $y = (x + 9)^2 + 12$?

   _____

3. Based on the graph of $y = x^2 + 4x + 5$ shown below, what are the solutions to the equation $x^2 + 4x + 5 = 5$?

   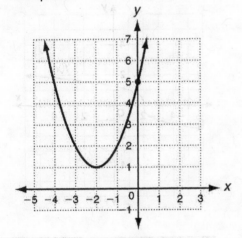

   _____

4. Given $f(x) = x^2 - 5$ and $g(x) = (x + 4)^2 + 5$, choose True or False for each statement.

   A $g(x)$ is $f(x)$ translated up 10 units and left 4 units.

   ○ True    ○ False

   B $g(x)$ is $f(x)$ translated down 10 units and right 4 units.

   ○ True    ○ False

   C $g(x)$ is wider than $f(x)$.

   ○ True    ○ False

   D $g(x)$ is the same shape as $f(x)$.

   ○ True    ○ False

5. What is $y = \begin{cases} x^2 & \text{if } x < -4 \\ -2x + 4 & \text{if } x \geq -4 \end{cases}$ evaluated for $x = 6$?

   _____

6. Which equation is graphed below?

   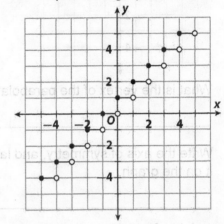

   A $y = |x| + 1$    C $y = [x] + 1$

   B $y = |x|$        D $y = [x]$

7. What is the vertex of the graph of $y = 3|x - 2.5| + 0.125$?

   _____

8. In an Algebra class, students get one extra credit point for each minute of tutoring for 10 minutes or less and double extra credit points for over 10 minutes of tutoring. Which equation gives the number of extra credit points where $m$ is the number of minutes of tutoring?

   A $y = \begin{cases} m & \text{if } 0 \leq m < 10 \\ 2m & \text{if } m \geq 10 \end{cases}$

   B $y = 2|m|$

   C $y = \begin{cases} m & \text{if } 0 \leq m \leq 10 \\ 2m & \text{if } m > 10 \end{cases}$

   D $y = 2|m| + 10$

# Functions and Modeling

## Unit Test: B

9. a.  Graph $y = x^2 - 4x + 1$ below.

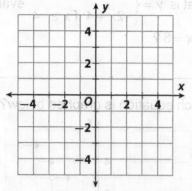

b.  What is the vertex of the parabola?

_____

c.  Write the axis of symmetry, and label it on the graph.

_____

10. The height of a ball in meters is modeled by $f(x) = -5x^2 + 40x$, where $x$ is the time in seconds after it is hit.

a.  Graph $f(x) = -5x^2 + 40x$.

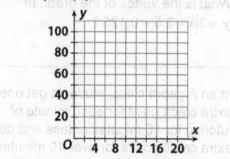

b.  How long is the ball in the air?

_____

c.  Find and interpret the vertex of the graph.

_____

_____

11. Solve $-\dfrac{1}{2}|6 - 3x| = -6$.

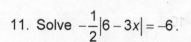

12. Solve $\begin{cases} y = x^2 - 6x + 6 \\ 3 - \dfrac{1}{2}y = 3x \end{cases}$

_____

13. Find the domain and range of $y = (x - 6)^3 + 1$.

_____

_____

_____

14. a.  Write the function $f(x)$ which is graphed below.

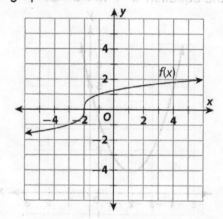

_____

_____

b.  Find and graph the inverse of $f(x)$.

_____

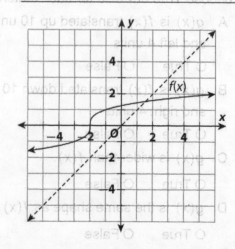

**UNIT 5**

# Functions and Modeling

*Unit Test: C*

1. Which is **not** a quadratic function?

   A  $f(x) = (x-8)(x+4)$

   B  $f(x) = \dfrac{x^4 + 5x^3}{x^2}$

   C  $f(x) = 6x^2 + 17x - 8$

   D  $f(x) = \dfrac{5x - 7}{x^2}$

2. What is the axis of symmetry of a parabola that contains the points $(9, -4)$ and $(14, -4)$?

   _____

3. Based on the graph of $y = x^2 + 4x + 5$, what are the solutions to the equation $x^2 + 4x + 5 = 2$?

   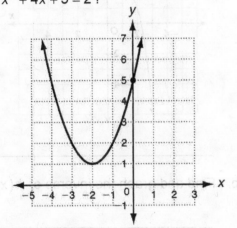

   _____

4. Given $f(x) = (x-4)^2 + 6$ and $g(x) = x^2 - 8x + 24$, choose True or False for each statement.

   A  $g(x)$ is $f(x)$ translated up 2 units.

   ○ True      ○ False

   B  $g(x)$ is $f(x)$ translated left 2 units.

   ○ True      ○ False

   C  $g(x)$ is $f(x)$ translated down 6 units.

   ○ True      ○ False

   D  $g(x)$ is $f(x)$ translated right 4 units.

   ○ True      ○ False

5. What is $f(x) = \begin{cases} 3x^2 & \text{if } x < -4 \\ -\dfrac{1}{2}x + 12 & \text{if } x \geq -4 \end{cases}$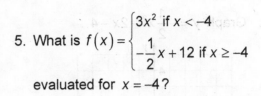

   evaluated for $x = -4$?

   _____

6. Which equation is graphed below?

   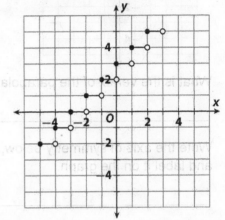

   _____

7. Which function has a graph with a vertex at $(-14, -5)$?

   A  $f(x) = 2|x + 14| - 5$

   B  $f(x) = -5|x + 14|$

   C  $f(x) = \dfrac{2}{3}|x + 5| - 14$

   D  $f(x) = 7|x - 5| - 14$

8. Which equation equals $-4$ when $x = -128$?

   A  $y = \dfrac{1}{2}\sqrt[3]{x}$        C  $y = -\dfrac{1}{2}\sqrt[3]{x}$

   B  $y = \sqrt[3]{\dfrac{x}{2}}$          D  $y = -\sqrt[3]{\dfrac{x}{2}}$

# UNIT 5

## Functions and Modeling
### Unit Test: C

9. a. Graph $y = -\frac{1}{2}x^2 - 2x - 4$.

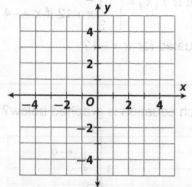

b. What is the vertex of the parabola?

_____

c. Write the axis of symmetry below, and label it on the graph.

_____

d. Find the maximum or minimum value of the parabola.

_____

10. Are the first differences or the second differences of the values described on the table below invariant? Is the relation linear, quadratic, or neither?

| x | −2 | −1 | 0 | 1 | 2 |
|---|----|----|---|---|---|
| y | −10 | −10 | −8 | −4 | 2 |

_____

_____

11. Solve $\begin{cases} y = x^2 - 4 \\ y = x^2 + 16x + 4 \end{cases}$

_____

12. Solve $8 = \dfrac{|-5x + 12|}{2}$.

_____

13. Find the domain and range of $y = 8x^3 + 7.5$.

_____

_____

14. a. Write the function $h(x)$ which is graphed below.

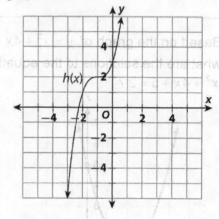

_____

b. Find and graph the inverse of $h(x)$.

_____

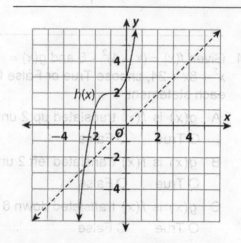

UNIT
5

# Functions and Modeling

*Unit Test: D*

1. Which is a quadratic function?

   A  $f(x) = x^2 + 6$

   B  $f(x) = 2x$

   C  $f(x) = x + 5$

2. What is the axis of symmetry of the parabola graphed below?

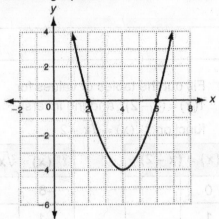

   A  $y = -4$

   B  $x = 4$

   C  $x = 2$

3. What are the zeros of $y = x^2 - 9$?

   A  $-9$

   B  $-9$ and $9$

   C  $-3$ and $3$

4. $f(x) = x^2$ and $g(x) = x^2 + 4$.
   Which statement is true?

   A  $g(x)$ is $f(x)$ translated up 4 units.

   B  $g(x)$ is $f(x)$ translated right 4 units.

   C  $g(x)$ is $f(x)$ translated down 4 units.

5. What is $y = \begin{cases} x \text{ if } x < 0 \\ x + 11 \text{ if } x \geq 0 \end{cases}$ evaluated for $x = -3$?

   A  $-3$

   B  $8$

   C  $14$

6. Which equation is graphed below?

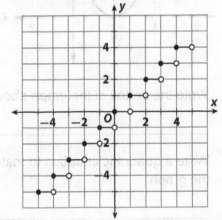

   A  $y = x - 1$

   B  $y = |x|$

   C  $y = [x]$

7. What is the vertex of the graph of $y = 6|x|$?

   A  $(0, 6)$

   B  $(6, 0)$

   C  $(0, 0)$

8. A bank gives customers points equal to the amount they deposit or withdraw from their accounts. Which equation represents the points awarded if $x$ is the change in a customer's account total?

   A  $y = |x|$

   B  $y = \begin{cases} x \text{ if } x \leq 0 \\ -x \text{ if } x > 0 \end{cases}$

   C  $y = [x]$

9.

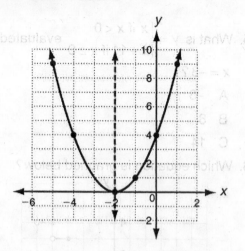

a. Write the vertex of the graph above.

_____

b. Write a quadratic equation to match the graph.

_____

10. The height of a ball in meters is modeled by $f(x) = -5x^2 + 50x$, shown on the graph below, where $x$ is the time in seconds after it is hit.

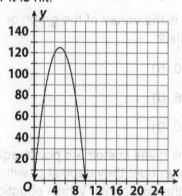

How long is the ball in the air?

_____

11. Solve $11 = |x + 7|$.

_____

12. Solve the system by substitution.

$$\begin{cases} y = x^2 - 2 \\ y = x \end{cases}$$

_____

13. Find the domain and range of $y = \sqrt[3]{x}$.

_____

_____

14. a. Fill out the tables of values for $t(x) = (x - 2)^3$ and the inverse function $t^{-1}(x) = \sqrt[3]{x} + 2$.

| $t(x) = (x - 2)^3$ | | $t^{-1}(x) = \sqrt[3]{x} + 2$ | |
|---|---|---|---|
| 0 | | −8 | |
| 1 | | −1 | |
| 2 | | 0 | |
| 3 | | 1 | |
| 4 | | 8 | |

b. Graph $t^{-1}(x) = \sqrt[3]{x} + 2$.
$t(x) = (x - 2)^3$ has already been graphed below.

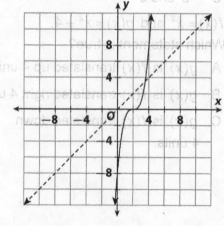

# UNIT 5 Functions and Modeling
## *Performance Task*

**Mirror, Mirror on the Plane**

The graph depicts an upward facing mirror on the *x*-axis. A beam of light passes through Quadrant II at a 45° angle to the *x*-axis, strikes the mirror at the origin, and is reflected upward into Quadrant I.

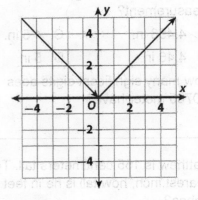

1. Write the equations of two lines, one that includes the Quadrant II section of the ray and one that includes Quadrant I.

   _____  _____
   
   Quadrant II    Quadrant I

2. Complete to write the co-ordinates of two points on the lines:

   $(-4, \_\_\_), (4, \_\_\_)$

3. Write an absolute value equation representing the path for the entire light beam.

   _____

4. The mirror is moved down 3 units and the beam adjusted so that its incoming and outgoing paths are still 45° to the mirror. The beam now strikes the mirror at $(-5, -3)$. Write an absolute value representing the path for the entire light beam.

   _____

5. Complete to write the co-ordinates of two points on the lines:

   $(-4, \_\_\_), (4, \_\_\_)$

6. The mirror is moved again and the angle of the beam adjusted so that the equation of the beam is now $y = \frac{1}{3}|x - 2| + 7$.

   a. Describe the location of the mirror.

   _____

   b. At what point does the beam strike the mirror? _____

   c. Complete to write the co-ordinates of two points on the lines:

   $(-1, _____), (8, \_\_\_\_\_)$

   d. Compare the shape of the beam with the shape of the original beam.

# Benchmark Test Modules 1–5

1. Which of the following is the most precise measurement?

   A   4.458 in.        C   4.5 in.

   B   4.46 in.         D   5 in.

2. How many significant digits does 0.0705 meter have?

   _____

3. Matthew is 165 centimeters tall. To the nearest inch, how tall is he in feet and inches?

   _____

4. The length of $r$ of the circle $O$ below is 6.50 inches. What is the circumference of the circle to the nearest centimeter?

   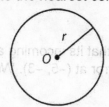

   _____

5. A living room of a house is 20.5 feet wide and 32.5 feet long. What is the approximate area of the room in square meters?

   A   61.9 m$^2$        C   666 m$^2$

   B   203 m$^2$         D   2,180 m$^2$

6. Which expression is equivalent to $\sqrt[5]{a^3}$ ?

   A   $a^{\frac{5}{3}}$        C   $a^{\frac{3}{5}}$

   B   $a^2$            D   $a^{-2}$

7. $81^{\frac{3}{4}}$ is equal to which of the following?

   A   3           C   27

   B   9           D   61

8. Which of the following is equivalent to $\dfrac{x^{15}}{x^3}$ ?

   A   $x^5$            C   $x^{-12}$

   B   $x^{12}$         D   $x^{-5}$

9. What is $\left(\dfrac{16}{144}\right)^{\frac{1}{2}}$ simplified?

   A   $\dfrac{1}{36}$        C   $\dfrac{1}{9}$

   B   $\dfrac{1}{18}$        D   $\dfrac{1}{3}$

10. Does each of the following numbers belong to the set of irrational numbers?

    A   $0.\overline{32}$                 O Yes    O No

    B   $\dfrac{2}{3}$                   O Yes    O No

    C   $\sqrt{3}$                  O Yes    O No

11. Is the set $\{-1, 1\}$ closed under each operation?

    A   addition            O Yes    O No

    B   subtraction         O Yes    O No

    C   multiplication      O Yes    O No

    D   division            O Yes    O No

12. What is $x(7 - x) + 12$ when evaluated for $x = -4$?

    _____

# Benchmark Test Modules 1–5

13. Which of the following is equivalent to $5(z+3)-4(1+p)$ ?

   A   $15z-4p$

   B   $5z+19+4p$

   C   $5z+11-4p$

   D   $11zp$

14. Oran bought seven oranges for $0.25 each. He also bought $b$ bananas for $0.15 each. Which expression best represents the total amount Oran spent?

   A   $1.75

   B   $1.90

   C   $1.05b + $1.75

   D   $0.15b + $1.75

15. Which of the following expressions has two terms and a coefficient of 6?

   A   $6-12y$        C   $6y^2-18$

   B   $6y^2-2x+10$    D   $-y^2+6$

16. What is $-7x+\dfrac{y}{3}$ when evaluated for $x=3$ and $y=-12$ ?

_____

17. What is the solution of $50=-x-23$ ?

_____

18. Solve $15x-7.5=30$. What is the value of $x$?

_____

19. Solve $x+72=-9x$. What is the value of $x$?

_____

20. Does each equation have at least one solution?

   A   $-8x+2=-8x-4$    ○ Yes    ○ No

   B   $12-x=5x+12$     ○ Yes    ○ No

   C   $6x+9=6x+9$      ○ Yes    ○ No

   D   $15-x=10-x$     ○ Yes    ○ No

21. Which inequality has solutions that best match those graphed on the number line below?

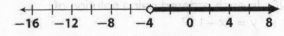

   A   $x<-4$         C   $x>-4$

   B   $x\le-4$        D   $x\ge-4$

22. Which statement describes the solutions of $2-5x<42$ ?

   A   Real numbers less than $-8$

   B   Real numbers greater than $-8$

   C   Real numbers less than or equal to $-8$

   D   Real numbers greater than or equal to $-8$

23. What are the solutions to $3(x+5)\le 3x+20$ ?

   A   $x\le 0$

   B   $x\ge 15$

   C   all real numbers

   D   no solutions

24. The equation a company uses to calculate pay checks is $p = 12h + 0.25s$ where $h$ is the number of hours worked and $s$ is total sales. What is the equation solved for $s$?

_____

25. Which values of $u$ and $v$ make $3u^2 + v = 68$ true?

A  $u = -5$ and $v = -7$

B  $u = 5$ and $v = 7$

C  $u = -5$ and $v = 6$

D  $u = -5$ and $v = -6$

26. Is each ordered pair a solution of $y = 7x - 11$?

A  $(-2, -16)$     ○ Yes    ○ No

B  $(17, 4)$     ○ Yes    ○ No

C  $(5, 24)$     ○ Yes    ○ No

27. Which equation matches the graph shown?

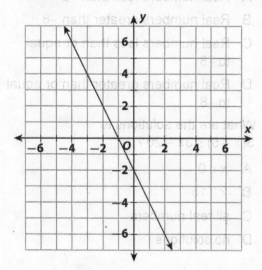

A  $y = 2x - 2$      C  $y = \dfrac{1}{2}x - 2$

B  $y = -\dfrac{1}{2}x + 2$      D  $y = -2x - 2$

28. Which values of $x$ and $y$ make $x^2 = 75 + y$ true?

A  $x = -9$ and $y = 6$

B  $x = 9$ and $y = -6$

C  $x = 8$ and $y = 9$

D  $x = -8$ and $y = -9$

29. Which of the following sets of ordered pairs does **not** describe a function?

A  $\{(7, -2), (5, 0), (3, 3), (1, -2)\}$

B  $\{(7, 2), (5, 4), (3, 6), (1, 8)\}$

C  $\{(7, 2), (7, 0), (3, -2), (1, -4)\}$

D  $\{(7, 7), (5, 5), (3, 3), (1, 1)\}$

30. What is the range of the relation represented on the mapping diagram?

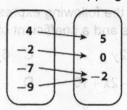

_____

31. The recursive rule of a sequence is $f(n) = f(n - 1) - 6$. If the first term is 20, what is the fourth term of the sequence?

_____

# Benchmark Test Modules 1–5

32. What is the product of 75.0 feet and 2.05 feet written with the correct number of significant digits?

_____

33. Turtles can swim at a speed of 0.2 miles per minute. To the nearest whole number, find the speed of a turtle in kilometers per hour.

_____

34. Simplify $125^{\frac{1}{3}}$.

_____

35. The side length of the base a square prism with a height of 18 centimeters can be found with the equation $b = \left(\dfrac{v}{18}\right)^{\frac{1}{2}}$ where $v$ is the volume of the prism. Find the side length of the base if the volume of the prism is 3,042 cubic centimeters.

_____

36. List the sets that the following numbers belong to. Use the following sets: whole numbers, integers, rational numbers, irrational numbers, and real numbers.
   −13

_____

   $\pi$

_____

37. Evaluate $25 - 2(x^2 + 5)$ for $x = 6$.

_____

38. Simplify $7z + 19 + z^2 - 8z + 5$.

_____

39. Solve $17(9 - x) - 50 = 52$.

_____

40. Solve $1.5x - 2 \leq 10$, and graph the solutions on the number line.

_____

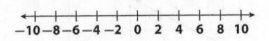

41. Solve $15x + 2 \geq 15x + 25$.

_____

42. Graph the solutions to $f(x) = 4x - 6$.

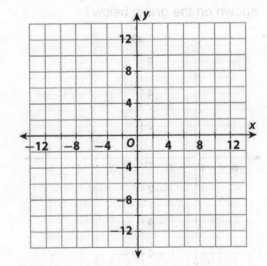

43. Write an explicit rule for the sequence −8, −3, 2, 7.

_____

# Mid-Year Test Modules 6–11

1. What is the *x*-intercept of the line graphed below?

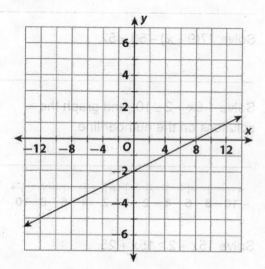

_____

2. What best describes the slope of the line shown on the graph below?

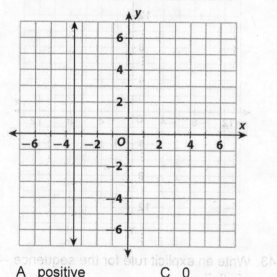

A  positive        C  0

B  negative       D  undefined

3. What is the slope of the line below?

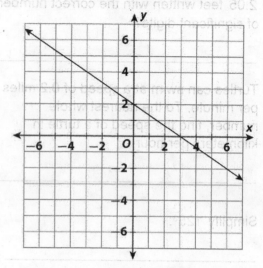

4. Which of the following equations describes a line with an *y*–intercept of 5?

A  $y + 16 = -4x - 21$    C  $y = 5x - 25$

B  $9 + y = 3x + 14$      D  $x - 10 = y + 5$

5. Which equation describes a line that passes through (2, −5) and (6, −3)?

A  $y = -2x - 1$        C  $y = \frac{1}{2}x - 6$

B  $y = -\frac{1}{2}x - 4$     D  $y = 2x - 9$

6. Does each sequence have a common difference of −9?

A  $\frac{1}{81}, \frac{1}{9}, 1, 9, 81, \ldots$

    ○ Yes      ○ No

B  9, 18, 27, 36, 45, …

    ○ Yes      ○ No

C  16, 7, −2, −11, −20, …

    ○ Yes      ○ No

D  4.5, −4.5, −13.5, −22.5, …

    ○ Yes      ○ No

# Mid-Year Test Modules 6–11

7. $f(x) = 18x + 6$, and $g(x) = 21 - 2x$.
   What is $h(x) = f(x) - g(x)$?

   _____

8. Which of the following is the inverse
   of $f(x) = -\dfrac{1}{2}x + 9$?

   A  $f^{-1}(x) = -2x + 18$

   B  $f^{-1}(x) = 2x + 9$

   C  $f^{-1}(x) = 2x - 9$

   D  $f^{-1}(x) = -2x - 18$

9. Which linear inequality is represented on
   the graph?

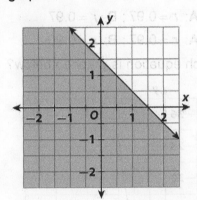

   A  $y \le x + 1.5$         C  $y \le -x + 1.5$

   B  $y \ge -x + 1.5$        D  $y \ge x + 1.5$

10. Is each ordered pair a solution of
    $y \le 5x - 40$?

    A  (8, 0)          ○ Yes      ○ No

    B  (8, –4)         ○ Yes      ○ No

    C  (6, 0)          ○ Yes      ○ No

    D  (6, –12)        ○ Yes      ○ No

11. Which of the following correlation
    coefficients indicates a strong negative
    correlation?

    A  –0.98                    C  0

    B  –0.61                    D  0.89

12. What is the sum of the squared residuals
    based on the data shown on the table?

| $y = -0.75x + 14$ | | |
|---|---|---|
| $x$ | $y$ (actual) | $y$ (predicted) |
| 0 | 13.5 | 14 |
| 2 | 11.5 | 12.5 |
| 4 | 11 | 11 |
| 6 | 9.8 | 9.5 |

    _____

13. How many solutions does the system
    $$\begin{cases} 12x = y - 5 \\ \dfrac{1}{2}y = 6x - \dfrac{5}{9} \end{cases}$$ have?

    A  none               C  exactly two

    B  exactly one        D  infinitely many

14. What is the solution to the system
    $$\begin{cases} 3y = 5x + 22 \\ y = -5x + 8 \end{cases}?$$

    _____

15. Is each ordered pair a solution to the
    system $\begin{cases} y + 7 < -5x \\ y \ge -4.5x - 10 \end{cases}?$

    A  (–1, –2)         ○ Yes      ○ No

    B  (–1, –5)         ○ Yes      ○ No

    C  (–2, –1)         ○ Yes      ○ No

    D  (–2, 3)          ○ Yes      ○ No

# Mid-Year Test Modules 6–11

16. Which set of ordered pairs satisfies an exponential equation?

   A   $\{(0,\ 5),(1,\ 8),(2,\ 11),(3,\ 14)\}$

   B   $\{(0,\ 3),(1,\ 9),(2,\ 27),(3,\ 81)\}$

   C   $\{(0,\ 0),(1,\ 1),(2,\ 4),(3,\ 9)\}$

   D   $\{(0,\ -2),(1,\ 4),(2,\ -6),(3,\ -8)\}$

17. The Twisted River had approximately 5,300 Chinook salmon in 2008. The population has been decreasing at a rate of 8% per year. Write a function that gives the population in terms of $y$ years after 2008.

   _____

18. What is the tenth term of the geometric sequence $-\dfrac{1}{16},\ \dfrac{1}{4},\ -1,\ 4,\ ...$?

   _____

19. Solve $27^2 = 3^{5+x}$. What is the value of $x$?

   _____

20. $g(x) = 5^x$, and $h(x) = \dfrac{1}{3} \times 5^x$. Choose True or False for each statement.

   A   $h(x)$ is greater than $g(x)$ for all values of x except for 0

   ○ True        ○ False

   B   $g(x)$ is greater than $h(x)$ for all values of x except for 0

   ○ True        ○ False

   C   $h(x)$ is greater than $g(x)$ for all values of x

   ○ True        ○ False

   D   $g(x)$ is greater than $h(x)$ for all values of x

   ○ True        ○ False

21. Which regression equation best fits the data shown on the table?

| x | 0 | 1 | 2 | 3 |
|---|---|---|---|---|
| y | 2.5 | 17.0 | 178.2 | 1,305.4 |

   A   $y \approx 2.4(8.3)^x$         C   $y \approx 8.3(2.4)^x$

   B   $y \approx 8.3^x$              D   $y \approx 2.4^x$

22. Regression equation **A** is $y = 12 \times 4^x$. Regression equation **B** is $y = 2x^3$. Which of the following describes a situation in which the exponential regression equation better fits the data?

   A   **A**: $r = 0.87$; **B**: $r = 0.93$

   B   **A**: $r = 0.89$; **B**: $r = 0.99$

   C   **A**: $r = 0.97$; **B**: $r = 0.97$

   D   **A**: $r = 0.97$; **B**: $r = 0.90$

23. Which equation is graphed below?

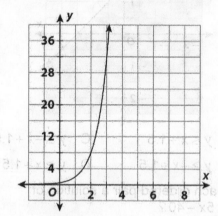

   A   $f(x) = \dfrac{1}{2} \times 4^x$         C   $f(x) = \dfrac{1}{2} \times 2^x$

   B   $y = 2 \times 2^x$              D   $y = 2 \times 4^x$

# Mid-Year Test Modules 6–11

24. Graph and label $x = -3$ and $y = 0.5$.

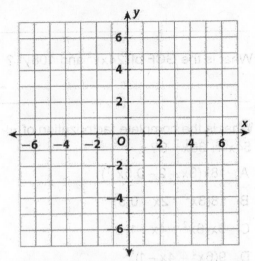

25. Write an equation in standard form for a line with a slope of –6 that includes the point (3, 2).

_____

26. The table below shows the relationship between the number of hours Rhonda works and the amount she is paid.

| Hours (x) | 4 | 6 | 8 | 10 |
|-----------|-----|-----|-----|-----|
| Pay (y) | $122 | $158 | $194 | $230 |

Write a linear equation that describes the relationship in terms of x and y.

_____

27. Write a recursive rule for the sequence $-8, -12, -16, -20, \ldots$.

_____

28. Meredith has $5.10 in quarters and dimes. She has 24 coins in all. To find how many quarters and dimes she has, write and solve a system of equations.

_____

29.

| Age (yrs) | 28 | 36 | 42 | 48 | 56 |
|-----------|-----|-----|-----|-----|-----|
| Annual salary (in thousands) | 32 | 40 | 39 | 42 | 46 |

The table above shows the age and salary of employees at a clothing store. Draw a scatter plot and trend line for the data.

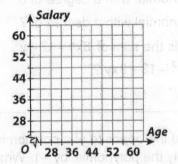

30. Solve $8 \times 5^x = 1{,}000$.

_____

31. Louisa has $4,500 in her savings account. She has to choose between two savings plans. Under plan A, she will increase her account balance by 10% per year. Under plan B, her account balance will increase by $525 per year.
If she plans to keep her money in savings for 3 years, which plan should she choose? How much more will she save under that plan?

_____

# Benchmark Test Modules 12–16

1. Which monomial has a degree of 5?

   A  $5x^3y$          C  $-9xy^2z^2$

   B  $12xy^2z$        D  $8x^2y^3z$

2. Which is the correct classification of $6x^4y^2z + 7xy$?

   A  binomial with a degree of 6

   B  binomial with a degree of 7

   C  trinomial with a degree of 6

   D  trinomial with a degree of 7

3. What is the sum of $8x^2 + 12 - y^2$ and $x^2 - 13 + 8xy$?

   _____

4. To find the opposite of a polynomial, multiply the polynomial by −1. What is the opposite of $14xy - 6x + 12$?

   _____

5. Does each polynomial represent the area of the rectangle shown below?

   ```
   ┌─────────────────┐
   │                 │ 2x in.
   └─────────────────┘
       8x − 2.5 in.
   ```

   A  $16x^2 - 5x$ in$^2$       ○ Yes   ○ No

   B  $4(5x - 1.25)$ in$^2$     ○ Yes   ○ No

   C  $20x - 5$ in$^2$          ○ Yes   ○ No

   D  $5(3.2x^2 - x)$ in$^2$    ○ Yes   ○ No

6. What is the product of $(x - 15)(x + 15)$?

   _____

7. What is the GCF of $24xy^2$ and $108y^3$?

   _____

8. What is the complete factorization of $54x^2 + 36x - 9$?

   A  $18x(3x + 2 - 0.5x^{-1})$

   B  $18(3x^2 + 2x - 0.5)$

   C  $9x(6x^2 + 4x - 1)$

   D  $9(6x^2 + 4x - 1)$

9. What is the correct factorization of $x^2 - 9x - 36$?

   A  $(x - 12)(x + 3)$

   B  $(x + 9)(x - 4)$

   C  $(x + 12)(x - 3)$

   D  $(x - 9)(x + 4)$

10. What is the correct factorization of $8xy - 16x + 2y - y^2$?

   A  $(8x - y)(y - 2)^2$

   B  $(8x - y)(y - 2)$

   C  $(8x + y)(y - 2)$

   D  $(8x + y)(y + 2)$

# Benchmark Test Modules 12–16

11. Does each value of $c$ make $4x^2 + 12x + c$ factorable?

    A  −16    ○ Yes   ○ No

    B  −8     ○ Yes   ○ No

    C  5      ○ Yes   ○ No

    D  7      ○ Yes   ○ No

12. What is the complete factorization of $x^4 - 16$?

    _____

13. Which statement best describes the data distribution shown on the dot plots below?

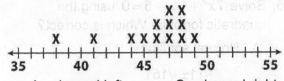

    A  skewed left       C  skewed right

    B  symmetric         D  bimodal

14.

| What types of music do you like? | | | |
|---|---|---|---|
| | Classical | | |
| Pop | Yes | No | Total |
| Yes | 102 | 62 | 164 |
| No | 35 | 81 | 116 |
| Total | 137 | 143 | 280 |

What is the joint relative frequency that a person surveyed likes Classical music and Pop music?

_____

15. For the set {−12, −12, −4, 8, 16, 20}, would each measure be affected if the value of 22 were included?

    A  mode     ○ Yes   ○ No

    B  median   ○ Yes   ○ No

    C  mean     ○ Yes   ○ No

    D  range    ○ Yes   ○ No

16. What is the mean and standard deviation of the data set {32, 35, 35, 45, 49, 50}?

    A  mean: 41; standard deviation: 7.2

    B  mean: 39.2; standard deviation: 6.4

    C  mean: 39.2; standard deviation: 7.2

    D  mean: 41; standard deviation: 6.4

17. What is the interquartile range of the data represented on the plot below?

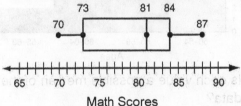

    Math Scores

18. The histogram below represents the fuel economy of a company's fleet of vehicles.

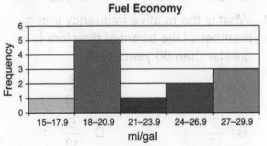

What is the relative frequency that the fuel economy of a car from the fleet is between 27 and 29.9 miles per gallon?

    A  $\dfrac{1}{12}$        C  $\dfrac{1}{5}$

    B  $\dfrac{1}{10}$        D  $\dfrac{1}{4}$

19. The amount of cereal in a carton is listed as 24 ounces. The cartons are filled by machine, and the amount filled follows a normal distribution with a mean of 24 ounces and standard deviation of 0.3 ounces.

What is the probability that a carton of cereal contains between 24 ounces and 24.6 ounces?

A  81.5%          C  47.5%

B  49%            D  13.5%

**For 20–21, refer to the histogram below.**

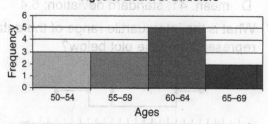

20. Is each value a possible median of the data?

A  57          ○ Yes   ○ No

B  59          ○ Yes   ○ No

C  62          ○ Yes   ○ No

D  64          ○ Yes   ○ No

21. What is the relative frequency that a member of the board of directors is greater than 60 years old?

A  $\dfrac{1}{6}$          C  $\dfrac{7}{13}$

B  $\dfrac{3}{13}$          D  $\dfrac{6}{13}$

22. What are the solutions of $3x^2 + 24x = 0$?

A  $x = 0$

B  $x = 0$ or $x = -8$

C  $x = -8$ or $x = 8$

D  $x = 0$ or $x = 8$

23. Solve $81x^2 - 9 = 0$ for $x$.

_____

24. Use factorization to solve
$4x^2 - 28x + 49 = 0$ for $x$.

_____

25. Solve $7x^2 + 11x - 5 = 0$ using the quadratic formula. Which is correct?

A  No real solutions

B  $x = \dfrac{-11 \pm \sqrt{151}}{14}$

C  $x = \dfrac{-11 \pm \sqrt{261}}{14}$

D  $x = \dfrac{11 \pm \sqrt{140}}{14}$

26. What is the discriminant of $-2x^2 + 14x - 10$, and how many real solutions does the equation have?

_____

# Benchmark Test Modules 12–16

27. Simplify:
$(7m^2n + 12m - 45) - (6mn^2 + 20m + 17)$

_____

28. Find the product of –5 and
$23r^2s - 8r + 11$.

_____

29. Simplify $(6x - 5)^2$.

_____

30. Factor $24st^2 + 66st$.

_____

31. Factor $-10 - 5x + 2y + xy$.

_____

32. Factor $25z^4 - 100$.

_____

33. The area of a square is $x^2 - 6x + 9$ square centimeters. Find a side length of the square.

_____

34. Ana interviewed 125 people to see if they liked jogging. 35 of the people surveyed were males. 54 females like jogging and 23 males liked jogging.

What is the conditional frequency that a person does not like jogging given that the person is a female?

_____

35. a. Complete the frequency table.

| Gender | Preferred Pet | | | |
|--------|-----|-----|------|-------|
|        | Dog | Cat | Fish | Total |
| Male   |     | 197 | 16   | 323   |
| Female | 180 |     | 12   |       |
| Total  | 290 |     |      | 565   |

b. How many males prefer dogs?

_____

c. How many females do not prefer cats?

_____

36. Mindy conducted a survey to find the eye colors of her neighbors.
Use the following information to complete the frequency table.

– She surveyed 36 children,
28 teenagers, and 23 adults.

– Five adults had blue eyes, and six adults had hazel eyes.

– Eight teenagers had green eyes.

– No teenagers had hazel eyes.

– The same number of teenagers had green eyes as blue eyes.

– In all 33 people had brown eyes.

|          | Blue | Green | Hazel | Brown |
|----------|------|-------|-------|-------|
| Child    | 6    | 5     | 10    | 15    |
| Teenager |      |       |       |       |
| Adult    |      |       |       |       |

# End-of-Year Test Modules 1–19

1. Which measurement is the most precise?

   A  5.52 m      C  5.516 m

   B  552 cm      D  550 cm

2. A rectangle has a length of 3.750 inches and a width of 1.52 inches What is the perimeter of the rectangle with the correct number of significant digits?

   _____

3. Duncan's dog weighs 25.5 pounds. Approximately how many kilograms does the dog weight?

   A  11.6 kg      C  25.5 kg

   B  12.8 kg      D  56.1 kg

4. A van is traveling 1.5 kilometers per minute. Approximately how fast is the van traveling in miles per hour?

   _____

5. Is each of the following expressions equivalent to $p^5 \times p^{-3}$?

   A  $p^{-2} \times p^4$    ○ Yes   ○ No

   B  $p^{-5} \times p^3$    ○ Yes   ○ No

   C  $p^2$         ○ Yes   ○ No

   D  $p^8$         ○ Yes   ○ No

6. Which of the following expressions is equivalent to $x^{\frac{2}{7}}$?

   A  $\sqrt[2]{x^7}$      C  $\sqrt[7]{x^2}$

   B  $\dfrac{x^2}{x^7}$      D  $x^{-5}$

7. Which set is closed under multiplication?

   A  {2}      C  {−1, 0}

   B  {−1, 0, 1}      D  {−2, −1, 0, 1, 2}

8. Which set does **not** contain any irrational numbers?

   A  $\left\{ -\dfrac{2}{3}, \sqrt{9}, -\sqrt{121} \right\}$

   B  $\{ -1.05, 7, \pi \}$

   C  $\left\{ \dfrac{1}{9}, \sqrt{11}, 18 \right\}$

   D  $\left\{ \sqrt{16}, \sqrt{20}, 100 \right\}$

9. What is $5(x-14)+20$ evaluated for $x = -4$?

   _____

10. What is $9r - 4s - 27$ evaluated for $r = 5$ and $s = -2$?

    _____

11. Which expression is equivalent to $15x + 8y$?

    A  $5(3x + y) - 3y$

    B  $15x - 2y - 10$

    C  $3(5x + 2y) + 2y$

    D  $10(x + y) + 5y - 2x$

12. Franco has $x$ quarters, 12 one-dollar bills and half as many ten-dollar bills as quarters. Which expression represents the amount of money Franco has?

    A  $20.25x + 12$

    B  $10.25x + 12$

    C  $5.25x + 12$

    D  $0.25x + 10x + 12$

13. Solve $6 - 1.5x = 24$. What is the solution?

    _____

# End-of-Year Test Modules 1–19

14. Which is the solution to
$9q + 24 = 3(3q - 4)$?

   A $q = -2$

   B $q = 2$

   C no solution

   D $q$ is all real numbers

15. Which graph best represents the
solutions of $-12x \leq 90$?

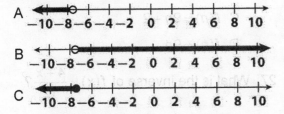

16. The formula a university uses to charge
tuition is $T = \$500h - \$275$ where $h$ is the
number of class hours a student is taking.
What is the formula solved for $h$?

_____

17. Which ordered pair is **not** a solution to
the equation $y = \dfrac{x}{2} - 12$?

   A $(-6, -15)$        C $(0, -12)$

   B $(-4, 16)$          D $(26, 1)$

18.

| $x$ | $-2$ | $-1$ | 0 | 1 |
|-----|------|------|---|---|
| $y$ | $-2$ | 3 | 8 | 13 |

Which equation matches the solutions in
the table of values above?

   A $y = -4 - x$        C $5x = y - 8$

   B $4y + 6 = x$        D $8x + 14 = y$

19. Which equation is graphed below?

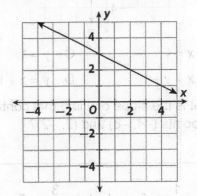

   A $y = \dfrac{1}{2}x + 3$        C $y = -\dfrac{1}{2}x + 3$

   B $y = 2x + 3$          D $y = -2x + 3$

20. What is the fourth term of a sequence
with the recursive rule $f(n) = -2f(n - 1)$;
$f(1) = -3.5$?

_____

21. What are the $x-$ and $y-$intercepts of
$7x - \dfrac{7}{2}y = -49$?

   A $x-$intercept: $-7$; $y-$intercept: $-14$

   B $x-$intercept: $-7$; $y-$intercept: 14

   C $x-$intercept: 14; $y-$intercept: $-7$

   D $x-$intercept: 14; $y-$intercept: 7

# End-of-Year Test Modules 1–19

**22.** Which equation is graphed below?

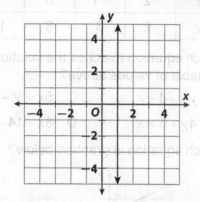

A  $x = 1$      C  $y = 1$

B  $x = y + 1$      D  $y = x + 1$

**23.** What is the slope of a line that contains the points $(-4, -8)$ and $(2, -2)$?

_____

**24.** $f(x) = \dfrac{1}{3}x + 5$, and $g(x) = \dfrac{3}{4}x + 5$.

Choose True or False for each statement.

A  $f(x)$ has a steeper slope than $g(x)$.

     O True      O False

B  $g(x)$ has a steeper slope than $f(x)$.

     O True      O False

C  $f(x)$ has a greater $x$-intercept than $g(x)$.

     O True      O False

D  $g(x)$ has a greater $x$-intercept than $f(x)$.

     O True      O False

**25.** $s(x) = 22x - 8$, and $t(x) = -5$.
What is $s(x) \times t(x)$?

A  $22x - 13$      C  $-110x - 8$

B  $17x - 13$      D  $-110x + 40$

**26.** Which of the following rules for an arithmetic sequence match the pay scale represented on the table below?

| Hours of work | 1 | 2 | 3 | 4 |
|---|---|---|---|---|
| Pay | $11 | $20 | $29 | $38 |

A  $f(n) = 9n + 20$

B  $f(n) = 9n + 11$

C  $f(n) = 9n + 2$

D  $f(n) = 9n$

**27.** What is the inverse of $f(x) = \dfrac{4 + x}{12}$?

_____

**28.** Does each linear inequality have the ordered pair $(0, 8)$ as a solution?

A  $y < -4x + 32$      O Yes    O No

B  $y + 4 \leq \dfrac{x}{2} + 10$      O Yes    O No

C  $y > -2x + 17$      O Yes    O No

D  $y + 6 \geq x + 14$      O Yes    O No

**29.** Which type of correlation best describes the data represented on the table below?

| Price of stock over time | | | | |
|---|---|---|---|---|
| 1998 | 2002 | 2006 | 2010 | 2014 |
| $21 | $22 | $20 | $17 | $14 |

A  Strong positive

B  Negative

C  Positive

D  None

# End-of-Year Test Modules 1–19

30. What is the correlation coefficient based on the scatterplot below?

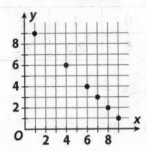

   A  −1            C  0

   B  −0.85         D  1

31. What is the best prediction for the number of runners in 2016?

| Year | '12 | '13 | '14 | '15 |
|---|---|---|---|---|
| Number of Runners | 61 | 70 | 75 | 82 |

   A  83            C  92

   B  89            D  98

32. The squared residuals of lines of fit **A** and **B** are calculated. Line **A** better fits the data. Which of the following could be true?

   A  The sum of the squared residuals of **A** and **B** is 1.25.

   B  The sum of the squared residuals of **A** is 1 and the sum of the squared residuals of **B** is 0.25.

   C  The sum of the squared residuals of **A** is 0.82 and the sum of the squared residuals of **B** is 1.01.

   D  The sum of the squared residuals of **A** is 4.5 and the sum of the squared residuals of **B** is 2.8.

33. How many solutions does the system of equations graphed below have?

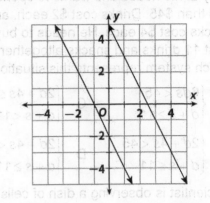

34. Which equation would make this system have an infinite number of solutions?

$$\begin{cases} y = x + 2 \\ \underline{\hspace{2cm}} \end{cases}$$

   A  $2y = 2x + 2$       C  $y = 2x$

   B  $y - 2 = x$         D  $y = 3x - 1$

35. Which ordered pair is not a solution of the system graphed below?

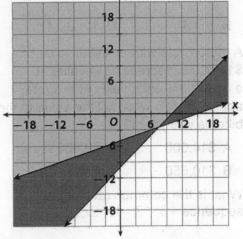

   A  (−5, −10)       C  (0, −4)

   B  (−4, −12)       D  (12, 0)

# End-of-Year Test Modules 1–19

36. Alex is buying drinks and snacks for a party at his house and wants to spend less than $45. Drinks cost $2 each, and snacks cost $4 each. He needs to buy at least 11 drinks and snacks altogether. Which system represents this situation?

A $\begin{cases} 6ds < 45 \\ d+s \geq 11 \end{cases}$    C $\begin{cases} 2d+4s \leq 45 \\ d+s < 11 \end{cases}$

B $\begin{cases} 2d+4s < 45 \\ d+s \leq 11 \end{cases}$    D $\begin{cases} 2d+4s < 45 \\ d+s \geq 11 \end{cases}$

37. A scientist is observing a dish of cells. The dish contains six cells that are splitting every second. Which function best represents this situation?

A $f(x) = 6 \times 2^x$    C $f(x) = 2 \times 6^x$

B $f(x) = 6^x$    D $f(x) = 2^x$

38. The ordered pairs $\left(-3, \dfrac{1}{2}\right)$ and (2, 16) are solutions to an exponential equation. What is the equation?

A $y = \dfrac{8^x}{4}$    C $y = 4(2)^x$

B $y = 4^x$    D $y = 32(4)^x$

39. A motorcycle with an initial value of $14,000 is decreasing in value at a rate of 3% each year. At this rate, approximately what will the value of the bike be in 9 years?

A $14,000    C $9,800

B $10,650    D $550

40. What is the common ratio of the sequence −8, 12, −18, 27, ... ?

_____

41. Which regression equation best fits the data shown on the table?

| x | 0 | 1 | 2 | 3 |
|---|---|---|---|---|
| y | 5 | 2.3 | 1.3 | 0.63 |

A $y \approx 5.2 \times \left(\dfrac{1}{4}\right)^x$

B $y \approx 5.1 \times 2^x$

C $y \approx 5 \times \left(\dfrac{3}{2}\right)^x$

D $y \approx 4.8 \times \left(\dfrac{1}{2}\right)^x$

42. The regression equation for a set of data is $y = \dfrac{3^x}{4}$. The observed value of $y$ when $x = 3$ is 6.7. What is the residual?

A −0.05    C 0.05

B −0.5    D 0.5

43. Would each of the following data sets be best described by an exponential model?

A {(2, 4), (3, 9), (4, 16), (5, 25)}
   O Yes    O No

B {(−2, −1), (−3, 0), (−4, 1), (−5, 0)}
   O Yes    O No

C {(2, 64), (3, 16), (4, 4), (5, 1)}
   O Yes    O No

44. Is each of the following polynomials a trinomial with a degree of 6?

A $3x^4y^2 - 5x^2$    O Yes    O No

B $-x^6 + 5x^2 - 3$    O Yes    O No

C $10x^3y^2 - 7x - 9y$    O Yes    O No

D $-7xy^5 + 15x - 11$    O Yes    O No

45. What is the sum of $(32rs + 9r - 15)$ and $(-17rs - 18s + 12)$?

_____

# End-of-Year Test Modules 1–19

46. What is the area of the square modeled below?

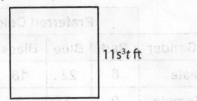

$11s^3t$ ft

_____

47. What is the product of $2x-15$ and $2x+15$?

   A  $2x^2-225$

   B  $4x^2-225$

   C  $4x^2+225$

   D  $4x^2-30x+225$

48. What is the GCF of $28m^3n^3$ and $84mn^4$?

_____

49. What is the complete factorization of $-12x^3+18xy-42x$?

_____

50. What is the complete factorization of $9x^2-60x+100$?

   A  $(3x-10)(3x+10)$

   B  $(3x-10)^2$

   C  $(3x+10)^2$

   D  $(9x-10)(x-10)$

51. Which function is graphed below?

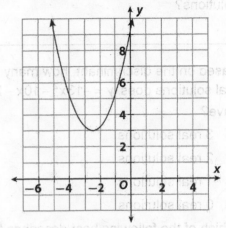

   A  $f(x)=(x-2.5)^2+3$

   B  $f(x)=(x-2.5)^2-3$

   C  $f(x)=(x+2.5)^2+3$

   D  $f(x)=(x+2.5)^2-3$

52. What is the vertex of the graph of $y=-3x^2-6$?

_____

53. Does $f(x)=x^2+4x$ have a maximum or minimum value, and what is the value?

   A  Maximum: –4

   B  Minimum: –4

   C  Maximum: 0

   D  Minimum: 0

54. What are the solutions to $(x-3)^2+8=12$?

_____

# End-of-Year Test Modules 1–19

55. Solve $x^2 + 14x = -48$. What are the solutions?

    _____

56. Based on the discriminant, how many real solutions does $y = -13x^2 - 10x - 2$ have?

    A  3 real solutions

    B  2 real solutions

    C  1 real solutions

    D  0 real solutions

57. Which of the following best describes the end behavior of $f(x) = -x^2 + 2x - 8$?

    A  As $x \to \infty$, $f(x) \to -\infty$;
       As $x \to -\infty$, $f(x) \to -\infty$

    B  As $x \to \infty$, $f(x) \to -\infty$;
       As $x \to -\infty$, $f(x) \to \infty$

    C  As $x \to \infty$, $f(x) \to \infty$;
       As $x \to -\infty$, $f(x) \to -\infty$

    D  As $x \to \infty$, $f(x) \to \infty$;
       As $x \to -\infty$, $f(x) \to \infty$

58. Is each ordered pair a solution to the system: $\begin{cases} y = 2x^2 + 4 \\ y = x + 5 \end{cases}$?

    A  (−0.5, 4.5)      ○ Yes    ○ No

    B  (0.5, 4.5)       ○ Yes    ○ No

    C  (1, 4)           ○ Yes    ○ No

    D  (1, 6)           ○ Yes    ○ No

59. The following is a frequency table from a survey of 90 elementary school students.

| Gender | Preferred Color | | | |
|---|---|---|---|---|
| | Red | Blue | Black | Total |
| Male | 6 | 22 | 18 | 42 |
| Female | 9 | ? | ? | 48 |
| Total | 15 | 36 | 39 | 90 |

How many female students preferred black?

_____

60. The frequency table below shows a survey about whether people have a pet.

| Age in years | Do they have a pet? | |
|---|---|---|
| | Yes | No |
| 21–35 | 20 | 8 |
| 36–50 | 10 | 12 |
| 51–65 | 21 | 4 |

What was the joint relative frequency that a person surveyed was 51–65 years old and owned a pet?

_____

61. Given that the outlier 73 is added to the set {21, 25, 18, 23, 20, 16}, choose True or False for each of the following.

    A  The range increases by 55.
       ○ True      ○ False

    B  The range increases by 48.
       ○ True      ○ False

    C  The mean increases by 28.
       ○ True      ○ False

    D  The mean increases by 7.5.
       ○ True      ○ False

# End-of-Year Test Modules 1–19

62. What is $y = [x] - 12$ evaluated for $x = -0.6$?

_____

63. What is the vertex of the graph of $y = -2|x - 4| + 11$, and is it a maximum or a minimum?

_____

64. Which is not a one–to–one function?

A $f(x) = -5\sqrt{x}$    C $f(x) = x^2 - 7x$

B $f(x) = \sqrt[3]{x} + 1$    D $f(x) = x + 12$

65. Which is a one–to–one function?

A $f(x) = 3x^2$     C $f(x) = 10x^3$

B $f(x) = 2|x| + 2$    D $f(x) = [x]$

66. Which equation is graphed below?

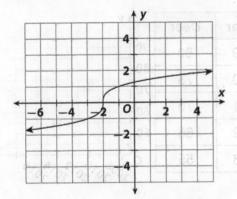

A $y = (x + 2)^3$     C $y = \sqrt[3]{x - 2}$

B $y = (x - 2)^3$     D $y = \sqrt[3]{x + 2}$

67. How many significant digits does 1,020 mm have?

68. Find the approximate perimeter of the triangle modeled below to the nearest centimeter.

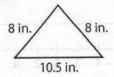

8 in.        8 in.

10.5 in.

_____

69. Simplify the expression $8^2 - 27^{\frac{2}{3}}$.

_____

70. The population of a town can be represented with the formula

$P = 20,000(1.21)^{\frac{t}{3}}$ where $t$ is the number of years since 2012. Find the population of the town in 2014.

_____

71. Monday, Meghan earned $16 per hour for $m$ hours of work. Tuesday, she earned $20 per hour for $t$ hours of work. She also got a $75 bonus. Write an expression to represent how much Meghan earned in total.

_____

72. Simplify $7(x + 11y) - 15(x - y)$.

_____

73. Solve $-8t + 16 = 7(10 - 8t)$. Write the answer as a mixed number.

_____

# End-of-Year Test Modules 1–19

74. Solve the inequality $-\dfrac{3}{4} < \dfrac{y}{8} - \dfrac{5}{4}$, and graph the solution.

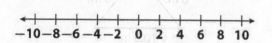

75. Complete the table of value for the equation $y = \dfrac{-3x}{10}$.

| x | 0 | 2 | 4 | 6 |
|---|---|---|---|---|
| y |   |   |   |   |

76. Graph the functions $h(x) = -x + 1$. and $g(x) = 2x - 5$, and determine when $h(x) = g(x)$.

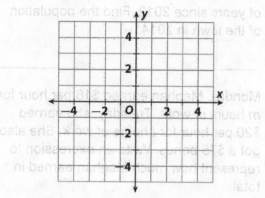

77. Write an equation in slope–intercept for a line with a $y$–intercept of $-1$ that contains the point $(-4, -18)$.

78. Write a recursive rule for the arithmetic sequence 22, 15, 8, 1, ….

79. Write the inequality shown on the graph below.

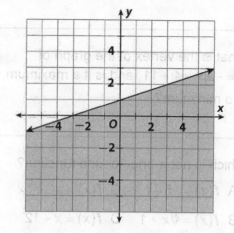

80. The table below shows the number of deer in a certain forest over five years. Draw a scatter plot and trend line.

| Year | Deer |
|------|------|
| '09 | 80 |
| '10 | 78 |
| '11 | 70 |
| '12 | 66 |
| '13 | 55 |

81. Solve $\begin{cases} 2y = 3x + 4 \\ 3y - 2x = -4 \end{cases}$

82. Solve $\begin{cases} 6y = 6x - 40 \\ 4y = 12x + 48 \end{cases}$.

# End-of-Year Test Modules 1–19

83. $f(x)$ is $g(x)$ translated 4 units down. Use the graph of $g(x)$ below to write $f(x)$.

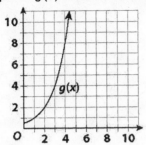

_____

84. $81^4 = 3^{-y+7}$. What is the value of $y$?

_____

85. Multiply $6xyz(x^2 - 14yz^3)$.

_____

86. Factor $8x^2 + 22x - 40$.

_____

87. Determine which of the following polynomials is a difference of squares and factor that polynomial: $4x^2 - 8$, $9x^3 - 100$, or $25x^4 - 1$?

_____

88. A quadratic equation with a vertex at $(-3, 5)$ contains the point $(2, -10)$. Write the equation.

_____

89. Find the zeros and axis of symmetry of the graph of $f(x) = x^2 - 16x + 64$.

_____

90. Use the quadratic formula to solve $0 = 8x^2 + 10x - 2$.

_____

91. Graph $y = \begin{cases} 2x & \text{if } x < 1 \\ -\dfrac{1}{3}x + 4 & \text{if } x \geq 1 \end{cases}$.

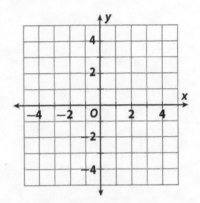

92. Fill in the table of values for $y = -\dfrac{1}{2}|x| + 8$.

| $x$ | $f(x)$ |
|-----|--------|
| –3 | |
| 0 | |
| 3 | |
| 6 | |

93. Find the inverse of $y = 5x^2 + 11$ for $x \geq 0$.

_____

# Answer Key

## *Placement Test*

1. C
2. B
3. D
4. A
5. D
6. A
7. A
8. C
9. A
10. A
11. B
12. C
13. A
14. B
15. A
16. B
17. D
18. B
19. A
20. C
21. B
22. A
23. D
24. C
25. A
26. A
27. B
28. B
29. A

# Answer Key

## Beginning-of-Year Diagnostic Test

1. **D** Correct

   21.25 is the only measurement that includes hundredths of an inch.

   ***TEST PREP DOCTOR:*** Students who answered **A**, **B**, or **C** may not know the meaning of precise.

2. **A** Correct

   The only significant digit is 2, since the 0s are to the right of 2 and do not precede a decimal point.

   ***TEST PREP DOCTOR:*** Students who answered **B**, **C**, or **D** need to review the rules for identifying significant digits.

3. **B** Correct

   30.2 has 3 significant digits, and 12 has 2 significant digits. The sum will have 2 significant digits.

   ***TEST PREP DOCTOR:*** Students who answered **C** need to review the rules for the significant digits in a sum of measurements. Students who answered **A** or **D** did not find the perimeter of the rectangle.

4. **C** Correct

   Multiply 63 by 2.54 to convert inches to centimeters.

   ***TEST PREP DOCTOR:*** Students who answered **B** divided 63 by 2.54. Students who answered **A** or **D** did not multiply or divide correctly.

5. **C** Correct

   Multiply 1 by 0.62, or divide 1 by 1.609 to convert kilometers to miles. Then, multiply by 60 to convert miles per minute to miles per hour.

   ***TEST PREP DOCTOR:*** Students who answered **A** did not convert miles per minute to miles per hour. Students who answered **B** or **D** did not convert kilometers to miles correctly.

6. **C** Correct

   Since the bases are the same, add the exponents to find the product of $x^6$ and $x^2$.

   ***TEST PREP DOCTOR:*** Students who answered **A**, **B**, or **D** need to review the property of exponents for multiplying powers with the same base.

7. **B** Correct

   The cubed root of $y$ is the same as $y$ raised to the power of $\frac{1}{3}$.

   ***TEST PREP DOCTOR:*** Students who answered **A**, **C**, or **D** need to review the relationship between radicals and rational exponents.

8. **D** Correct

   The set $\{-1, 0\}$ is not closed under multiplication. $-1 \times -1 = 1$, and 1 is not included in the set.

   ***TEST PREP DOCTOR:*** Students who answered **A**, **B**, or **C** may not understand what it means for a set to be closed under multiplication.

9. **A** Correct

   The set $\left\{-\frac{2}{5}, \sqrt{16}\right\}$ does not contain any irrational numbers, since $\sqrt{16} = 4$.

   ***TEST PREP DOCTOR:*** Students who answered **B**, **C**, or **D** need to review the definition of an irrational number.

10. C Correct

Multiply 2 by −8 before subtracting the product from 12.

***TEST PREP DOCTOR:*** Students who answered **A** or **D** need to review the order of operations. Students who answered **B** or **D** need to review integer rules of multiplication, subtraction, and addition.

11. B Correct

Multiply 8 by −3 and divide 16 by 2 before subtracting: $-24 - 8 = -32$.

***TEST PREP DOCTOR:*** Students who answered **A** or **D** need to review the order of operations. Students who answered **C** need to review integer rules of subtraction and addition.

12. B Correct

Factor the GCF, 7, from both terms.

***TEST PREP DOCTOR:*** Students who answered **A**, **C**, or **D** need to review factoring and the distributive property.

13. A Correct

Wednesday, Diana made $8y$ dollars. On Thursday, she made $4y$ dollars. Add $45 to the sum of $8y$ and $4y$.

***TEST PREP DOCTOR:*** Students who answered **B** and **C** did not use the correct variable. Students who answered **B** and **D** did not correctly translate the verbal description into an expression.

14. B Correct

Subtract 25 from both sides of the equation to get $4x = 26$. Then, divide both sides of the equation by 4, to get $x = 6.5$.

***TEST PREP DOCTOR:*** Students who answered **A**, **C**, or **D** need to review how to isolate a variable in an equation.

15. D Correct

Distribute on the right side of the equation to get $2x - 8$. Since the right and left sides of the equation are equivalent, the solution is all real numbers.

***TEST PREP DOCTOR:*** Students who answered **A** or **B** need to review how to solve an equation with variables on both sides of the equation. Students who answered **C** need to review the rules for equations with no solution and equations with a solution of all real numbers.

16. A Correct

Divide both sides of the inequality by 8 to get $x \le -6$. The solution will be a ray with a closed circle at −6 that points left.

***TEST PREP DOCTOR:*** Students who answered **B**, **C**, or **D** need to review how to graph solutions to single variable inequalities on a number line.

17. B Correct

Substitute the $x$ value of 3 and $y$ value of 12. These values make $y = 8x - 12$ a true statement.

***TEST PREP DOCTOR:*** Students who answered **A** made a mistake with combining integers. Students who answered **C** or **D** switched the $x$ and $y$ values.

18. A Correct

All the pairs of $x$ values and $y$ values from the table make $y = 2x + 3$ a true statement.

***TEST PREP DOCTOR:*** Students who answered **B**, **C**, or **D** may have made a mistake substituting $x$ and $y$ values from the table into the equations.

19. C Correct

The ordered pairs (2, 3) and (2, 5) have the same $x$-value and different $y$-values, so it is not a function.

**_TEST PREP DOCTOR:_** Students who answered **A** may have thought that a function cannot have different $x$-values that share the same $y$-value. Students who answered **A**, **B**, or **D** need to review the definition of a function.

20. B Correct

The solutions to $f(x) = -2x + 4$, such as (0, 4) and (2, 0), are included in the line on the graph.

**_TEST PREP DOCTOR:_** Students who answered **A**, **C**, or **D** need to review how to find solutions to a function and how to graph ordered pairs.

21. D Correct

The first four terms of the sequence are –3, –6, –12, and –24.

**_TEST PREP DOCTOR:_** Students who answered **A**, **B**, or **C** may not understand how to interpret a recursive rule of a sequence.

22. A Correct

To find the $x$-intercept, set $y = 0$ and solve $-12x + 3y = 48$ for $x$. To find the $y$-intercept, set $x = 0$ and solve $-12x + 3y = 48$ for $y$.

**_TEST PREP DOCTOR:_** Students who answered **C** switched the $x$ and $y$-intercept. Students who answered **B** or **D** need to review how to solve an equation for a variable.

23. C Correct

All of the $y$-values of the line on the graph are –3. Therefore, it's the graph of $y = -3$.

**_TEST PREP DOCTOR:_** Students who answered **A** switched the form of horizontal and vertical linear equations. Students who answered

**B** or **D** need to review equations of vertical and horizontal lines.

24. D Correct

To find the slope, find the quotient of the difference of the $y$-values and the difference of the $x$-values.

**_TEST PREP DOCTOR:_** Students who answered **B** divided the difference of the $x$-values by the difference of the $y$-values. Students who answered **A** or **C** should review how to find the slope of a line given two points.

25. A Correct

The point at which $f(x) = g(x)$ is the point at which the lines intersect when graphed.

**_TEST PREP DOCTOR:_** Students who answered **B** or **D** found an $x$- or $y$-intercept. Students who answered **C** switched the $x$- and $y$-value of the point of intersection of the lines.

26. C Correct

The $y$-intercept of $f(x)$ is 5, and the $y$-intercept of $g(x)$ is –3. The $y$-intercept of $f(x)$ is greater than that of $g(x)$. The slopes are the same.

**_TEST PREP DOCTOR:_** Students who answered **A**, **B**, or **D** should review the parts of a linear equation in slope-intercept form.

27. B Correct

To multiply $x + 5$ by $-7$, distribute $-7$ to both terms of $x + 5$.

**_TEST PREP DOCTOR:_** Students who answered **A**, **C**, or **D** should review the distributive property and how to multiply functions.

28. C Correct

The sequence represented by the table is 25, 35, 45, 55, ... This is an arithmetic function that has a constant difference of 10, and an unwritten 0 term of 15.

**TEST PREP DOCTOR:** Students who answered **B** may have forgotten that the first term has an $n=1$ not 0. Students who answered **A**, **B**, or **D** should review how to write a function as the explicit rule of an arithmetic sequence.

29. **A** Correct

One way to find the inverse of a function is to change the $f(x)$ to $y$ in the original equation and solve for $x$.

**TEST PREP DOCTOR:** Students who answered **B** may have divided both sides of the equation by 7 before adding 12 to both sides. Students who answered **B**, **C**, or **D** need to review how to find the inverse of a function.

30. **C** Correct

When $y > -8x + 32$ is evaluated for (2, 18), the inequality is satisfied. 18 is greater than 16.

**TEST PREP DOCTOR:** Students who answered **A**, **B**, or **D** need to review how to evaluate an inequality.

31. **A** Correct

The correlation coefficient of the data on the table is 0.998, which is indicates that the variables have a strong positive correlation.

**TEST PREP DOCTOR:** Students who answered **B**, **C**, or **D** need to review how to interpret correlation coefficients.

32. **D** Correct

The values are on a straight, positively sloping line. The correlation coefficient is 1.

**TEST PREP DOCTOR:** Students who answered **A**, **B**, or **C** need to review how scatterplots of data relate to various correlation coefficients.

33. **C** Correct

The line of best fit for the data is $y \approx -7.4x + 78.6$ where $x = 0$ to represent the number of years since 2009. Evaluate the equation for $x = 7$ to predict the deer population in 2016.

**TEST PREP DOCTOR:** Students who answered **A**, **B**, or **D** may have misinterpreted the meaning of the $x$ value in the equation of the line of best fit. These students may not have plugged in 7 for $x$.

34. **D** Correct

The sum of the squared residuals is. $0.5^2 + (-1)^2 + 0^2 + 2^2 = 5.25$.

**TEST PREP DOCTOR:** Students who answered **A** may have found the sum of the residuals. The students who answered **B** may have found $(-1)^2$ to be $-1$. The students who answered **C** may have found the sum of the absolute values of the residuals.

35. **B** Correct

When a system of linear equations is graphed and the lines intersect, the system has one answer.

**TEST PREP DOCTOR:** Students who answered **A**, **C**, or **D** need to review how to solve systems of linear equations by graphing.

36. **C** Correct

If the equations in a system of linear equations have the same slope, but are not equivalent, the system has no solution. In this case, the slope is 3.

**TEST PREP DOCTOR:** Students who answered **A**, **B**, or **D** need to review when systems of equations have no solution versus infinitely many solutions or exactly one solution.

37. A Correct

One way to solve this system is to multiply $2y = 4x + 20$ by 2 to get $4y = 8x + 40$. Then, subtract the equations and solve for $x$.

***TEST PREP DOCTOR:*** Students who answered **C** may not have multiplied every term of $2y = 4x + 20$ when multiplying by 2. Students who answered **B**, **C**, or **D** need to practice solving systems of equations by multiplication, combination, or substitution.

38. A Correct

The point $(-4, -2)$ falls in the section of the graph that includes solutions to both inequalities. Therefore, it is a solution to the system.

***TEST PREP DOCTOR:*** Students who answered **B**, **C**, or **D** may not understand when a point is a solution to a system of inequalities.

39. C Correct

Solutions to an exponential equation will have $y$ values that increase by a constant ratio like the set $\{(5, 3), (6, 9), (7, 27), (8, 81)\}$ which has a ratio of 3.

***TEST PREP DOCTOR:*** Students who answered **B** may not have noticed the absence of the $3^3 = 27$ term. Students who answered **A** or **D** need to review the behavior of exponents applied to the same base.

40. D Correct

The mice are doubling in number, so the equation will be exponential with 2 as the base. Since there are originally 4 mice, the function is $f(x) = 4 \times 2^x$.

***TEST PREP DOCTOR:*** Students who answered **A** may have forgotten to consider the four original mice. Students who answered **B** or **C** did not correctly interpret the real–world situation.

41. B Correct

The only equation that has both ordered pairs as solutions is $y = 2.5 \times 2^x$.

***TEST PREP DOCTOR:*** Students who answered **A**, **C**, or **D** did not check that **both** ordered pairs are solutions of the equations.

42. B Correct

One way to solve this exponential growth problem is to evaluate $y = 140,000 \times (1.02)^3$ for $x = 3$, which evaluates to 148,569.

***TEST PREP DOCTOR:*** Students who answered **A** did not use an exponential equation to solve the problem. Students who answered **C** or **D** may have incorrectly written the exponential equation.

43. A Correct

The common ratio for a geometric sequence is the number that is multiplied by each term to get the subsequent term. For this sequence, the common ratio is $-3$.

***TEST PREP DOCTOR:*** Students who answered **B** or **C** may have divided 2 by $-6$ to get the ratio. Students who answered **D** disregarded the changing signs of the integers in the sequence.

44. B Correct

Rewrite the equation so the bases on both sides of the equation are 2. $2^{2(6)} = 2^{3(x-1)}$. With equivalent bases, solve the equation formed by the exponents for $x$.

***TEST PREP DOCTOR:*** Students who answered **A**, **C**, or **D** need to review how to solve exponential equations.

45. **B** Correct

One way to find an exponential regression equation is to use a graphing calculator. Also, the values on the table should be close to the solutions of the equation.

**TEST PREP DOCTOR:** Students who answered **A**, **C**, or **D** need to review what a regression equation is and how to find one on a graphing calculator.

46. **C** Correct

The regression equation evaluated for $x = 2$ is $-95$. To find the residual, subtract $-95$ from the observed value.

**TEST PREP DOCTOR:** Students who answered **B** may have subtracted the observed value from $-95$. Students who answered **A** or **D** may have squared the residual.

47. **B** Correct

A binomial has 2 terms. The degree of a polynomial is the highest sum of the exponents of the variables of the terms of the expression.

**TEST PREP DOCTOR:** Students who answered **A** may not have remembered to add the invisible exponent of 1 with the base $y$. Students who answered **C** or **D** did not remember that a binomial has only 2 terms, while a trinomial has 3 terms.

48. **A** Correct

Combine like terms when adding polynomials.

**TEST PREP DOCTOR:** Students who answered **B**, **C**, or **D** need to practice combining like terms.

49. **A** Correct

To find the area of a rectangle, multiply the length by the width. When multiplying powers, add the exponents. $6 \times 5 = 30$.
$xy \times x^3 y = x^4 y^2$.

**TEST PREP DOCTOR:** Students who answered **D** found the perimeter of the rectangle. Students who answered **B** or **C** need to practice multiplying powers.

50. **C** Correct

When multiplying binomials, use the following pattern of distribution: first terms, outside terms, inside terms, and last terms.

**TEST PREP DOCTOR:** Students who answered **A**, **B**, or **D** need to revisit multiplying binomials and FOILing.

51. **A** Correct

The greatest common factor, or GCF, of 8 and 12 is 4. The greatest common factor of $x^3$ and $x^2 y$ is $x^2$.

**TEST PREP DOCTOR:** Students who answered **C** or **D** found the least common multiple of 8 and 12. Students who answered **B** multiplied the variables together instead of finding the least number of each variable in all the terms.

52. **D** Correct

The GCF of $25x^3$ and $75xy$ is $25x$. Factor $25x$ from both terms.

**TEST PREP DOCTOR:** Students who answered **A**, **B**, or **C** did not completely factor the expression.

53. **A** Correct

To factor $x^2 - 8x + 16$ find factors of 16 whose sum is $-8$, or $-4$ and $-4$. Also, $x^2 - 8x + 16$ is a perfect square trinomial.

**TEST PREP DOCTOR:** Students who answered **B**, **C**, or **D** need to revisit perfect square trinomials.

54. **B** Correct

$9x^4$ and 1 are perfect squares. $9x^4 - 1$ is the difference of squares.

**TEST PREP DOCTOR:** Students who answered **A**, **C**, or **D** need to revisit perfect square trinomials.

55. B Correct

The graph of $y = \frac{1}{2}x^2 + 2$ is a basic parabola that has been moved up 2 units and vertically shrunk. The basic parabola has a vertex at (0, 0), so this parabola has a vertex that is at (0, 2).

***TEST PREP DOCTOR:*** Students who answered **A**, **C**, or **D** need to revisit transformations to quadratic equations.

56. A Correct

The parabola is a parent quadratic function, $f(x) = x^2$ that has been translated right 6 units and reflected over the *x*–axis.

***TEST PREP DOCTOR:*** Students who answered **B** may have thought translations to the right are represented by adding units to *x* instead of subtracting units from *x*. Students who answered **B**, **C**, or **D** need to revisit transformations to quadratic equations.

57. B Correct

$g(x) = (x + 4)^2 - 2$. This function translated up 6 units is $f(x) = (x + 4)^2 + 4$.

***TEST PREP DOCTOR:*** Students who answered **A** may have found $g(x)$, but did not translate it up 6 units. Students who answered **A**, **C**, or **D** need to review transformations of quadratic equations.

58. A Correct

The equation $y = 3x^2 + 2$ has the solutions (0, 2) and (2, 14).

***TEST PREP DOCTOR:*** Students who answered **B**, **C**, or **D** should revisit how to create quadratic functions.

59. D Correct

Find the square root of both sides of the equation which changes the equation to $x - 11 = \pm 7$. Then, add 11 to +7 and −7.

***TEST PREP DOCTOR:*** Students who answered **A** may have forgotten to take the square root of 49. Students who answered **B** and **C** need to revisit how to solve equations with one variable.

60. A Correct

One way to solve this equation is to subtract 30 from both sides and factor $x^2 + 7x - 30$. Set $(x + 10)$ and $(x - 3)$ equal to zero. Solve both equations for *x*.

***TEST PREP DOCTOR:*** Students who answered **D** may have forgotten to set the factors of $x^2 + 7x - 30$ equal to zero. Students who answered **B** and **C** may not have factored correctly.

61. B Correct

To find the discriminant, use $\sqrt{b^2 - 4ac}$ from the quadratic equation. The discriminant is 1. When the discriminant is a positive integer, the quadratic equation has 2 real number solutions.

***TEST PREP DOCTOR:*** Students who answered **A**, **C**, or **D** should revisit how to find the discriminant and how to interpret the discriminant.

62. D Correct

The graph of $f(x) = x^2 - 12$ is a basic parabola that has been translated down 12 units. As the *x* values approach infinity, the *y* values approach infinity. As the *x* values approach negative infinity, the *y* values approach infinity.

***TEST PREP DOCTOR:*** Students who answered **A**, **B**, or **C** should revisit the end behavior of parabolas.

63. B Correct

   The graph of $y = 6$ intersects the parabolic graph of $y = 3(x - 2)^2 + 6$ at (2, 6).

   ***TEST PREP DOCTOR:*** Students who answered **A**, **C**, or **D** should revisit how to graph parabolas and lines and how to solve systems of equations.

64. C Correct

   The rectangle at the intersection of male and blue is 3, and the intersection of female and blue is 9. The difference is 6.

   ***TEST PREP DOCTOR:*** Students who answered **B** or **D** did not subtract as was necessary. Students who answered **A, B** or **D** should revisit how to interpret two–way frequency tables.

65. C Correct

   There were twelve 51–65 years olds that liked cats out of a total of 50 people who were surveyed. $12 \div 50 = 0.24$.

   ***TEST PREP DOCTOR:*** Students who answered **A** may have divided 12 by 100. Students who answered **B** or **D** found the incorrect numbers on the frequency table.

66. A Correct

   To find the mean, add the data and divide by the number of pieces of data. To find the range, subtract the least number, 16, from greatest number, 26.

   ***TEST PREP DOCTOR:*** Students who answered **B** or **C** may have found the maximum value instead of the range. Students who answered **D** may have made an error while calculating the mean.

67. A Correct

   The histogram shows that two ages are from 21 to 25. Six ages are from 26 to 30. One age is from 31 to 35, and one age is from 36 to 40.

   ***TEST PREP DOCTOR:*** Students who answered **B, C,** or **D** may have miscounted or may not understand how to interpret a histogram.

68. C Correct

   The interquartile range is Q3 minus Q1, or $24 - 14 = 10$.

   ***TEST PREP DOCTOR:*** Students who answered **D** may have found the range. Students who answered **A** may have subtracted the minimum value from Q1. Students who answered **B** may have subtracted Q1 from the median.

69. B Correct

   The median annual salary at Alpha is $32,000, and the median annual salary at Beta is $34,000. The median salary at Beta is higher than that at Alpha.

   ***TEST PREP DOCTOR:*** Students who answered **A** may have switched the meaning of mean and median. Also, the box–and–whisker plot does not indicate the number of salaries. Students who answered **A, C,** or **D** should revisit how to compare two sets of data.

70. A Correct

   $y = \lceil x \rceil$ is a least integer equation. Values of $x$ are rounded to the next least integer. In this case, $-7.2$ is changed to $-8$.

   ***TEST PREP DOCTOR:*** Students who answered **D** may have confused the least integer symbols for absolute value symbols. Students who answered **B, C,** or **D** should revisit how to evaluate least integer equations.

71. A Correct

   The equation on the graph is a piecewise function. It is $2x + 4$ when $x$ is less than or equal to 0, and $x - 3$ when $x$ is greater than 0.

**TEST PREP DOCTOR:** Students who answered **B** should revisit the meaning of open and closed dots on a graph. Students who answered **C** or **D** need to revisit how to translate linear graphs into equations.

72. A   Correct

The graph of $y = |x + 5| - 15$ is the absolute value parent function that has been translated 5 units left and 15 units down. The original shape has not been flipped over the $x$–axis, so the vertex is a minimum.

**TEST PREP DOCTOR:** Students who answered **C** need to revist the rules for translating functions. Students who answered **B**, or **D** should revisit the meaning of maximum and minimum.

73. C   Correct

A one-to-one function has a domain and range of all real numbers. $f(x) = x^2 - 13$ has a range of all numbers greater than or equal to $-13$.

**TEST PREP DOCTOR:** Students who answered **A**, **B**, or **D** need to revisit the definition of one-to-one.

74. B   Correct

$y = 3\sqrt{x + 12}$ is the parent graph of a square root equation that has been translated 12 units to the left. The parent graph has a domain of all numbers greater than or equal to 0, so this equation has a domain of all numbers greater than or equal to $-12$.

**TEST PREP DOCTOR:** Students who answered **A**, **C**, or **D** need to revisit how to translate square root functions.

75. D   Correct

The inverse of $f(x) = x^3 + 15$ can be found by changing $f(x)$ to $y$ and solving the new equation for $x$.

**TEST PREP DOCTOR:** Students who answered **A**, **B**, or **C** need to revisit how to find the inverse of a cubic function.

76. D   Correct

The graph shows a cube root function that has been translated 3 units to the left.

**TEST PREP DOCTOR:** Students who answered **A**, **B**, or **C** need to revisit how to translate cube root functions.

# Answer Key
## *Module Quizzes*

## MODULE 1 Relationships Between Quantities

### Module Quiz 1: B

1. C
2. 30.5 cm to 31.5 cm
3. 5
4. A No B Yes C No D No
5. C
6. 45.6 ft
7. 4.9 in.
8. 16 cm
9. A
10. 1 $\frac{kg}{L}$
11. C
12. 1,032 cm$^2$
13. 8 years old
14. a. 41.25; b. 4
15. a. 40; b. 1
16. 53.8 in.
17. 68 in.
18. 14 feet
19. 95 liters
20. 9.5 $\frac{km}{liter}$
21. 7.4 $\frac{km}{h}$
22. 7 in.
23. 19 g

### Module Quiz 1: D

1. B
2. A
3. B
4. C
5. B
6. A

7. C
8. A
9. C
10. A
11. B
12. A
13. 3 years old
14. a. 37.25; b. 4
15. a. 43; b. 2
16. 17.9 in.
17. 67 m$^2$
18. 41 cm
19. 72 liters
20. 8.1 $\frac{km}{L}$
21. 11 $\frac{km}{h}$
22. 15.2 in.
23. 23 m$^2$

## MODULE 2 Exponents and Real Numbers

### Module Quiz 2: B

1. D
2. D
3. A Yes B No C Yes D Yes
4. −8
5. B
6. 500
7. B
8. 1
9. A No B Yes C No D Yes
10. A False B False C True
11. A Yes B Yes C No
12. D
13. A

14. 823 cm$^2$

15. $18^{\frac{1}{3}}$

16. $10 = 1000^{\frac{1}{3}}$

17. 19

18. 64

19. $2,824.25

20. a. irrational numbers, real numbers

b. integers, rational numbers, real numbers

c. rational numbers, real numbers

d. irrational numbers, real numbers

21. a. not closed; $-1-1 = -2$, and $-2$ is not in the set.

b. closed; Every product of every pair is in the set. $-1 \times 0 = 0$; $-1 \times 1 = -1$; $0 \times 1 = 0$; $-1 \times -1 = 1$; $0 \times 0 = 0$; $1 \times 1 = 1$.

## Module Quiz 2: D

1. A
2. C
3. B
4. A
5. B
6. B
7. A
8. C
9. C
10. A
11. C
12. B
13. 70.9 in.
14. $11^{\frac{1}{3}}$
15. $\frac{1}{2}$
16. 14
17. 4
18. $24.00
19. a. whole numbers, integers, rational numbers, real numbers

b. irrational numbers, real numbers

c. integers, rational numbers, real numbers

d. rational numbers, real numbers

20. a. not closed; $-1 + (-1) = -2$, and $-2$ is not in the set.

b. closed; Every quotient of every pair is in the set. $-1 \div 1 = -1$; $1 \div -1 = -1$; $-1 \div -1 = 1$; $1 \div 1 = 1$.

# MODULE 3 Expressions

## Module Quiz 3: B

1. A No B Yes C No D Yes
2. 3
3. D
4. −13
5. 14
6. −24
7. C
8. A
9. A No B No C Yes D Yes
10. D
11. $21y$
12. $9s + 2p$
13. 3
14. 7, −1
15. 29
16. 2
17. a. $8\left(\dfrac{85}{h}\right) + 12$

b. $148

18. 726 miles

19. Possible answer: $-8 + 2y$; $2y - 8$

20. $4x + 5$

21. $42z + y$

22. $10x^2 + 18$

23. a. $0.42x$

b. $0.42x + $1.19y$

## Module Quiz 3: D

1. B
2. B
3. C
4. B
5. C

6. A

7. B

8. B

9. C

10. B

11. 22

12. $3t^2$ and $5t$

13. 66

14. 30

15. $15c + 8$

16. 405 miles

17. Possible answer: $21p - 28$

18. $-3x$

19. $20r - 5s$

20. $-5x^2 + 6x + 4$

21. a. $\$2.50b + \$3.25c$

    b. $\$5.75x$

    c. $\$17.25$

# MODULE 4 Equations and Inequalities in One Variable

## Module Quiz 4: B

1. 7

2. $x = -8$

3. C

4. $m = -11.4$

5. A Yes B No C Yes

6.
    −1 0 1 2 3 4 5 6 7 8 9 10 11 12

7. A False B True C True D True

8. $y \geq \dfrac{1}{2}$

9. B

10. $s = 15r - 2$

11. $6x - 8y$

12. $x = 15$

13. $z = -2$

14. $p = \dfrac{1}{2}$

15. infinitely many solutions

16. a. $\$45 + \$0.25t = \$0.15t + \$70$

    b. $t = 250$; The companies will charge the same amount for 250 text messages in a month.

17. $p > -3$;
    −4 −3 −2 −1 0 1 2 3 4

18. $d \geq -2$;
    −4 −3 −2 −1 0 1 2 3 4

19. $x \leq \dfrac{2}{3}$

20. all real numbers are solutions

21. $80 + 6.25x < 16x$; 9 birdhouses

22. $r = \sqrt{\dfrac{A}{\pi}}$

23. $t = \dfrac{u + 63}{9}$

## Module Quiz 4: D

1. C

2. B

3. A

4. A

5. C

6. C

7. A

8. C

9. C

10. B

11. $7x + 3y$

12. $x = 5$

13. $z = 5$

14. $\dfrac{z}{5} - 7 = -1$

    $\dfrac{z}{5} = \underline{6}$

    $z = \underline{30}$

15. infinitely many solutions

16. a. $x + 2x = 135$

    b. $\$45$

17.
    −4 −3 −2 −1 0 1 2 3 4

18. a. $p > -2$

b.

$$-4\ -3\ -2\ -1\ \ 0\ \ 1\ \ 2\ \ 3\ \ 4$$

19. $17x + 6 \geq 9x - 10$

$\underline{8x} + 6 \geq -10$

$8x \geq \underline{-16}$

$x \geq \underline{-2}$

20. no solutions

21. $115 \geq 90 + x$

22. $b = \dfrac{p - 15}{30}$

23. $t = 5u$

# MODULE 5 Equations in Two Variables and Functions

## Module Quiz 5: B

1. $x = 26$

2. A Yes B No C Yes D No

3. A No B Yes C No D Yes

4. C

5. 13

6. D: {3, 6, 8}

7. A Yes B No C Yes

8. 6

9. 22

10. D

11. $m = 10$

12. $(3, -2)$ is a solution, but $(6, 1)$ is not.

13. a.

| $x$ | $3 - 2x = y$ | $y$ |
|---|---|---|
| $-1$ | $3 - 2(-1) = y$ | 5 |
| 0 | $3 - 2(0) = y$ | 3 |
| 2 | $3 - 2(2) = y$ | $-1$ |
| 4 | $3 - 2(4) = y$ | $-5$ |

b.

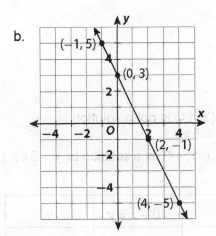

14. $f(4) = 19$

15. a.

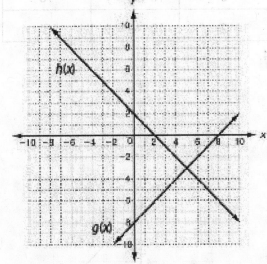

b. $(5, -3)$

16. $\dfrac{1}{6}$

17. 7, 11, 15, 19

18. $f(n) = f(n - 1) - 3$ where $f(1) = 1$

## Module Quiz 5: D

1. A

2. B

3. A

4. B

5. C

6. C

7. A

8. B

9. B

10. A

11. $y = 4$

12. a. No, (3, 14) is not a solution
to $y = 5x + 1$.

b. Yes, (−1, −4) is a solution to $y = 5x + 1$.

13.

| $x$ | $10 - x = y$ | $y$ |
|---|---|---|
| −2 | $10 - (-2) = y$ | 12 |
| 0 | $10 - 0 = y$ | 10 |
| 2 | $10 - 2 = y$ | 8 |

14.

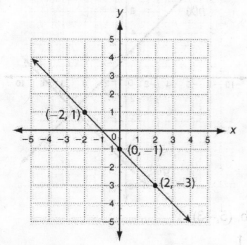

15. $f(3) = 12$

16. Yes, the graph does represent a function, because each $x$-value is matched to one and only one $y$-value.

17. (5, −3)

18. 23

19. 1, −3

20. $f(n) = 7n$ or $f(n) = f(n-1) + 7$ for $f(1) = 7$

# MODULE 6 Linear Functions

## Module Quiz 6: B

1. A Yes B No C Yes D No

2. A Yes B No C No

3. C

4. 2

5. −18

6. A Yes B No C Yes

7. $y = \dfrac{5}{2}x - 3$

8. C

9. $f(-4) = 75$

10. a. $x$-int: 2; $y$-int: −5

b. $\dfrac{5}{2}$

c. $y = \dfrac{5}{2}x - 5$

11.

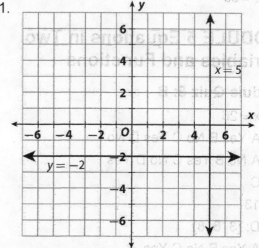

12. Domain: All real numbers; Range: All real numbers

13. $y = \dfrac{3}{5}x + \dfrac{34}{5}$

14. $3x - y = 6$

15. a. $c(x) = 0.5x + 1.5$

b. $g(x) = 0.5x + 0.5$

c.

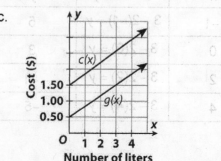

d. $g(x)$ and $c(x)$ have the same slope.
$g(x)$ is $c(x)$ translated down 1 unit.

**Module Quiz 6: D**

1. B
2. C
3. C
4. A
5. A
6. C
7. C
8. B
9. $f(8) = 31$
10. a. –2
    b. 4
    c. 2
    d. $y = 2x + 4$
11. a.

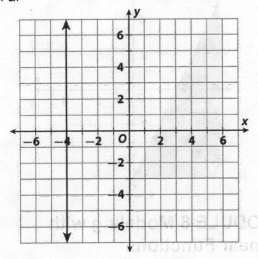

    b. –4
    c. All real numbers
12. $y = -7x + 6$
13. x-int: –16; y-int: –2
14. a.

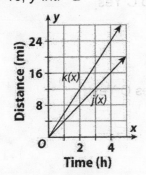

    b. Katherine; 24 miles
    c. $k(x)$

# MODULE 7 Building Linear Functions

## Module Quiz 7: B

1. $\dfrac{4}{5}$
2. A Yes B No C Yes
3. 5
4. $t(d) = 246d + 1{,}200$
5. $3x + 27$
6. $f^{-1}(x) = 8x + 40$
7. $-60x + 15$
8. B
9. A
10. x-int: $4\dfrac{2}{3}$; y-int: 2
11. a. –4, –2, 0, 2, 4, 6
    b. 2
    c. $f(1) = -4$; $f(n) = f(n-1) + 2$
    d. $f(n) = 2n - 6$
12. $s(x) = -\dfrac{5}{2}x + \dfrac{3}{2}$
13. $d(x) = -\dfrac{7}{2}x + \dfrac{23}{2}$
14. $p(x) = 6x - 13$
15. a. $f^{-1}(x) = 4(x - 2) = 4x - 8$
    b.

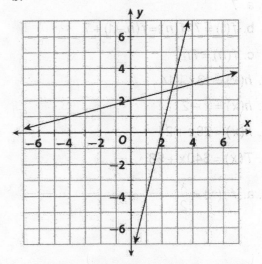

    c. $f(x): (-8, 0), (0, 2)$; $f^{-1}(x): (2, 0), (0, -8)$

16. Yes, $\left(10, -7\frac{1}{2}\right)$ is a solution.

17.

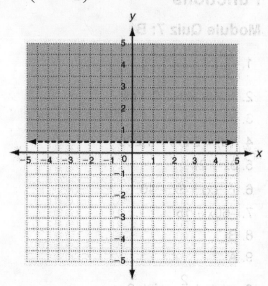

## Module Quiz 7: D

1. B
2. B
3. C
4. B
5. C
6. B
7. C
8. B
9. A

10. x-int: $4\frac{2}{3}$; y-int: $-3$

11. a. 7

    b. $f(1) = 7$; $f(n) = f(n-1) + 7$

    c. $f(n) = 7n$

12. $h(x) = 13x + 14$

13. $h(x) = x - 2$

14. $h(x) = 28x + 24$

15. $T(x) = \$40x + \$8$

16. a. $f^{-1}(x) = \dfrac{x}{2}$

b.

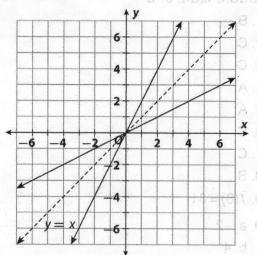

17. No, (4, 3) is not a solution.

18.

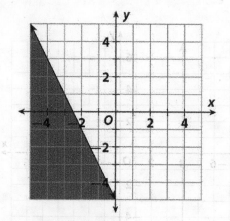

# MODULE 8 Modeling with Linear Functions

## Module Quiz 8: B

1. $h(x) = 13x - 14$
2. A
3. A No B No C Yes
4. D
5. D
6. 9.36
7. A No B Yes C Yes

8. $f^{-1}(x) = -\dfrac{x}{4} + 0.6625$

9. a.

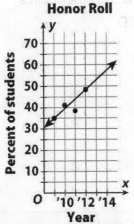

**Honor Roll**

b. $y = 3.5x + 34$

c. 60%

d. Yes; this makes me make my prediction higher, because the line of fit is going to be steeper

10. a.

| $p = -1.5x + 4.4$ | | | |
|---|---|---|---|
| x | p (actual) | p (predicted) | residuals |
| –2 | 6 | 7.4 | –1.4 |
| 0 | 5.5 | 4.4 | 1.1 |
| 2 | 1 | 1.4 | –0.4 |
| 4 | –1.2 | –1.6 | 0.4 |

b. 3.49

11. a. 13

b. 25

c. $y = \dfrac{1}{2}x + 2$ better fits the data, because it has a lower squared residual.

**Module Quiz 8: D**

1. B

2. A

3. A

4. B

5. C

6. B

7. B

8. $f(x)^{-1} = -11x$

9.

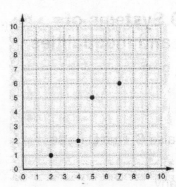

10. a.

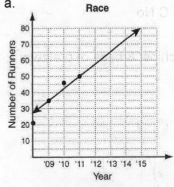

**Race**

b. 72; the trend line is closer to 72 than 40 when the year is 2013.

11. a.

| $p = 5x + 4$ | | | |
|---|---|---|---|
| x | p (actual) | p (predicted) | residuals |
| –2 | –5 | –6 | 1 |
| 0 | 6 | 4 | 2 |
| 2 | 13 | 14 | –1 |
| 4 | 27 | 24 | 3 |

b. 15

12. a.

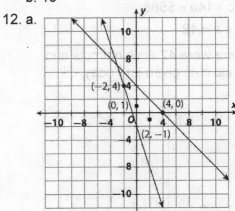

b. 22

c. 254

d. $y = -x + 4$

# MODULE 9 Systems of Equations and Inequalities

## Module Quiz 9: B

1. B

2. (3.5, −2.5)

3. A True B False C True D False

4. (7, 27)

5. infinitely many

6. A No B Yes C No

7. C

8. 15 bags of chips; 8 bags of pretzels

9. 5.25

10.

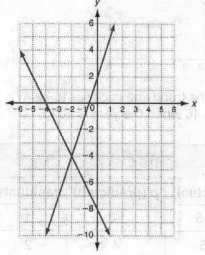

(−2, −4)

11. No solutions

12. (3, 5)

13. a. $\begin{cases} 4c + 14a = \$588 \\ c + a = 42 \end{cases}$

    b. There were 42 adult haircuts and no kid cuts given on Friday.

14. a.

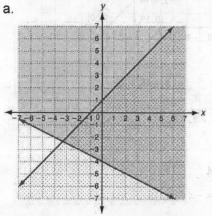

b. Solutions: Any points in the shaded and cross-hatched area; Not solutions: All other points

## Module Quiz 9: D

1. B

2. C

3. B

4. B

5. C

6. B

7. A

8. A

9. a.

| $y = -2x + 9$ | | | |
|---|---|---|---|
| x | p (actual) | p (predicted) | residuals |
| −2 | 14 | 13 | 1 |
| 0 | 9 | 9 | 0 |
| 2 | 3 | 5 | −2 |

b. 5

10. (2, 2)

11. (4, 1)

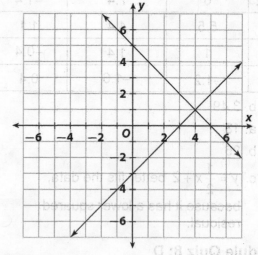

12. (−6, −4)

13. a. $35 + 5x = y$

    b. $100 - 8x = y$

    c. (5, 60); 5 minutes, 60 gallons

14. (−6, 0) is a solution.

15. a. Solutions: Any points in the shaded and cross hatched area

    b. Not solutions: All other points

# MODULE 10 Exponential Functions and Equations

## Module Quiz 10: B

1. B
2. 8
3. –20
4. C
5. 7.6 ft
6. A
7. A Yes B No C No D Yes
8. 729
9. A True B False C True D False
10. $x = 4$
11. $x = 6$
12. $(-5, -3)$
13. a.

| $x$ | $-2\left(\dfrac{1}{2}\right)^x = y$ | $y$ |
|---|---|---|
| –2 | $-2\left(\dfrac{1}{2}\right)^{-2} = -2\left(\dfrac{4}{1}\right)$ | –8 |
| –1 | $-2\left(\dfrac{1}{2}\right)^{-1} = -2\left(\dfrac{2}{1}\right)$ | –4 |
| 0 | $-2\left(\dfrac{1}{2}\right)^{0} = -2(1)$ | –2 |
| 1 | $-2\left(\dfrac{1}{2}\right)^{1} = -2\left(\dfrac{1}{2}\right)$ | –1 |
| 2 | $-2\left(\dfrac{1}{2}\right)^{2} = -2\left(\dfrac{1}{4}\right)$ | $-\dfrac{1}{2}$ |

b.

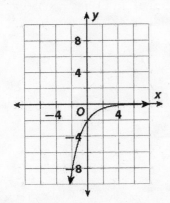

14. $y = 5(3)^x$
15. $17,910
16. a. –4

   b. $f(1) = -5$, $f(n) = f(n-1) \times -4$

   c. $f(n) = -5(-4)^{n-1}$

17. The graph of $y = 3(2)^x - 4$ is vertically stretched and translated down 4 units.
18. $x = 4$
19. $y = 3$

## Module Quiz 10: D

1. B
2. C
3. C
4. A
5. B
6. B
7. A
8. B
9. A
10. A
11. B
12. (6, 16)
13. a.

| $x$ | $4(2)^x = y$ | $y$ |
|---|---|---|
| –2 | $4(2)^{-2} = 4\left(\dfrac{1}{4}\right)$ | 1 |
| –1 | $4(2)^{-1} = 4\left(\dfrac{1}{2}\right)$ | 2 |
| 0 | $4(2)^{0} = 4(1)$ | 4 |
| 1 | $4(2)^{1} = 4(2)$ | 8 |
| 2 | $4(2)^{2} = 4(4)$ | 16 |

b.

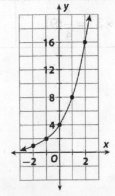

14. $y = 3^x$

15. 289

16. a. 3

   b. $f(1) = 6$, $f(n) = f(n-1) \times 3$

   c. $f(n) = 6(3)^{n-1}$

17. $y = 3 \times 2^x - 2$ is vertically stretched and has been translated 2 units down.

18. $y = 9$

# MODULE 11 Modeling with Exponential Functions

## Module Quiz 11: B

1. 7,604

2. A

3. A

4. $209

5. A No B Yes C No D Yes

6. **A**: 48; **B**: 7

7. A No B No C Yes D Yes

8. a.

| $x$ | $\frac{1}{4} \times 3^x = y$ | $y$ |
|---|---|---|
| -2 | $\frac{1}{4} \times 3^{-2} = \frac{1}{4}\left(\frac{1}{9}\right)$ | $\frac{1}{36}$ |
| -1 | $\frac{1}{4} \times 3^{-1} = \frac{1}{4}\left(\frac{1}{3}\right)$ | $\frac{1}{12}$ |
| 0 | $\frac{1}{4} \times 3^0 = \frac{1}{4}(1)$ | $\frac{1}{4}$ |
| 1 | $\frac{1}{4} \times 3^1 = \frac{1}{4}(3)$ | $\frac{3}{4}$ |
| 2 | $\frac{1}{4} \times 3^2 = \frac{1}{4}(9)$ | $2\frac{1}{4}$ |

b.

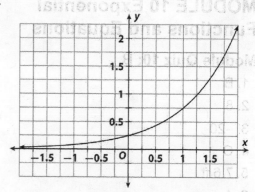

9. An exponential function would be better than a linear function, because the differences are increasing from 0.7 to 2.5.

10. a.

| $x$ | $y$ observed | $y$ predicted | residual |
|---|---|---|---|
| -1 | 0 | $0.\overline{2}$ | $-0.\overline{2}$ |
| 0 | 1.2 | 1 | 0.2 |
| 1 | 4.4 | 4.5 | -0.1 |
| 2 | 20.4 | 20.25 | 0.15 |

b. There is an even number of positive and negative residuals, and they remain low as $x$ increases. The equation fits the data well.

11. a. Job A: $f(x) = 24,000(1.02)^x$

   b. Job B: $f(x) = 24,000 + 500x$

   c. 6 years

## Module Quiz 11: D

1. C

2. B

3. B

4. A

5. B

6. C

7. A

**8. a.**

| $x$ | $\frac{1}{2} \times 2^x = y$ | $y$ |
|---|---|---|
| $-2$ | $\frac{1}{2} \times 2^{-2} = \frac{1}{2}\left(\frac{1}{4}\right)$ | $\frac{1}{8}$ |
| $-1$ | $\frac{1}{2} \times 2^{-1} = \frac{1}{2}\left(\frac{1}{2}\right)$ | $\frac{1}{4}$ |
| $0$ | $\frac{1}{2} \times 2^0 = \frac{1}{2}(1)$ | $\frac{1}{2}$ |
| $1$ | $\frac{1}{2} \times 2^1 = \frac{1}{2}(2)$ | $1$ |
| $2$ | $\frac{1}{2} \times 2^2 = \frac{1}{2}(4)$ | $2$ |

**b.**

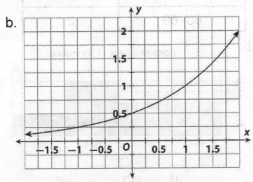

**9.** A linear function would be better than an exponential function, because the differences are constantly $110.

**10. a.**

| $x$ | $y$ observed | $y$ predicted | residual |
|---|---|---|---|
| $-1$ | $\frac{1}{4}$ | $\frac{1}{4}$ | $0$ |
| $0$ | $2$ | $1$ | $1$ |
| $1$ | $6$ | $4$ | $2$ |
| $2$ | $22$ | $16$ | $6$ |

**b.** As $x$ increases, the residuals get larger, which indicates a growing disparity between the data and the model.

**11. a.** Job A: $f(x) = 2{,}000 + 85x$

**b.** Job B: $f(x) = 2{,}000(1.04)^x$

**c.** 5 months

## MODULE 12 Descriptive Statistics

### Module Quiz 12: B

1. D
2. 15
3. 14
4. 29
5. $\frac{4}{5}$ or 80%
6. 0.52
7. A
8. 0.40
9. a.

| Gender | Preferred Pet | | | |
|---|---|---|---|---|
| | Dog | Cat | Fish | Total |
| Male | 110 | 208 | 5 | 323 |
| Female | 190 | 50 | 2 | 242 |
| Total | 300 | 258 | 7 | 565 |

b. 110
c. 192

10.

| | Blue | Green | Hazel | Brown |
|---|---|---|---|---|
| Child | 5 | 2 | 6 | 10 |
| Teenager | 3 | 3 | 0 | 8 |
| Adult | 6 | 5 | 10 | 15 |

11. 40 liked both oranges and bananas
12. a. 0.04
   b. 0.24
   c. 21–35 year old, because the conditional frequency of 21–35 year olds that recycle, or 0.30, is higher than the conditional frequency for 51–60 year olds that recycle, or 0.24.

### Module Quiz 12: D

1. A
2. A
3. B
4. C

5. C

6. B

7. A

8. A

9. a.

| Preferred Pet | | | | |
|---|---|---|---|---|
| Gender | Dog | Cat | Fish | Total |
| Male | 16 | 12 | 3 | 31 |
| Female | 19 | 25 | 7 | 51 |
| Total | 35 | 37 | 10 | 82 |

   b. 16

   c. 26

10.

| | Blue | Green | Hazel | Brown |
|---|---|---|---|---|
| Child | 3 | 4 | 9 | 14 |
| Teenager | 3 | 0 | 6 | 6 |
| Adult | 10 | 10 | 7 | 25 |

11. 0.17

12. a. 0.02

   b. 0.25

   c. 0.33

   d. 21–35 year old

# MODULE 13 Data Displays

## Module Quiz 13: B

1. 0.70

2. mean: 54.6; median: 55; mode: 51

3. A No B Yes C Yes

4. A False B False C True D True

5. A

6. C

7. C

8. 0.84

9.

| Eye Color | | | | |
|---|---|---|---|---|
| | Blue | Green | Brown | Total |
| Child | 15 | 9 | 12 | 36 |
| Teenager | 3 | 3 | 8 | 14 |
| Adult | 19 | 13 | 8 | 40 |
| Total | 37 | 25 | 28 | 90 |

10. mean = 82.5; standard deviation ≈ 9.54

11. a.

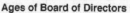

| Age | Frequency |
|---|---|
| 50–54 | 3 |
| 55–59 | 3 |
| 60–64 | 5 |
| 65–69 | 2 |

   b.

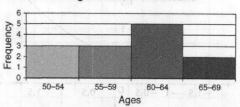

Ages of Board of Directors

12. a.

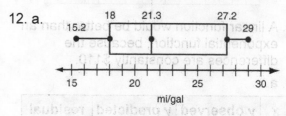

   b. Possible answer: The median and Q3 of A is greater than B. Also, the interquartile range of A is greater than B.

13. a. 5

   b. 0.025

## Module Quiz 13: D

1. C

2. C

3. C

4. A

5. A

6. B

7. B

8. B

9.

|  | Eye Color | | | |
|---|---|---|---|---|
|  | Blue | Green | Brown | Total |
| Child | 15 | 9 | 12 | 36 |
| Teenager | 3 | 3 | 8 | 14 |
| Adult | 19 | 13 | 8 | 40 |
| Total | 37 | 25 | 28 | 90 |

10. Mean: 91; Standard deviation: 6.8

11. a.

| Age | Frequency |
|---|---|
| 50–54 | 2 |
| 55–59 | 4 |
| 60–64 | 4 |
| 65–69 | 3 |

b.

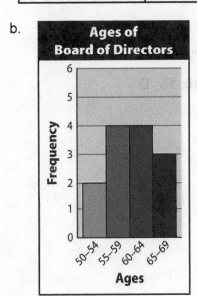

12. a. 55

b. 27

c. Possible answer: The median from Week 1 is less than that from Week 2. The range from Week 1 is greater than that from Week 2. The interquartile range from Week 2 is slightly greater the interquartile range from Week 1.

# MODULE 14 Polynomials and Operations

## Module Quiz 14: B

1. 216

2. C

3. 6

4. A Yes B No C Yes D No

5. D

6. $12x^3 - 3x + 4$

7. $6mn^2 - 8m$

8. $-5x^2 - 5x - 10$

9. A No B No C Yes D No

10. $24x^2y - 56xy^2$

11. $9x^2 - 9x - 4$

12. D

13. 80

14. a. polynomial; trinomial with a degree of 4

b. neither

c. polynomial; binomial with degree 2

15. $14x^2 + 21xy + 4y^2 - 20$

16. a. $61x^2 - 28x$

b. $20x^3 - 10x^2$

c. 120 ft$^3$

17. $22mn^2 + 66m^2n - 64$

18. $-15x^3 + 5x^2 - 20$

19. $-7x^2 + 5x$

20. a. $2h^2 + h$

b. $7\frac{2}{9}$ in$^2$

21. $3t^2 + 17t - 56$

22. $r^2s^6 - 144$

23. $x^3 - 3x^2y + 3xy^2 - y^3$

## Module Quiz 14: D

1. B

2. C

3. C

4. B

5. A

6. C
7. B
8. A
9. A
10. B
11. C
12. B
13. B
14. 43
15. $-6m^2 + 4m$
16. a. polynomial
    b. neither
    c. monomial
17. $8mn^2 + 16n$
18. $-15y + 2$
19. a. $20b^2 + 40bh$
    b. 1,120 in$^2$
20. $45r^5$
21. $-7x^2 + 5x$
22. a. $45x^2 + 75x$
    b. 630 ft$^2$
23. $2x^2 + 7x - 4$
24. $t^2 + t - 56$
25. $p^2 - 24p + 144$

# MODULE 15 Factoring Polynomials

## Module Quiz 15: B

1. $36x^3y^2 - 21x^2y^2$
2. 18
3. $18xy$
4. $3(36x^2 - 33y + 1)$
5. B
6. $(12x - 3)$ in.
7. D
8. C
9. $(2x + 5)(x - 1)$
10. A Yes B No C No D Yes

11. A Yes B No C No D No
12. C
13. $8x^2 - 6xy - 14y^2$
14. $19s$
15. Possible answer: $7x^3y, 21x^3y^2$
16. a. $4x(5x^2 - 16)$
    b. $t(17s^2 + 11)$
    c. not factorable
    d. $(7 + z)(8 - x)$
17. a. not factorable
    b. $(x - 9)(x + 4)$
18. $(7x + 1)(x + 4)$
19. $5x(x + 10)(x - 2)$
20. $(m^2 + 4)(m - 2)(m + 2)$
21. a. $z + 6$
    b. 72 ft
22. Yes, both $4x^4$ and 49 are perfect squares.
23. $(2x - 7)(2x + 7)$
24. $(3n + 7)^2$
25. $(5a^2 - 2)(3a + 4)$

## Module Quiz 15: D

1. A
2. C
3. C
4. B
5. B
6. C
7. B
8. C
9. A
10. B
11. A
12. C
13. C
14. $x^2 - 2x - 35$

15. 15

16. $3y$

17. a. $7(x-11)$

   b. not factorable

   c. $x(8-x)$

   d. $(7+z)(8-x)$

18. a. not factorable

   b. $(x-5)(x+2)$

19. a. $x^2+12x+20$

   b. $(x+10)(x+2)$

20. $(x+7)(x-3)$

21. $(3x+1)(x+2)$

22. No, $4x^2+16$ is not a difference of two squares, because it is the sum of two squares.

23. $(p-10)(p+10)$

24. $(n+5)^2$

25. $(x-8)^2$

# MODULE 16 Solving Quadratic Equations

## Module Quiz 16: B

1. 0 and –2

2. $\dfrac{-9}{8}$ and $\dfrac{9}{8}$

3. B

4. $5+2\sqrt{3}$ and $5-2\sqrt{3}$

5. A Yes B No C Yes D No

6. $x=-\dfrac{1}{2}$

7. –13 and 3

8. B

9. 161; 2 real solutions

10. 7 and 11

11. 5

12. a. $x^2-21x-46=0$

   b. 23 and –2

   c. 23 and 24

13. 8 seconds

14. $x=1$ or $x=-3$

15. $x=-1$ or $x=\dfrac{8}{3}$

16. –16; no real solutions

17. yes; $(n+5)^2$

18. yes; $(x+4)(x-4)$

19. –3 and 9

20. $\dfrac{a}{2}$ and $\dfrac{-2}{b}$

21. –2 and 8

22. –2 and 17

23. –5 and –1

## Module Quiz 16: D

1. C

2. B

3. C

4. A

5. B

6. B

7. C

8. B

9. B

10. $x^2-34x+289$

11. 13

12. a. 12 and –1

   b. 12 and 13, or –1 and 0

13. $x=1$ or $x=-9$

14. $x=-1$, $x=\dfrac{8}{3}$

15. 76; two real solutions

16. $x=-3$, $x=5$

17. $x=-\dfrac{1}{3}$

18. $x=-5$ and 7

19. $x=-\dfrac{1}{4}$

20. $x=-\dfrac{2}{3}$ and 20

# MODULE 17 Quadratic Functions

## Module Quiz 17: B

1. A Yes B No C Yes
2. A No B Yes C Yes
3. (0, –4)
4. A True B False C True
5. B
6. A
7. B
8. 2 and 3
9. A
10. $x = 0$ or $x = 6$
11. A
12. a.

| $x$ | $-2x^2 + 4 = y$ | $y$ |
|---|---|---|
| –2 | $-2(-2)^2 + 4 = y$ | –4 |
| –1 | $-2(-1)^2 + 4 = y$ | 2 |
| 0 | $-2(0)^2 + 4 = y$ | 4 |
| 1 | $-2(1)^2 + 4 = y$ | 2 |
| 2 | $-2(2)^2 + 4 = y$ | –4 |

b.

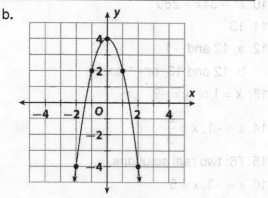

13. As $x \to \infty$, $f(x) \to \boxed{-\infty}$

   As $x \to -\infty$, $f(x) \to \boxed{-\infty}$

14. Linear; the $y$-values are increasing at a constant rate.
15. Sample answer: $y = x^2 - 8x + 18$
16. a. (–5, 4); Maximum $y = 4$

   b. $x = -5$

   c. Domain: All real numbers;
      Range: $y \le 4$

17. (4, 54) and (–4, –10)
18.

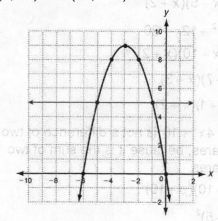

   $x = -1$ and $x = -5$

## Module Quiz 17: D

1. B
2. C
3. B
4. A
5. A
6. C
7. C
8. A
9. C
10. a.

| $x$ | $2x^2 = y$ | $y$ |
|---|---|---|
| – 2 | $2(-2)^2 = y$ | 8 |
| – 1 | $2(-1)^2 = y$ | 2 |
| 0 | $2(0)^2 = y$ | 0 |
| 1 | $2(1)^2 = y$ | 2 |
| 2 | $2(2)^2 = y$ | 8 |

b.

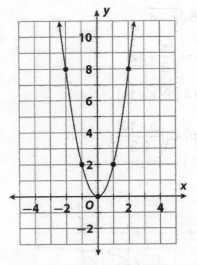

11. $f(x) = (x - 2)^2 - 4$

12. $(t - 8)(t + 8)$

13. $(1, -4)$

14. As $x \to \infty$, $f(x) \to \boxed{\infty}$

   As $x \to -\infty$, $f(x) \to \boxed{\infty}$

15. $(-2, 8)$

# MODULE 18 Piecewise and Absolute Value Functions

## Module Quiz 18: B

1. 17

2. –6

3. B

4. A Yes B No C Yes

5. $y = \{-3, -2, -1, 0, 1, 2\}$

6. A

7. A Yes B No

8. $x = -4.5, -0.5$

9.

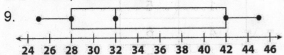

10. $y = 19$

11. $y = 6$

12. $y = -29$

13.

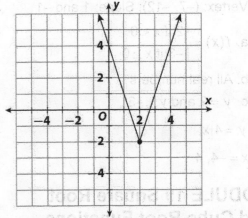

14. a. They have the same vertex, $(9, 7)$.

   b. $f(x)$ is less steep than $g(x)$. In other words, the values of $f(x)$ are closer to the $x$–axis than those of $g(x)$ for the same values of $x$.

15. a. $y = -0.5|x - 1| + 3$

   b. Domain: All real numbers
      Range: $y \le 3$

## Module Quiz 18: D

1. A

2. C

3. B

4. A

5. C

6. A

7. C

8. Range: 16; IQR: 13

9. $y = 15$

10. $y = 4$

11. $y = 6$

12.

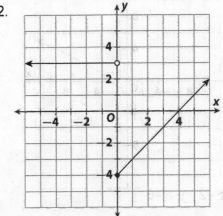

13. Vertex: (−7, −12); Slope: 1 and −1

14. a. $f(x) = \begin{cases} 2 \text{ if } x < 0 \\ -3 \text{ if } x \geq 0 \end{cases}$

    b. All real numbers

    c. $y = 2$ and $y = -3$

15. $y = 4|x|$

16. $x = -4, 4$

# MODULE 19 Square Root and Cube Root Functions

## Module Quiz 19: B

1. C

2. A Yes B Yes C No D Yes

3. $\{x \mid x \geq -14\}$; $\{y \mid y \geq -7\}$

4. $y = \dfrac{1}{3}\sqrt{x} - 8\dfrac{1}{2}$

5. $r(V) = \sqrt[3]{\dfrac{3V}{4\pi}}$

6. −22

7. C

8. $y = 15.2$

9. a.

| x | $f(x)$ |
|---|---|
| −2 | −6 |
| −1 | −3 |
| 2 | 0 |
| 7 | 3 |

b.

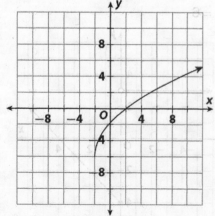

c. $x \geq -2$; $y \geq -6$

10. $y = -5\sqrt{x-4}$

11. $f^{-1}(x) = \sqrt{\dfrac{x}{6}} + 12$

12. $f^{-1}(x) = \sqrt[3]{9(x-11)}$

13. a. $N(p) = \sqrt{\dfrac{p-10}{0.2}}$

    b. 20

14.

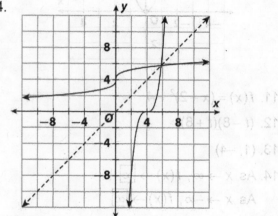

## Module Quiz 19: D

1. C

2. B

3. B

4. C

5. A

6. A

7. A

8. $y = 10$

9. a.

| x | y |
|---|---|
| 0 | 4 |
| 1 | 5 |
| 4 | 6 |
| 9 | 7 |

b.

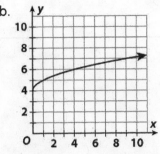

c. Domain: $x \geq 0$; Range: $y \geq 4$

10. $y^{-1} = \sqrt{x - 11}$

11. $f^{-1}(x) = \sqrt[3]{x} + 2$

12. a. $P(r) = \sqrt[3]{r - 10}$

   b. 4 pets

13. a.

| $f(x) = x^3 + 2$ | |
|---|---|
| **x** | **f(x)** |
| −2 | −6 |
| −1 | 1 |
| 0 | 2 |
| 1 | 3 |
| 2 | 10 |

| $f(x)^{-1} = \sqrt[3]{x - 2}$ | |
|---|---|
| **x** | **f(x)⁻¹** |
| −6 | −2 |
| 1 | −1 |
| 2 | 0 |
| 3 | 1 |
| 10 | 2 |

b.

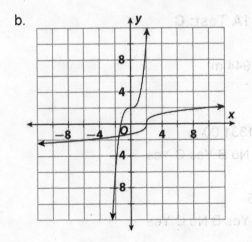

# Answer Key

## UNIT 1A Numbers and Expressions

### Unit 1A Test: A

1. C
2. 4
3. A
4. A
5. $y^4$
6. 4
7. A No B No C No
8. A Yes B No C Yes
9. 6
10. 9
11. C
12. A
13. 6.7 m
14. $7.1\ \dfrac{mi}{h}$
15. 568 cm$^2$
16. 40
17. 7
18. 64
19. not closed; $-1 \times -1 = 1$, and 1 is not included in the set.
20. 38
21. $2.50x$
22. a. $32 + 0.25y$
    b. $33.50

### Unit 1A Test: B

1. C
2. 90.10 m
3. A
4. D
5. $7y^{-9}$
6. $108.00
7. A No B No C Yes D Yes

8. B
9. 30
10. −36
11. A No B No
12. A
13. 320 km
14. $1.14\ \dfrac{mi}{h}$
15. 899 m$^2$
16. 8 cm
17. 800
18. $\dfrac{1}{625}$
19. The set is not closed under any operation, since the product, quotient, and sum of −3 and −3 is not included in the set, for example, and neither is the difference of −3 and 3.
20. 14
21. $4.80 + $0.79x + $0.75y$
22. $1.69z$

### Unit 1A Test: C

1. D
2. 1,944 m$^2$
3. B
4. A
5. $1331.00
6. A No B Yes C Yes
7. C
8. 55
9. A Yes B No C Yes
10. A
11. 831 ft
12. $80\ \dfrac{km}{h}$
13. 5.9 yd$^3$
14. 6 in.

15. 2

16. 3

17. Possible answer: The set {0, 1} is closed under multiplication, since the product of any pair of numbers from the set is included in the set. $0 - 1 = -1$, and $-1$ is not included in the set, so it is not closed under subtraction.

18. 130

19. a. $\$2.54x + \$5.25$

 b. $\$12.87$

## Unit 1A Test: D

1. A

2. B

3. B

4. A

5. B

6. A

7. C

8. A

9. B

10. A

11. C

12. A

13. 312 ft

14. $14\dfrac{\text{km}}{\text{h}}$

15. $\dfrac{160 \text{ in}^2}{1} \times \dfrac{2.54 \text{ cm}}{1 \text{ in.}} \times \dfrac{2.54 \text{ cm}}{1 \text{ in.}} =$
 $1{,}032 \text{ cm}^2$

16. 10

17. 80

18. 3

19. not closed; $1 + 1 = 2$, and 2 is not included in the set.

20. real numbers and rational numbers

21. 84

22. 14

23. a. $7x$

 b. 98

24. a. $\$2x + \$6$

 b. $\$12$

## Unit 1A Performance Task

1. a. Multiply the number of tickets sold by $12 and subtract $275.

 a. $12n - 275$

 b. $\$1{,}213$

2. Multiply $20 by $r$ and multiply the product by 20, since there are 20 seats in each row. Then multiply $15 times $40 - r$ and multiply the product by 20. Finally, find the sum of the two quantities.

3. a. $\$6{,}400$

 b. $\$7{,}200$

 c. $\$13{,}600$

4. $100r + 12{,}000$

5. $100r + 12{,}000 = 100\,(16) + 12{,}000 =$
 $1{,}600 + 12{,}000 = 13{,}600$

# UNIT 1B Equations and Functions

## Unit 1B Test: A

1. $x = 6$

2. $m = 5$

3. A Yes B Yes C No D No

4. C

5.

6. A No B Yes C Yes D No

7. A

8. C

9. C

10. 2

11. $x = \dfrac{2}{5}$

12. $p = 8$

13. a. $\dfrac{77 + t}{2} = 84$

 b. 91

14. a. $p \le -4$

 b.

15. $x$ can be any real number, because 7 is always greater than 6.

16. $x = \dfrac{y+1}{3}$

17. $h = \dfrac{V}{\ell w}$

18. Yes

19. Yes

20. a.

| $x$ | $-2x = y$ | $y$ |
|---|---|---|
| $-2$ | $-2(-2) = y$ | 4 |
| 0 | $-2(0) = y$ | 0 |
| 2 | $-2(2) = y$ | $-4$ |

b.

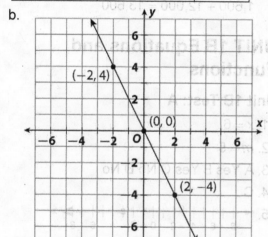

c. The equation is a function, because each $x$-value has exactly one corresponding $y$-value.

21. 41

22. 7, 14, 28

## Unit 1B Test: B

1. $x = -8$

2. $t = 8$

3. A Yes B Yes C Yes D No

4. C

5.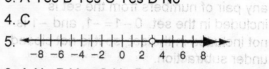

6. A No B Yes C No D Yes

7. B

8. B

9. C

10. 3

11. $y = 31$

12. $x = -14$

13. a. $\dfrac{p - 445}{3} = 592;$

   b. $2,221

14. a. $z \le 4$

   b.

15. All real numbers are solutions.

16. $y = \dfrac{-9 - 3x}{18}$ or $y = -\dfrac{1}{2} - \dfrac{x}{6}$

17. $h = \dfrac{t - 25}{13.25}$

18. $(-12.5, 4)$ is a solution, $(1, -4)$ is not.

19. a.

| $x$ | $-\dfrac{1}{2}x + 3 = y$ | $y$ |
|---|---|---|
| $-2$ | $-\dfrac{1}{2}(-2) + 3 = y$ | 4 |
| 0 | $-\dfrac{1}{2}(0) + 3 = y$ | 3 |
| 2 | $-\dfrac{1}{2}(2) + 3 = y$ | 2 |

b.

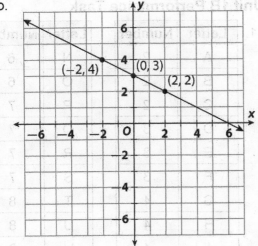

20. 1, −2, −7

21. a. 9, 11

   b. $f(n) = f(n-1) + 2$ ; $f(1) = 1$

## Unit 1B Test: C

1. $x = 15$

2. $p = -\dfrac{1}{2}$

3. A

4. A

5. ![number line with ray shaded from −4 to the right]
   $-8\ -6\ -4\ -2\ \ 0\ \ 2\ \ 4\ \ 6\ \ 8$

6. A No B Yes C No D Yes

7. $y = -2x + 3$

8. −19

9. C

10. D

11. $x = 11\dfrac{1}{3}$

12. $y = -\dfrac{1}{2}$

13. a. $3s^2 = 168.75$

    b. 7.5 mm

14. a. $z \le -2$

    b. ![number line with ray shaded from −2 to the left]
    $-8\ -6\ -4\ -2\ \ 0\ \ 2\ \ 4\ \ 6\ \ 8$

15. Answers may vary; any number less than 14 is a correct answer.

16. $y = \dfrac{21 + 3x}{2}$ or $y = 10.5 + 1.5x$

17. $r = \sqrt[3]{\dfrac{3V}{4\pi}}$

18. $\left(\dfrac{1}{2}, \dfrac{1}{4}\right)$ is a solution, (−9, 9) is not.

19. a.

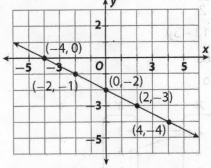

   b. The equation is a function, because each x-value has exactly one corresponding y-value.

20. a. 13, 16

    b. $f(n) = 3n - 2$

    c. $f(n) = f(n-1) + 3$ ; $f(1) = 1$

## Unit 1B Test: D

1. A

2. B

3. A

4. A

5. A

6. C

7. B

8. B

9. B

10. C

11. C

12. $x = 72$

13. $z = -6$

14. a. $26 + p = 31$

    b. 5

15. a. $s < -1$

b.

16. All real numbers are solutions.

17. $x = \dfrac{y}{2}$

18. $z = 13 - 3y$

19. a. yes

b. no

20. a.

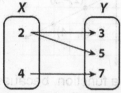

b. The points cannot represent a function, because the x-value 2 has more than one corresponding y-value, 3 and 5.

21. a. 7

b. 11, 13

22. 7, 4, 1, -2

## Unit 1B Performance Task

1.

| Letter | Number | | Letter | Number |
|--------|--------|---|--------|--------|
| A | 2 | | N | 6 |
| B | 2 | | O | 6 |
| C | 2 | | P | 7 |
| D | 3 | | Q | 7 |
| E | 3 | | R | 7 |
| F | 3 | | S | 7 |
| G | 4 | | T | 8 |
| H | 4 | | U | 8 |
| I | 4 | | V | 8 |
| J | 5 | | W | 9 |
| K | 5 | | X | 9 |
| L | 5 | | Y | 9 |
| M | 6 | | Z | 9 |

2. the letters of the alphabet

3. the whole numbers 2 through 9

4. Yes, because for each letter there is exactly one corresponding number.

5. 5, 5, 5, 2, 6, 6, 5

6. the whole numbers 2 through 9

7. the letters of the alphabet

8. No, because for each number there are three or four corresponding letters.

9. DMG, DMH, DMI, DNG, DNH, DNI, DOG, DOH, DOI, EMG, EMH, EMI, ENG, ENH, ENI, EOG, EOH, EOI, FMG, FMH, FMI, FNG, FNH, FNI, FOG, FOH, and FOI.

# UNIT 2A Linear Relationships

## Unit 2A Test: A

1. x-intercept: 1; y-intercept $1\frac{1}{2}$

2. $m = 3$; $b = -6$

3. C

4. $(4, \frac{1}{2})$

5. A False B True C False

6. C

7. $(0, -2)$

8. 4

9. a. $-4$

   b. 3, Opal takes 3 hours to walk from school to home.

   c. 12, Opal starts 12 miles from home, so she has 12 miles to walk in all.

   d. $y = -4x + 12$

10. $s(x) = 3x + 4$

11. $d(x) = 17x - 20$

12. $p(x) = 40x - 32$

13. a.

| $s = 2r - 6$ | | | |
|---|---|---|---|
| r | s (actual) | p (predicted) | residuals |
| −1 | −7 | −8 | 1 |
| 0 | −7 | −6 | −1 |
| 1 | −3 | −4 | 1 |
| 2 | 0 | −2 | 2 |

| $s = 2r - 5$ | | | |
|---|---|---|---|
| r | s (actual) | p (predicted) | residuals |
| −1 | −7 | −7 | 0 |
| 0 | −7 | −5 | −2 |
| 1 | −3 | −3 | 0 |
| 2 | 0 | −1 | 1 |

   b. 7; 5

   c. $s = 2r - 5$ ; The lower the squared residual, the better the line fits the data.

14. a.

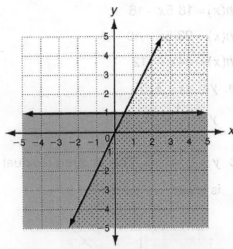

   b. Solution: Any points in the shaded, cross-hatched section of the graph or on the portions of the line bordering that section

   Not-solutions: Points or portions of the lines from any other section of the graph

## Unit 2A Test: B

1. x-int: 5, y-int: 10          6. B

2. $y = 3x - 2$          7. (−1, 2)

3. B          8. 8

4. no solution          9. a

5. A No B Yes C No D Yes

6. B

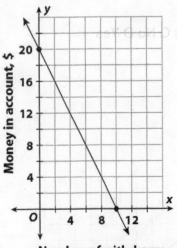

Number of withdraws

$y = 200 - 20x$

   b. 10, Carla can withdraw $20 10 times.

   c. 200, Carla starts with $200.

   d. Domain: $0 \le x \le 10$, Range: $0 \le y \le 200$

10. $h(x) = 18.5x - 16$

11. $h(x) = 23.5x - 40$

12. $h(x) = 84x - 112$

13. a. $y = -x - 3$, 10

  $y = -\dfrac{1}{2}x - 3$, 3.75

  b. $y = -\dfrac{1}{2}x - 3$; The squared residual is lower.

14.

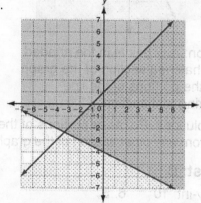

## Unit 2A Test: C

1. $x$-int: 3; $y$-int: 12

2. $y = \dfrac{1}{2}x + \dfrac{7}{2}$

3. B

4. (−2.5, 6.5)

5. A No  B Yes  C No  D Yes

6. B

7. $\left(\dfrac{5}{2}, -\dfrac{17}{4}\right)$

8. 8

9. a.

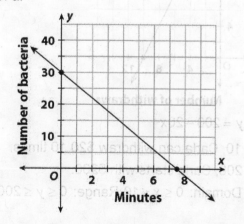

$y = 30 - 4x$

  b. 7.5; In 7.5 minutes, all the bacteria will die.

  c. 30, Weasley starts with 30 bacteria.

  d. Domain: $0 \le x \le 7.5$, Range: $0 \le y \le 30$

10. $h(x) = -17.5x + 59$

11. $h(x) = 2x - \dfrac{27}{5}$

12. $h(x) = -25x + 91$

13. a. $y = \dfrac{1}{2}x + 3.5$, 7.5

  b. Possible answer: $y = \dfrac{1}{2}x + 3$, The squared residual is 3.75, which is lower than 7.5.

14.

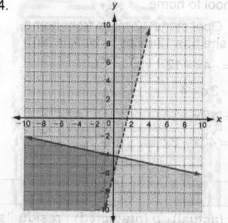

## Unit 2A Test: D

1. C

2. C

3. B

4. (4, 13)

5. B

6. C

7. A

8. A

9. a. −4

  b. 3

  c. 12

  d. $y = -4x + 12$

10. $s(x) = 12x + 6$

11. $d(x) = -2x - 2$

12. $p(x) = 42x + 24$

13. a.

| $s = 2r - 6$ | | | |
|---|---|---|---|
| $r$ | $s$ (actual) | $p$ (predicted) | residuals |
| −1 | −7 | −8 | 1 |
| 0 | −7 | −6 | −1 |
| 1 | −3 | −4 | 1 |
| 2 | 0 | −2 | 2 |

b. 7

c. The first line of fit, $s = 2r - 6$

14. (2, 4)

15. Solutions: Any point in the shaded, cross-hatched area, or on the solid line bordering the shaded area; No solutions: Any other points

## Unit 2A Performance Task

1. a. $4 \dfrac{\text{mi}}{\text{h}}$

   b. $5 \dfrac{\text{mi}}{\text{h}}$

2. a. $y = 4x$

   b. $y = 5x - 0.5$

3.

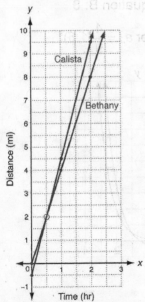

4. a. Bethany

   b. 0.5 hr

   c. 2 mi

   d. Calista

5. (0.5, 2); After 0.5 hour, Calista catches up with Bethany 2 miles after the starting line.

6. Calista; On the graph, Calista's line is above Bethany's for every time past 0.5 hour, so Calista will always be ahead of Bethany after the first half-hour and will cross the finish line first.

# UNIT 2B Exponential Relationships

## Unit 2B Test: A

1. 32

2. B

3. 1.25, 0.625, 0.3125

4. A

5. C

6. $x = 3$

7. A False B True C True D False

8. A

9. A No B No C Yes

10. $a_n = 6 \cdot (2)^{n-1}$ or $a_n = 3(2)^n$

11. a.

| $x$ | $4(3)^x = y$ | $y$ |
|---|---|---|
| −2 | $4(3)^{-2} = 4\left(\dfrac{1}{9}\right)$ | $\dfrac{4}{9}$ |
| −1 | $4(3)^{-1} = 4\left(\dfrac{1}{3}\right)$ | $\dfrac{4}{3}$ |
| 0 | $4(3)^0 = 4(1)$ | 4 |
| 1 | $4(3)^1 = 4(3)$ | 12 |
| 2 | $4(3)^2 = 4(9)$ | 36 |

b.

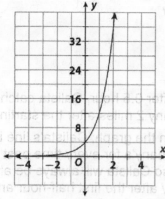

12. 107

13. a. $y = 500 + 150x$

b. $y = 500(1.25)^x$

c. $26.56

14. Exponential, the $y$-values are increasing at increasing intervals, from 1 to 7.

## Unit 2B Test: B

1. $\dfrac{2}{9}$

2. B

3. $\dfrac{1}{3}, -\dfrac{1}{9}$

4. C

5. B

6. $x = 3$

7. B

8. A Yes B No C No D Yes

9. Equation A: 4; Equation B: 2

10. $a_n = 567 \cdot \left(\dfrac{1}{3}\right)^{n-1}$ or $a_n = 1701\left(\dfrac{1}{3}\right)^n$

11. a.

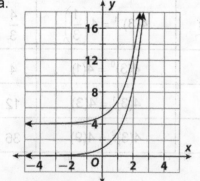

b. The graph of $y = 3^x + 4$ is translated up 4 units. Other than the vertical translation, the graphs are the same.

12. $y = 1,350(0.8)^x$; 442

13. a. A: $y = 900 + 250x$; B: $y = 900(1.25)^x$

b. $596.58

14. a.

| $x$ | $y$ observed | $y$ predicted | residual |
|---|---|---|---|
| $-2$ | $\dfrac{1}{14}$ | $\dfrac{1}{16}$ | $\dfrac{1}{112}$ |
| $-1$ | $\dfrac{1}{3}$ | $\dfrac{1}{4}$ | $\dfrac{1}{12}$ |
| 0 | 1 | 1 | 0 |
| 1 | 5 | 4 | 1 |
| 2 | 16 | 16 | 0 |

b. The model fits the data well, because the residuals are small or zero.

## Unit 2B Test: C

1. $\dfrac{1}{324}$

2. B

3. 1.25

4. B

5. −486

6. $y = 3$

7. C

8. A Yes B No C No D No

9. Equation A: 2; Equation B: 8

10. $a_n = \dfrac{2}{3} \cdot (1.5)^{n-1}$ or $a_n = \dfrac{4}{9}(1.5)^n$

11. a.

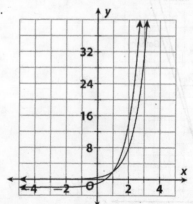

b. $f(x) = \frac{1}{2} \times 4^x$ is vertically shrunk, and

$f(x) = 4^x - 2$ has been translated
2 units down.

12. $y = 2{,}400(1.05)^x$; 3063

13. $121

14. a.

| x | y observed | y predicted | residual |
|----|-----------|-------------|----------|
| −2 | 1 | 1.50 | −0.50 |
| −1 | 5 | 3.76 | 1.24 |
| 0 | 15 | 9.40 | 5.60 |
| 1 | 25 | 23.50 | 1.50 |
| 2 | 40 | 58.75 | −18.75 |

b. The model does not fit the data well.
Perhaps a different type of model would
be better, such as a quadratic or quartic
model.

## Unit 2B Test: D

1. B
2. A
3. C
4. C
5. B
6. A
7. A
8. B
9. B
10. C
11. $a_n = 5 \cdot (5)^{n-1}$ or $a_n = (5)^n$ or $a_n = 1(5)^n$
12. a.

| x | $2(3)^x = y$ | y |
|----|-----------|-------|
| −2 | $2(3)^{-2} = 2\left(\frac{1}{9}\right)$ | $\frac{2}{9}$ |
| −1 | $2(3)^{-1} = 2\left(\frac{1}{3}\right)$ | $\frac{2}{3}$ |
| 0 | $2(3)^0 = 2(1)$ | 2 |
| 1 | $2(3)^1 = 2(3)$ | 6 |
| 2 | $2(3)^2 = 2(9)$ | 18 |

b.

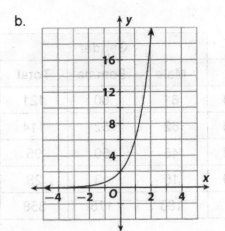

13. 107

14. a. $y = 100 + 10x$

b. $y = 100(1.10)^x$

c. Plan A: $130.00; Plan B: $133.10

15. Exponential, the y-values are increasing
at increasing intervals.

## Unit 2B Performance Task

1. 4, 8, 16, 32

2. $a_n = 4(2)^{n-1}$ or $a_n = 2^{n+1}$

3. 1, 4, 16, 64

4. $a_n = 1(4)^{n-1}$

5. perimeters: 64, 128, 256;
areas: 256, 1024, 4096

6. See students' drawings; Yes, the
perimeters and areas are the same.

# UNIT 3 Statistics and Data

## Unit 3 Test: A

1. 30
2. A
3. C
4. 5
5. A False B True C True D False
6. 13.1
7. A True B False

8. a.

| Age | Gender | | |
|---|---|---|---|
| | Male | Female | Total |
| 13–14 | 61 | 60 | 121 |
| 15–16 | 62 | 52 | 114 |
| 17–18 | 45 | 50 | 95 |
| 19–20 | 15 | 13 | 28 |
| Total | 183 | 175 | 358 |

b. 52

c. 183

d. 7 more 13–14 year old students

9. a. 0.15

b. 0.6

10.

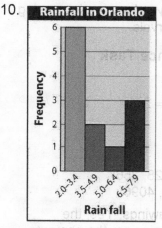

11. a. 68%

b. 0.16

## Unit 3 Test: B

1. 34

2. D

3. 78

4. A No B Yes C Yes D No

5. mean: 42.5; standard deviation 6.8

6. 11 °F

7. D

8. a.

| Age | Gender | | |
|---|---|---|---|
| | Male | Female | Total |
| 13–14 | 82 | 108 | 190 |
| 15–16 | 102 | 85 | 187 |
| 17–18 | 63 | 98 | 161 |
| 19–20 | 11 | 23 | 34 |
| Total | 258 | 314 | 572 |

b. 187

c. 121

9. a. 0.28

b. $\frac{8}{83}$

c. 0.4

10.

11. a. 97.5%

b. 0.815

## Unit 3 Test: C

1. 20

2. 0.75

3. 0.72

4. mean: 79.7; median: 81; mode: 84

5. A

6. A No B Yes C Yes

7. $\frac{6}{13}$

8. a.

| Age | Gender | | Total |
|---|---|---|---|
| | Male | Female | |
| 18–27 | 10 | 5 | 15 |
| 28–37 | 16 | 2 | 18 |
| 38–47 | 18 | 10 | 28 |
| 48–57 | 12 | 17 | 29 |
| Total | 56 | 34 | 90 |

b. 28

c. 14 more 48–57 year olds

9. a.

| | Bus | Bike | Car |
|---|---|---|---|
| Female | 20<br>= 0.16 | 15<br>= 0.12 | 30<br>= 0.24 |
| Male | 12<br>= 0.096 | 12<br>= 0.096 | 36<br>= 0.288 |

b. 0.216

c. 0.6

d. Female; 0.16 > 0.096

10. a.

32 34 36 38 40 42 44 46 48 50 52

b. The scores of the students in the afternoon class have a lower median and a smaller interquartile range than the morning class.

11. a. 0.75

b. 13.05

## Unit 3 Test: D

1. B
2. B
3. B
4. A
5. C
6. B
7. C

8. a.

| Age | Gender | | Total |
|---|---|---|---|
| | Male | Female | |
| 10–11 | 105 | 98 | 203 |
| 12–13 | 90 | 102 | 192 |
| 14–15 | 95 | 110 | 205 |
| Total | 290 | 310 | 600 |

b. 90

c. 205

d. 20 more females

9. a. 400

b. 0.1875

c. 0.4

10. a.

| Monthly rainfall | Frequency |
|---|---|
| 1–2 | 2 |
| 3–4 | 1 |
| 5–6 | 4 |
| 7–8 | 5 |

b.

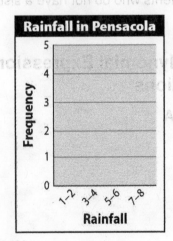

11. 34%

## Unit 3 Performance Task

1. 60% of 100 students said they had a sister. $60\% \cdot 100 = 60$

2. Of the 60 students with a sister, 30% had a brother. $30\% \cdot 60 = 18$

3. There are 100 student altogether. $100 - 60 = 40$

4. Of the 40 students who do not have a sister, 50% have a brother. $50\% \cdot 40 = 20$

5. The total of 60 includes 18 who have a brother. $60 - 18 = 42$

6–7.

|  | Has a brother | Does not have a brother | Total |
|---|---|---|---|
| Has a sister | 18<br>30% | 42<br>70% | 60<br>100% |
| Does not have a sister | 20<br>50% | 20<br>50% | 40<br>100% |
| Total | 38<br>38% | 62<br>62% | 100<br>100% |

8. It is the relative frequency of students who have a brother but no sister compared to all the students who do not have a sister.

9. 60%

# UNIT 4 Polynomial Expressions and Equations

## Unit 4 Test: A

1. D
2. B
3. $3x^3 - 2$
4. $56x^6$
5. $x^2 + x - 12$
6. A No B No C No D Yes
7. D
8. $(x + 2)(x + 6)$
9. $x = -4$ and $x = 10$

10. B
11. C
12. C
13. $-11m^2 + 4m$
14. $2x^2 + 2x$
15. $60p^3 - 48p + 12$
16. a. $12x^2 + 10$
    b. 310 ft
    c. $5x^4 + 21x^2 + 4$
    d. 168 in$^2$
17. $2x^2 + 15x + 27$
18. $x^2 - 8x - 65$
19. $25x^2 - 30x + 9$
20. 4 and 8
21. $x = -11 \pm \sqrt{17}$
22. $x = \dfrac{-10 \pm \sqrt{8}}{2} = -5 \pm \sqrt{2}$
23. $(8 + y)(x + 2)$
24. $4(y - 2)^2$
25. $x^2 + 20x - 100$ is not a perfect square trinomial because $10^2$ is 100, not $-100$.
26. $(b - 12)(b + 12)$
27. $5(5 - x)(5 + x)$

## Unit 4 Test: B

1. C
2. $21x^2 - 10x + 1$
3. $16a^5b^3$
4. C
5. A Yes B No C Yes D No
6. $6(5y^3 - y^2 + 2)$
7. $(x + 15)(x + 14)$
8. C
9. A
10. 68
11. A True B False C True D False

12. $9m^2 - 10m - 7$

13. $3.5x^2 + 18x - 12.5$

14. $35x^4 + 77x^3y$

15. a. $6x^2 + 8x - 16$

    b. 112 cm$^2$

    c. $x^3 + 2x^2 - 8x$

    d. 21 in$^3$

16. $6x^2 + 30x + 36$

17. $5x^2 + 12x - 65$

18. $36x^2 - 96x + 64$

19. 48

20. $y$

21. $-1$ and 4

22. $x = 1$ or $x = -\dfrac{2}{3}$

23. $x = 1$ or $x = -2\dfrac{1}{4}$

24. Possible answer: $x = 16$; $(4p - 8)(4p + 8)$

25. $(12 - b^3)(12 + b^3)$

## Unit 4 Test: C

1. A

2. D

3. $4.9x^5 - 5x^3 + 2.3$

4. C

5. $6x^2 + 14x - 12$

6. A No B No C Yes D Yes

7. A

8. $x = -\dfrac{1}{3}$ or $x = -\dfrac{1}{10}$

9. B

10. 100; 2

11. A True B True C False D True

12. $-5m^2n - 10m^2 + 7n$

13. $10x^2 + 5x + 11$

14. $-81x^3y - 45x^2y^2 + 9xy^4$

15. a. $6x^2 + 24x - 18$

    b. 108 m$^2$

    c. $x^3 + 6x^2 - 9x - 14$

    d. 216 in$^3$

16. $x^2 + \dfrac{77}{4}x + \dfrac{45}{2}$

17. $5t^3 + 12t^2 - 65t$

18. $x^3 - 12x^2 + 48x - 64$

19. $-1$ and 5

20. $c < \dfrac{25}{2}$

21. $x = \dfrac{5 \pm \sqrt{85}}{2}$

22. $(2m - 3)(m + 3)(m - 3)$

23. $5x(x - 10)(x + 2)$

24. $(3x - 20)^2$

25. $c = 25$; $(2p - 5)^2$

## Unit 4 Test: D

1. B

2. C

3. A

4. B

5. C

6. C

7. B

8. B

9. C

10. A

11. B

12. C

13. B

14. C

15. $22m^2 + m + 12$

16. $7x^2 + 5$

17. $49p^3 + 105p$

18. a. $14x - 16$

    b. 68 cm

    c. $6x^2 - 8x$

    d. 64 in$^2$

19. $x^2 + 15x + 56$

20. $x^2 - 5x - 36$

21. $x^2 - 8x + 16$

22. $x = 1$ or $x = -7$

23. $x = -4$

24. $(y - 2)^2$

25. $x^2 + 10x + 100$ is not a perfect square trinomial, because 2 times 10 is 20, not 10.

26. $(b - 11)(b + 11)$

27. $(2 - x)(2 + x)$

## Unit 4 Performance Task

1. $(4x + 3)(2x - 1)$

2. $4(4x + 3)(2x - 1)$

3. 2; Area B = 4 • Area A. Both dimensions were multiplied by the same number to get 4. Since 2(2) = 4, each dimension must have been multiplied by 2.

4. $\pi(2x - 5)^2$; $2x - 5$

5. $36\pi x^2 - 180\pi x + 225\pi$.

6. The scale factor of 3 is the square root of the GCF.

7. $x + 3$

8. $100\pi x^2 + 600\pi x + 900\pi$.

9. The scale factor of 5 is the square root of the GCF.

## Unit 5 Functions and Modeling

### Unit 5 Test: A

1. C

2. D

3. −2 and 2

4. A False B True C True D False

5. $f^{-1}(x) = \sqrt[3]{\dfrac{x}{4}}$

6. 4

7. B

8. $(-12, -10)$

9. A

10. a.

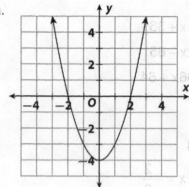

    b. $(0, -4)$

    c. $x = 0$

    d. Minimum: −4

11. a. 5 sec

    b. $(2.5, 100)$; At 2.5 seconds, the ball is at its highest distance from the ground, or 100 feet.

12. $(-4, -20)$

13. $x = -3$, or $x = 11$

14. Domain: $x \geq -5$; Range: $y \geq 0$

15. a.

| $f(x) = x^3 + 4$ | | $f^{-1}(x) = \sqrt[3]{x - 4}$ | |
|---|---|---|---|
| −2 | −4 | −4 | −2 |
| −1 | 3 | 3 | −1 |
| 0 | 4 | 4 | 0 |
| 1 | 5 | 5 | 1 |
| 2 | 12 | 12 | 2 |

b.

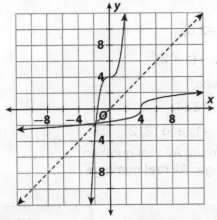

## Unit 5 Test: B

1. A
2. $x = -9$
3. $x = -4$ and $x = 0$
4. A True B False C False D True
5. $-8$
6. C
7. (2.5, 0.125)
8. C
9. a.

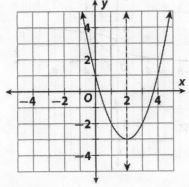

b. (2, $-3$)

c. $x = 2$

10. a.

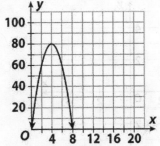

b. 8 seconds

c. (4, 80); the ball reaches a maximum height of 80 meters after 4 seconds.

11. $x = -2, 6$

12. (0, 6)

13. Domain: All real numbers
Range: All real numbers

14. a. $f(x) = \sqrt[3]{x + 2}$

b. $f^{-1}(x) = x^3 - 2$

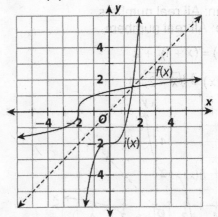

## Unit 5 Test: C

1. D
2. $x = 11.5$
3. $x = -3$ and $x = -1$
4. A True B False C False D False
5. 14
6. $y = [x] + 3$
7. A
8. B

9. a.
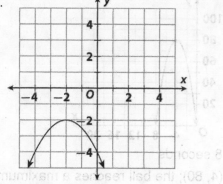

b. $(-2, -2)$

c. $x = -2$

d. Maximum: $-2$

10. The second differences are all 2, which indicates that the relation is quadratic.

11. $(-0.5, -3.75)$

12. $x = -0.8, 5.6$

13. Domain: All real numbers
Range: All real numbers

14. a. $h(x) = (x + 1)^3 + 2$

b. $h^{-1}(x) = \sqrt[3]{x - 2} - 1$

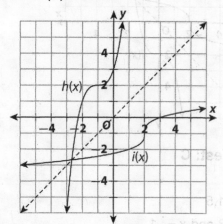

**Unit 5 Test: D**

1. A
2. B
3. C
4. A
5. A
6. C
7. C

8. A

9. a. $(-2, 0)$

b. $y = (x + 2)^2$

10. 10 sec

11. $x = -18, 4$

12. $(-1, -1)$ and $(2, 2)$

13. Domain: All real numbers
Range: All real numbers

14. a.

| $t(x) = (x - 2)^3$ | | $t^{-1}(x) = \sqrt[3]{x} + 2$ | |
|---|---|---|---|
| 0 | −8 | −8 | 0 |
| 1 | −1 | −1 | 1 |
| 2 | 0 | 0 | 2 |
| 3 | 1 | 1 | 3 |
| 4 | 8 | 8 | 4 |

b.

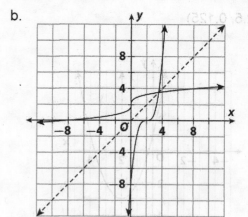

## Unit 5 Performance Task

1. Quadrant II: $y = -x$

   Quadrant II: $y = x$

2. $(-4, 4)$, $(4, 4)$

3. $y = |x|$

4. $y = |x + 5| - 3$

5. $(-4, -2)$, $(4, 6)$

6. a. The mirror is parallel to the $x$-axis and 7 units above it.

   b. $(2, 7)$

   c. $(-1, 8)$, $(8, 9)$

   d. The shape of the beam is that of the original beam shrunk by a factor of $\dfrac{1}{3}$.

# Answer Key

## Benchmark Test Modules 1–5

1. A

2. 3

3. 5 ft 5 in.

4. 104 cm

5. A

6. C

7. C

8. B

9. D

10. A No B No C Yes

11. A No B No C Yes D Yes

12. −32

13. C

14. D

15. C

16. −25

17. $x = -73$

18. $2\frac{1}{2}$

19. $-7\frac{1}{5}$

20. A No B Yes C Yes D No

21. C

22. B

23. C

24. $s = 4p - 48h$

25. A

26. A No B No C Yes

27. D

28. A

29. C

30. R: {5, 0, −2}

31. 2

32. 154 ft

33. $19\dfrac{\text{km}}{\text{hr}}$

34. 5

35. 13 cm

36. Real numbers, integers;
Real numbers, irrational numbers

37. −57

38. $z^2 - z + 24$

39. $x = 3$

40. $x \le 8$;

41. No solution

42.

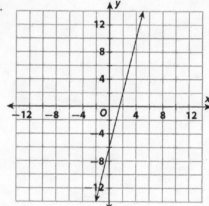

43. $f(n) = -13 + 5n$

# Answer Key

## Mid-Year Test Modules 6–11

1. 8

2. D

3. $-\dfrac{2}{3}$

4. B

5. C

6. A No B No C Yes D Yes

7. $h(x) = 20x - 15$

8. A

9. C

10. A Yes B Yes C No D Yes

11. A

12. 1.34

13. A

14. (0.1, 7.5)

15. A No B Yes C Yes D No

16. B

17. $P(y) = 5,300(0.92)^y$

18. 16,384

19. 1

20. A False B False C False D True

21. A

22. D

23. A

24.

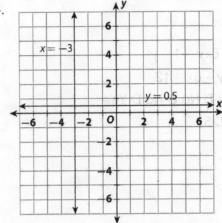

25. $6x + y = 20$

26. $y = 18x + 50$

27. $f(1) = -8$; $f(n) = f(n-1) - 4$

28. $\begin{cases} 5.10 = 0.25q + 0.10d; \\ 24 = q + d \end{cases}$

   6 dimes and 18 quarters

29. Trend lines will vary.

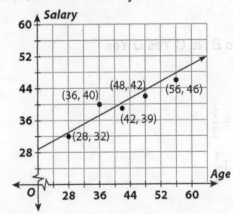

30. $x = 3$

31. Plan B; $85.50

# Answer Key

## Benchmark Test Modules 12–16

1. C

2. B

3. $9x^2 + 8xy - 1 - y^2$

4. $-14xy + 6x - 12$

5. A Yes B No C No D Yes

6. $x^2 - 225$

7. $12y^2$

8. D

9. A

10. B

11. A Yes B No C Yes D No

12. $(x - 2)(x + 2)(x^2 + 4)$

13. A

14. 0.36

15. A No B Yes C Yes D Yes

16. A

17. 11

18. D

19. C

20. A No B No C Yes D Yes

21. C

22. B

23. $x = \pm\dfrac{1}{3}$

24. $x = 3\dfrac{1}{2}$

25. C

26. 116; 2 real solutions

27. $7m^2n - 8m - 6mn^2 - 62$

28. $-115r^2s + 40r - 55$

29. $36x^2 - 60x + 25$

30. $6st(4t + 11)$

31. $(-5 + y)(2 + x)$

32. $25(z^2 - 2)(z^2 + 2)$

33. $(x - 3)$ cm

34. 0.4

35. a.

| Gender | Preferred Pet | | | |
| --- | --- | --- | --- | --- |
| | Dog | Cat | Fish | Total |
| Male | 110 | 197 | 16 | 323 |
| Female | 180 | 50 | 12 | 242 |
| Total | 290 | 247 | 28 | 565 |

b. 110

c. 192

36.

| | Blue | Green | Hazel | Brown |
| --- | --- | --- | --- | --- |
| Child | 6 | 5 | 10 | 15 |
| Teenager | 8 | 8 | 0 | 12 |
| Adult | 5 | 6 | 6 | 6 |

# Answer Key

## *End-of-Year Test Modules 1–19*

1. C

2. 10.5 in.

3. A

4. 56 mi/hr

5. A Yes B No C Yes D No

6. C

7. B

8. A

9. −70

10. 26

11. C

12. C

13. $x = -12$

14. C

15. D

16. $h = \dfrac{T + \$275}{\$500}$

17. B

18. C

19. C

20. 28

21. B

22. A

23. 1

24. A False B True C False D True

25. D

26. C

27. $f^{-1}(x) = 12x - 4$

28. A Yes B No C No D Yes

29. B

30. A

31. B

32. C

33. None

34. B

35. C

36. D

37. A

38. C

39. B

40. −1.5

41. D

42. A

43. A No B No C Yes

44. A No B Yes C No D Yes

45. $15rs - 18s + 9r - 3$

46. $121s^6t^2$ ft$^2$

47. B

48. $28mn^3$

49. $-6x(2x^2 - 3y + 7)$

50. B

51. C

52. (0, −6)

53. B

54. $x = 5$ and $x = 1$

55. $x = -8$ and $x = -6$

56. D

57. A

58. A Yes B No C No D Yes

59. 21

60. 0.28

61. A False B True C False D True

62. −13

63. (4, 11); maximum

64. C

65. C

66. D

67. 3

68. 67 cm

69. 55

70. 26,620

71. $16m + 20t + 75$

72. $-8x + 92y$

73. $t = 1\dfrac{1}{8}$

**74.** $y > 4$

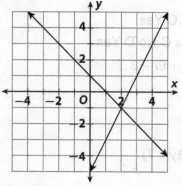

**75.**

| x | 0 | 2 | 4 | 6 |
|---|---|---|---|---|
| y | 0 | −0.6 | −1.2 | −1.8 |

**76.**

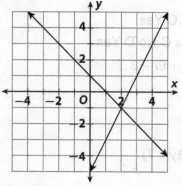

(2, −1)

**77.** $y = \dfrac{17}{4}x - 1$

**78.** $f(n) = (n-1) - 7; \ f(1) = 22$

**79.** $y \le \dfrac{1}{3}x + 1$

**80.**

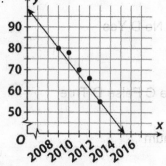

**81.** (−4, −4)

**82.** $\left(-9\dfrac{1}{3}, -16\right)$

**83.** $f(x) = 0.5(2)^x - 4$

**84.** $y = -9$

**85.** $6x^3yz - 84xy^2z^4$

**86.** $2(5x - 5)(x + 4)$

**87.** $25x^4 - 1 = (5x^2 - 1)(5x^2 + 1)$

**88.** $y = -\dfrac{3}{5}(x + 3)^2 + 5$

**89.** Zero: 8; Axis of symmetry: $x = 8$

**90.** $x = \dfrac{-5 \pm \sqrt{41}}{8}$

**91.**

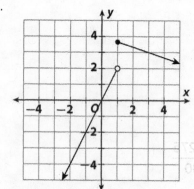

**92.**

| x | f(x) |
|---|------|
| −3 | 6.5 |
| 0 | 8 |
| 3 | 6.5 |
| 6 | 5 |

**93.** $y = \sqrt{\dfrac{x - 11}{5}}$